W9-CRX-615

FUNDAMENTALS
OF GAS
DYNAMICS

OTHER BOOKS BY THE AUTHOR

Handbook of Generalized Gas Dynamics
Plenum Press, 1966 (with W. G. Steltz)

Handbook of Specific Losses in Flow Systems
Plenum Press, 1966 (with N. A. Carlucci)

Manual on the Use of Thermocouples in
Temperature Measurement
STP470, STP470A, & STP470B, American Society for
Testing and Materials, 1970, 1974, & 1980 (Editor)

Journey Away From God
Fleming H. Revell Co., 1972

Fundamentals of Temperature, Pressure, and
Flow Measurements
John Wiley and Sons, 1969, 1977, 1984

Fundamentals of Pipe Flow
John Wiley and Sons, 1980

FUNDAMENTALS OF GAS DYNAMICS

ROBERT P. BENEDICT, P.E.

Fellow Mechanical Engineer
Westinghouse Electric Corporation
Adjunct Professor
Drexel University

JOHN WILEY & SONS, INC.

New York • *Chichester* • *Brisbane* • *Toronto* • *Singapore*

Library of Congress Cataloging in Publication Data:

Benedict, Robert P.
  Fundamentals of gas dynamics.

  Includes bibliographical references and indexes.
  1. Gas dynamics.   II. Title.
QC168.B448   1983   533'.2   83-1273
  ISBN 0-471-09193-6

Printed in the United States of America

10 9 8 7 6 5 4 3 2 1

To My Wife
Ruth

PREFACE

One might say that the subject of gas dynamics had its genesis primarily in the minds of two friends, Leonhard Euler and Daniel Bernoulli, about 1750, since they did much to advance the science of fluid flow in general. However, the low speed flows encountered then did not require analyses very different from that for liquids, and so it was hydraulics that remained the foremost subject of the day.

With man's attempts at flying, culminating at Kitty Hawk, North Carolina in 1903, the study of gas flow received its first real impetus. The work of men such as Ludwig Prandtl, Ernst Mach, F. W. Lanchester, N. E. Joukowsky, Samuel Langley, and Alexandre Eiffel, just before and just after World War I, laid the ground work for the study of gas dynamics as we currently know it.

Through the 1930s and into World War II, Geoffrey Taylor, Hugh Dryden, Aurel Stodola, Hermann Schlichting, William Sears, and others began the long task of formalizing the subject of gas dynamics. It was, however, only with the advent of the steam and gas turbines, rocketry, and space travel that gas dynamics received its true recognition as a field of study. The National Advisory Committee for Aeronautics (NACA and later NASA) in the United States, the National Gas Turbine Establishment in England, the schools at Göttingen and Braunschweig in Germany, and a host of other government agencies sponsored many research projects in the field of high-speed gas flow.

By the 1950s a number of textbooks appeared in the United States, including: Newman Hall's *Thermodynamics of Fluid Flow* and Ascher Shapiro's classic, *The Dynamics and Thermodynamics of Compressible Fluid Flow*, closely followed in the 1960s by the work of Rotty, Cheers, and John and in the 1970s by the texts of Zucrow and Hoffman. Zucker's book (completed at the U.S. Naval Postgraduate school) then followed in 1977.

The present work is based on an undergraduate course in gas dynamics that I have taught for the past 20 years at Drexel University. The introduction of the Γ function and the generalized approach to gas dynamics were first developed by the author and W. G. Steltz at the Westinghouse Steam Turbine Division around 1960.

Briefly, the book provides the following: Chapter 1, a review of the fundamentals of thermodynamics; Chapter 2, the conservation laws of mass, momentum, and energy; Chapter 3, the Mach number and corresponding equations; Chapter 4, the generalized gas dynamics equation that has application in all flow processes. Then, as in most textbooks on gas dynamics, the various simplified gas dynamics processes are dealt with separately. These include: Chapter 5, isentropic flow; Chapter 6, adiabatic flow; Chapter 7, diabatic-reversible flow; Chapter 8, isothermal flow (rarely treated in conventional texts); and Chapter 9, the normal shock process. Chapter 10 focuses on the generalized table that applies to all the simplified processes; Chapter 11 provides a stepwise method of solution for those processes that elude simplified solutions, such as the very realistic process involving simultaneous heat transfer and flow losses.

The unique features of this book include: specialized tables for each simplified gas dynamics process; dimensionless loss and heat transfer coefficients; rather complete tables based first on the experimentally-determined pressure ratio (R) as the independent variable, and then on the more academic Mach number (M) as the table entry; the consistent use throughout the text of the generalized Γ function that applies to all flow processes, and finally a stepwise solution method that has application in those gas dynamics processes that cannot be categorized as one or the other of the simplified processes.

I know of very few engineering companies in the United States that use the International System of Units (that is, SI units) in their engineering work. At the same time, I recognize that many schools and some government agencies (such as the National Bureau of Standards) employ this system. It is a fact that all codes and standards in this country are tabulated in U.S. Customary units, as are all engineering tables like the ASME Steam Tables, thermocouple tables, pipe sizes, and wire sizes. Engineering in the United States runs on psia, °F, ft, lbm/sec, and so on. Because of these conditions, I strongly feel that we should work in the current, more commonly used engineering units in gas dynamics, but that the student should have the ability to handle both systems of units. Consequently, while engineering units will be used throughout this text, many problems and examples will be given in both U.S. Customary and SI units.

The present text differs in many respects from its predecessors in that it is geared more toward engineering problem-solving than philosophical discussions.

With my best wishes, this book is presented to the engineering student, the teacher, and the practicing engineer.

Robert P. Benedict
Holly Hill, Pennsylvania
June 1982

CONTENTS

1 FUNDAMENTALS   **1**

  1.1 The Basic Gas Dynamics Problem   1
  1.2 Units and Dimensions   2
  1.3 Thermodynamic Definitions   5
  1.4 Gas Properties   6
  1.5 Thermodynamic Laws   7
  1.6 The Basic Gas Dynamics Identity   19
  1.7 The Perfect Gas   19
  1.8 Gas Dynamics Processes   25
  1.9 Stagnation States   27
  1.10 Viscosity   30
  1.11 Friction   34
  1.12 Concluding Remarks   41

     References   41
     Nomenclature   42
     Problems   44

2 CONSERVATION LAWS   **46**

  2.1 General Remarks   46
  2.2 General Conservation Principle   46
  2.3 Conservation of Mass   47
  2.4 Conservation of Momentum   49
  2.5 Conservation of Energy   53
  2.6 Concluding Remarks   56

     References   57
     Nomenclature   57
     Problems   58

3   MACH NUMBER   60

3.1   Velocity of Sound   60
3.2   Mach Number   63
3.3   The Mach Angle   64
3.4   Mach Number Equations   65
3.5   Concluding Remarks   70

    References   70
    Nomenclature   71
    Problems   71

4   GENERALIZED GAS DYNAMICS EQUATION   73

4.1   Generalized Gas Dynamics Equation   73
4.2   Normalized Gas Dynamics Function   75
4.3   Generalized Gas Dynamics Plot   79
4.4   The Dimensionless Multipliers   79
4.5   Concluding Remarks   81

    References   81
    Nomenclature   81
    Problems   82

5   ISENTROPIC FLOW   84

5.1   Isentropic Flow Equation   84
5.2   Isentropic Critical State   85
5.3   Convergent-Divergent Nozzle   90
5.4   Applications   91
5.5   Concluding Remarks   94

    References   95
    Nomenclature   95
    Problems   96

6   ADIABATIC FLOW AND THE LOSS COEFFICIENT   98

6.1   Adiabatic Flow Equation   98
6.2   Adiabatic Entropy Change   99
6.3   Adiabatic Critical State   100
6.4   Fanno Flow   101
6.5   Adiabatic Nozzle Flow With Loss   106
6.6   Adiabatic Loss Coefficient   107
6.7   Applications of K_{adi} 111
6.8   Generalized Fanno Flow Map   119
6.9   Generalized Fanno Flow Table   121
6.10 Concluding Remarks   125

References 125
Nomenclature 126
Problems 127

7 DIABATIC FLOW AND THE HEAT TRANSFER COEFFICIENT 129

7.1 Diabatic Flow Equation 129
7.2 Diabatic Entropy Change 130
7.3 Rayleigh Flow 131
7.4 Diabatic Heat Transfer Coefficient 135
7.5 Generalized Rayleigh Flow Map 139
7.6 Generalized Rayleigh Flow Table 142
7.7 Concluding Remarks 146

References 147
Nomenclature 147
Problems 148

8 ISOTHERMAL FLOW AND THE LOSS COEFFICIENT 150

8.1 Isothermal Flow Equation 150
8.2 Isothermal Entropy Change 151
8.3 Isothermal Critical State 152
8.4 Constant Area Isothermal Flow 153
8.5 Isothermal Loss Coefficient 158
8.6 K_{iso} and the Total Pressure Ratio 162
8.7 Generalized Isothermal Flow Map 163
8.8 Generalized Isothermal Flow Table 164
8.9 Concluding Remarks 167

References 168
Nomenclature 168
Problems 169

9 NORMAL SHOCK 171

9.1 The Normal Shock 171
9.2 Normal Shock Equations 174
9.3 Entropy Rise Across a Normal Shock 180
9.4 Nozzle Flow With Shock Waves 181
9.5 Pitot Tube and the Normal Shock 186
9.6 Concluding Remarks 187

References 188
Nomenclature 189
Problems 189

10 GENERALIZED GAS DYNAMICS TABLES   191

10.1   Development of a Generalized Table   191
10.2   Applications of the Generalized Tables   219

References   221
Nomenclature   221
Problems   221

11 STEPWISE SOLUTIONS   222

11.1   General Remarks   222
11.2   The Stepwise Differential Equations   223
11.3   Stepwise Solution Method   225
11.4   Stepwise FORTRAN Program Outline   227
11.5   Confirmations of the Stepwise Solution Method   228
11.6   Applications of the Stepwise Solution Method   231
11.7   Concluding Remarks   234

References   235
Nomenclature   235
Problems   236

1
FUNDAMENTALS

1.1 THE BASIC GAS DYNAMICS PROBLEM

Gas dynamics is the study of compressible fluid flow. It is a natural outgrowth of the older (1820–1930) classical disciplines: *fluid mechanics* (Bernoulli, Euler, Stokes, and Prandtl); *thermodynamics* (Carnot, Joule, Kelvin, Clausius, and Boltzmann); and *heat transfer* (Fourier, Kirchoff, Nusselt, and Planck).

For simplicity, in this introductory study, we will limit our interest to the macroscopic, one-dimensional, steady flow of a perfect gas characterized with little loss in generality by $\gamma = 1.4$. In this way the basic principles of gas dynamics will not be clouded by extraneous complications arising from molecular motions, multidimensional flow components, transient analyses, real fluid characteristics, and so on.

The fact that these four limitations are not as restrictive as they first appear can be seen from the following brief remarks [1].

1. The assumption of a *macroscopic* viewpoint, wherein the complicated substratum of molecular motion is ignored, is quite consistent with the study of thermodynamics and of empirical fluid flow.
2. The assumption of a *one-dimensional* flow implies that variations in gas properties normal to the mean direction of flow are negligible. Variations in flow area are still allowed, and effects associated with two- and three-dimensional gradients, such as wall friction and/or heat transfer, are still included by considering them as uniformly present across the flow passage.
3. The assumption of a *steady flow* implies that changes in flow conditions take place slowly enough so that dynamic effects (with time) can be neglected.
4. The assumption of a *perfect gas* implies that the equation of the state for the perfect gas (that is, $pv = \overline{R}T$) also applies to real gases in many practical situations. The perfect gas will be described in greater detail in Section 1.7.

As a prerequisite to solving gas dynamics problems, it is necessary to understand and be able to apply certain basic laws, principles. and definitions.

These include: the first and second laws of thermodynamics; the concepts of the total and static states of the fluid; the perfect gas relations; and the three conservation laws of mass, energy, and momentum. These fundamentals are discussed in this chapter and the next.

The objective of the overall study of gas dynamics is to be able to solve readily and with confidence the basic gas dynamics problem that, simply stated, is: Find the pressure, temperature, and flow rate in a pipe or duct where pressure losses and heat transfer may be present.

1.2 UNITS AND DIMENSIONS

Newton's second law of motion

$$F = Kma \tag{1.1}$$

serves to introduce the various systems of units in current use involving the dimensional concepts of force, mass, length, and time. Although all consistent systems of units are equally valid, it is important to avoid confusion between these systems by establishing a complete understanding of these systems at the onset.

In the U.S. Customary System (the system most often used in engineering), there are two sets of units in common use, each specified by appropriate definitions.

U.S. Definition One. A force of 1 lbf accelerates a mass of 1 lbm 32.174 ft/sec².

For the mathematical and dimensional homogeneity of (1.1) this definition requires that

$$K_2 = \left(\frac{1}{g_c}\right)\frac{\text{lbf-sec}^2}{\text{lbm-ft}} \tag{1.2}$$

where g_c is the gravitational constant of numerical value 32.174. K_2 is a pure number, in spite of the fact that it involves units. This is much the same case as with the common length conversion constant, $K_{\text{LENGTH}} = 12$ in./1 ft. The subscript in K_2 reminds us that this constant is consistent with the 2 lb system (that is, the lbf-lbm system).

Alternatively, in the U.S. Customary System we have the following definition

U.S. Definition Two. A force of 1 lbf accelerates a mass of 1 slug 1 ft/sec².

Again, for the homogeneity of (1.1), this definition requires that

$$K_1 = (1)\frac{\text{lbf-sec}^2}{\text{slug-ft}} \tag{1.3}$$

TABLE 1.1
USEFUL CONVERSION CONSTANTS (after [2])

PHYSICAL QUANTITY	SYMBOL	CONVERSION FACTOR
Area	A	1 ft^2 = 0.0929 m^2 1 in.^{2} = 6.452×10^{-4} m^2
Density	ρ	1 lbm/ft^3 = 16.018 kg/m^3 1 slug/ft^3 = 515.379 kg/m^3
Energy	Q or **W**	1 Joule ≡ 1 N·m 1 Btu = 1055.1 J 1 (ft)(lbf) = 1.3558 J 1 (hp)(hr) = 2.685 × 10^{6}J
Force	F	1 lbf = 4.448 N
Heat flow rate	$\dot{q}$	1 Btu/hr = 0.2931 W 1 Btu/sec = 1055.1 W
Heat transfer coefficient	h_c	1 Btu/(hr)(ft^2)(°F) = 5.678 W/m^2-K
Length	L	1 ft = 0.3048 m 1 in. = 2.54 cm = 0.0254 m 1 mile = 1.6093 km = 1609.3 m
Mass	m	1 lbm = 0.4536 kg 1 slug = 14.594 kg
Mass flow rate	$\dot{m}$	1 lbm/hr = 0.000126 kg/s 1 lbm/sec = 0.4536 kg/s
Power	$\dot{w}$	1 Watt ≡ 1 J/s 1 hp = 745.7 W 1 (ft)(lbf)/sec = 1.3558 W 1 Btu/sec = 1055.1 W 1 Btu/hr = 0.293 W
Pressure	p	1 pascal ≡ 1 N/m^2 1 lbf/in.^{2} = 6894.8 N/m^2 1 lbf/ft^2 = 47.88 N/m^2 1 atm = 101,325 N/m^2
Specific heat capacity	C	1 Btu/(lbm)(°F) = 4,187 J/kg-K
Specific energy	q	1 Btu/lbm = 2326.1 J/kg
Temperature	T	$T(°R) = (9/5)T(K)$ $T(°F) = [T(°C)](9/5) + 32$ $T(°F) = [T(K) - 273.15](9/5) + 32$
Thermal conductivity	k	1 Btu/(hr)(ft)(°F) = 1.731 W/m-K
Velocity	V	1 ft/sec = 0.3048 m/s 1 mph = 0.44703 m/s
Viscosity, dynamic	μ	1 lbm/(ft)(sec) = 1.488 N-s/m^2 1 centipoise = 0.00100 N-s/m^2
Viscosity, kinematic	ν	1 ft^2/sec = 0.0929 m^2/s 1 ft^2/hr = 2.581 × 10^{-5} m^2/s
Volume	V	1 ft^3 = 0.02832 m^3 1 in.^{3} = 1.6387 ×10^{-5} m^3 1 gal (U.S. liq.) = 0.003785 m^3

K_1 is a pure number, where the subscript 1 reminds us that this constant is consistent with the 1 lb system (that is, the lbf-slug system).

In the International System (SI), which is the current name for the metric system, we have this definition.

SI Definition.   A force of 1 newton accelerates a mass of 1 kilogram 1 meter/sec^2.

For the mathematical and dimensional homogeneity of (1.1), this definition requires that

$$K_{SI} = (1)\frac{\text{newton-sec}^2}{\text{kilogram-meter}} \tag{1.4}$$

Note that g_c in the SI system has the value 9.80665 kg-m/N-sec^2.

In the study of gas dynamics, all three systems of units have been used, although in engineering it is the 2 lb system that is still most commonly used in the United States.

It should be clear from this brief discussion of units that if (1.1) is properly understood, all systems of units can be used equally well, and units can be converted from one system to another with ease.

Table 1.1 provides some useful conversion factors between the U.S. Customary and the SI systems of units.

EXAMPLE 1.1

Express the weight of 1 lbm in lbf and in newtons if $g = g_c$.

Solution

In terms of weight, (1.1) becomes

$$W = Kmg$$

In the lbf-lbm system, $K_2 = 1/g_c$ and the following results:

$$W = \left(\frac{1}{g_c}\right)(1\text{ lbm})(g_c) = 1\text{ lbf}$$

In the SI system, $K_{SI} = 1$, $g_c = 9.80665$, and from Table 1.1, 1 lbm = 0.4536 kg. The following results

$$W = (1)(0.4536\text{ kg})(9.80665) = 4.448\text{ N}$$

in agreement with the Table 1.1 conversion.

1.3   THERMODYNAMIC DEFINITIONS

Some of the more important definitions used in the study of gas dynamics are given here [3]. Others will be defined as required.

1. **Working gas.** The gas under consideration, assumed to be of a homogeneous and invariable chemical composition.
2. **State.** The thermal condition of the working gas as defined by any two independent state properties.
3. **State property.** Any observable descriptive characteristic of the working gas, such as pressure, temperature, density.
4. **Process.** Any change of state—that is, any change in any property. If the process can be graphed, it is the path of successive states through which the working gas passes.
5. **System.** A specific region (container) of real or imaginary boundaries, rigid or not, whose contents are to be analyzed in terms of the transformations of energy within the boundaries and the passage of energy or matter across the boundaries.
6. **Surroundings.** The region outside the boundaries of the specific system under study.
7. **Isolated system.** A system in which no matter or energy crosses the boundaries—that is, the sum of all forms of energy within the system is conserved.
8. **Closed system.** A system that is impermeable to matter, and in which only mechanical and thermal energy can cross the boundaries (this implies a nonflow system).
9. **Adiabatic system.** A system that is isolated thermally from its surroundings, and in which only matter and mechanical energy can cross the boundaries (this implies perfectly insulated real boundaries).
10. **Diathermic system.** A system that is isolated mechanically from its surroundings, and in which only matter and thermal energy can cross the boundaries (this implies rigid boundaries).
11. **Work.** Interaction between a system and its surroundings such that the sole effect on the surroundings can be expressed in terms of the displacement of a weight.

To elaborate on the work definition, we draw from mechanics

$$W = \int F \cos \beta \, dx \tag{1.5}$$

where β is the angle between the force and the displacement. It follows that the boundaries of the system must deform if work is involved. Furthermore, this work can be exerted in two directions: it can operate *on* the system, or it can be performed *by* the system. Specifically, work is said to be done by the system if the sole effect on the surroundings can be expressed in terms of the *raising* of a weight.

A differential amount of work is expressed as δW rather than dW to remind us that the inexact differential must be considered. We recall from mathematics that the integral of an exact differential is independent of the path of integration; however, the work involved when the working substance passes from one state to another not only is a function of the end states (points) of the process but also, in general, is strongly dependent on the path followed. Thus, work, in general, is a path function as opposed to a point function:

$$\int_1^2 \delta W = W_{1,2} \tag{1.6}$$

It is meaningless to write $(W_2 - W_1)$ for the above integral since work represents energy in transition only. We do not speak of the work in a system at state 1 or 2, but only of how much work is involved in passing from state 1 to state 2. And, as we have pointed out, this depends on the specific path followed.

1.4 GAS PROPERTIES

In completing any flow analysis, it is necessary that the properties of the working gas be available. Such gas properties can be divided conveniently into three general categories: namely, state properties, thermodynamic properties, and transport properties. Definitions, symbols, and units for the gas properties required in this study are given in the following subsections.

1.4.1 State Properties

Pressure (p), lbf/in.², N/m².   A macroscopic measure of the average compressive stress on the working gas. Pressure may be expressed *empirically* in terms of an arbitrary base, such as gage or vacuum pressure, or it may be expressed *absolutely* in terms of a fixed zero base, that is, with respect to a perfect vacuum.

Temperature (T), °F, °R, °C, K.   Until the second law discussion, we take temperature as a measure of the thermal level of the gas. Temperature may be expressed empirically in terms of an arbitrary base, such as degrees Fahrenheit or degrees Celsius, or it may be expressed absolutely in terms of a fixed zero base, such as degrees Rankine or kelvins.

Density (ρ), lbm/ft³, kg/m³.   The local mass per unit volume of the gas. Note that the specific volume (v) is the reciprocal of density, that is $v = 1/\rho$.

1.4.2 Thermodynamic Properties [1]

Internal energy (u), Btu/lbm, J/kg.   Until the first law discussion, we consider internal energy as the energy possessed by the unit mass of a gas because of the state of molecular activity.

Enthalpy (h), Btu/lbm, J/kg.   A convenient summing of the internal energy and the pressure-volume product, that is,

$$h = u + pv \tag{1.7}$$

Entropy (s), Btu/lbm-°R, J/kg-K. Until the second law discussion, we consider entropy as a measure of the quality of the energy state of the gas.

Specific Heat (C), Btu/lbm-°R, J/kg-K. At constant volume, measures the rate of change of internal energy with temperature per unit mass. At constant pressure, measures the rate of change of enthalpy with temperature per unit mass of the gas.

1.4.3 Transport Properties

Thermal Conductivity (k), Btu/hr-ft-°F, W/m-K. This measures the molecular diffusion of heat (q) per unit area resulting from a temperature gradient (dT/dy), that is,

$$k = \frac{q/A}{dT/dy} \tag{1.8}$$

Dynamic Viscosity (μ), lbm/ft-sec, kg/m-sec. Dynamic viscosity is a measure of the molecular diffusion of momentum due to a shearing action in the gas, that is,

$$\mu = \frac{\tau}{dV/dy} \tag{1.9}$$

where dV/dy represents the velocity gradient. Gases following (1.9) are called Newtonian gases. Gas viscosity is a strong function of temperature, but is very nearly independent of pressure.

Kinematic Viscosity (v), ft²/sec, m²/sec. This is a convenient ratio of dynamic viscosity to density, that is,

$$v = \frac{\mu}{\rho} \tag{1.10}$$

1.5 THERMODYNAMIC LAWS

The discipline of thermodynamics is built on certain laws that are simply axioms or postulates serving as the basis of study [4] and that we take to be true.

1.5.1 Zeroth Law

The concepts of thermal equilibrium and empirical temperature are basic to thermodynamics. These are clarified in the zeroth law. If there is thermal interaction between a system and its surroundings, a change of state of the working substance will generally occur. However, it is a matter of experience that:

> *If no observable change takes place in the pressure or volume of either the system or its surroundings when each is individually in contact with an auxiliary diathermic-closed system, the system and its surroundings are said to be in thermal equilibrium with the auxiliary system and with each other.*

This generalization of experience introduces the concept of thermal equilibrium, and it is the essence of what we will call the zeroth law.

By virtue of the zeroth law, thermometers (auxiliary diathermic-closed systems) are made feasible. This law asserts the existence of a conserved property, an *empirical temperature*—empirical because it is measured from an arbitrary base, like Celsius or Fahrenheit temperature. The law ensures that each particular state of thermal equilibrium (that is, each *isotherm*) between the system and its surroundings can be labeled, although the assignment of numerical values to these isotherms is entirely arbitrary.

1.5.2 First Law

The concepts of internal energy and external heat are clarified by the first law. In addition, the concepts of friction and work are best examined in connection with the first law and its corollaries.

If there is a mechanical interaction between a system and its surroundings, a change of state of the working substance will generally occur. The work involved will, for the most part, be strongly dependent on the process. However, it is a matter of experience that:

> *For any closed, adiabatic system, the work done is fixed by the end states of the working substance.*

This generalization of experience, which we could not have expected in view of the general observation that work is a path function, is the essence of what we will call the first law of thermodynamics. It follows the general reasoning of Caratheodory [5].

The first law asserts the existence of a unique point function, the *internal energy;* empirical (that is, relative) since its base point is entirely arbitrary (the zero datum is conventionally at 32°F). The law ensures that each particular state of the working substance can be given a characteristic number with respect to an arbitrary base—that is, the increase in internal energy accompanying any specific change of state taking place in a closed, adiabatic system can be realized experimentally simply by evaluating the work done on the system during the process:

$$\delta(W_{on})_{\text{closed, adiabatic}} = dU$$

or

$$(\mathbf{W}_{on})_{1,\,2,\,\text{closed, adiabatic}} = U_2 - U_1 \qquad\qquad (1.11)$$

where the internal energy is represented by U.

Mathematically, dU is an exact differential, meaning that its integral is determined solely by the end states of the process, independently of the process. Physically, whenever we mean, recognize, observe, or encounter $\delta(\mathbf{W}_{on})_{\text{closed, adiabatic}}$, we will think, say, or write dU instead, for convenience only. In keeping with this viewpoint, note that Kelvin first called the internal energy the mechanical energy [6].

Once the internal energy is realized in practice for a process that takes place within the restrictive closed, adiabatic system, we can write by the first law:

$$0 = dU - \delta(\mathbf{W}_{on})_{\text{closed, adiabatic}} \qquad\qquad (1.12)$$

However, the adiabatic system is not generally encountered. The difference between the increase in internal energy of the working substance and the work done on the working substance in a closed system when the thermal-isolation restriction is removed (that is, a *diabatic* system) will not equal zero but will have a definite numerical value. That is, in general,

$$0 \neq dU - \delta(\mathbf{W}_{on})_{\text{closed}} \qquad\qquad (1.13)$$

This difference that will exist in a closed system because of interaction between the system and its surroundings we define to be the *external heat transferred* or, more simply, the *heat*. This heat can be transferred across the system boundaries in two directions—that is, heat can be absorbed or rejected by the system. Specifically, the *heat absorbed* is defined as the increase in internal energy plus the work done *by* the closed system:

$$\delta Q_{\text{added}} \equiv dU + \delta(\mathbf{W}_{by})_{\text{closed}} \qquad\qquad (1.14)$$

Equation (1.14) defines heat; it may be taken as a corollary of the first law and represents the complete *closed-system energy equation*. As a generalization of experience, there must be an empirical temperature difference between the system and its surroundings for an external heat transfer to be involved, and, of course, the system cannot be adiabatic.

A differential amount of heat is expressed as δQ rather than dQ to remind us that the inexact differential must be considered. This is so because the heat involved when the working substance passes from one state to another not only is a function of the end states of the process but also, in general, depends strongly on the path followed. Thus heat, like work, is a path function, and we write

$$\int_1^2 \delta Q = Q_{1,2} \tag{1.15}$$

From the discussion of path functions, we know that it is meaningless to write $(Q_2 - Q_1)$ for the above integral. It is also incorrect to speak of the heat in a system at states 1 or 2 because heat, like work, is a measure of energy in transition only.

Since the concepts of internal energy and external heat are both defined in terms of the work done on a closed system, as indicated by (1.13) and (1.14), it is evident that the question of work and its evaluation has again become pertinent to this study. Work must be defined in such a way as to ensure the concreteness of the first law and its corollaries. Additional definitions are required first.

Wholly Reversible Process. A quasi-static change of state in the absence of mechanical interference, fluid mixing, turbulence, and unrestrained expansions in the system and its surroundings. Note that the quasi-static restriction as used here signifies a succession of statistical equilibrium states in which all properties of all parts of the system and its surroundings are constant with time, and thus implies the absence of fluid-viscosity effects, any finite unbalanced forces, and any finite empirical temperature differences within and between the system and its surroundings. A wholly reversible process is an idealization that, contrary to our experience, can proceed equally well in either direction from a given state, without external effects.

Internally Reversible Process. A quasi-static change of state within the system such that any irreversibilities are confined to the surroundings. The system, however, behaves as though the process is not reversible in the natural sense since permanent changes must be produced somewhere in the surroundings if the process is to proceed in either direction from a given state.

For any internally reversible process, the work done by a closed system is defined from the mechanics, through (1.5), as

$$\delta(\mathbf{W}_{by})_{closed,\ reversible} = p\ d\mathbf{V} \tag{1.16}$$

where the volume must increase whenever work is done by the system, and the pressure must be absolute. This particular work term we call the *elastic work* since the boundaries of the closed system must deform if it is to exist. Like all work terms, the elastic work is, in general, a path function strongly dependent on the specific process involved.

An internally *reversible* process (and also a wholly reversible one) can always be drawn as a continuous curve on a property diagram, and the work involved in a closed system is always $\int p\ d\mathbf{V}$—that is, the area under the p versus $\mathbf{V}$ curve in Figure 1.1. Conversely, an internally *irreversible* process can never be drawn as a continuous curve on a property diagram, an the work involved in a closed system may or may not be well approximated by $\int p\ d\mathbf{V}$ (of course,

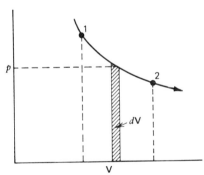

Figure 1.1 Area under $p\mathbf{V}$ curve is work $\left[\left(\mathbf{W}_{\text{by}}\right)_{\text{closed, reversible}} = \int_1^2 pd\mathbf{V}\right]$

it is meaningless to speak of the area under the p versus $\mathbf{V}$ curve since there is no curve). Thus, if a process is drawn as a continuous curve on a property diagram, internal reversibility (at least) is implied. See Figures 1.2 and 1.3.

Once the elastic work is realized in practice for the restrictive, internally reversible change of state of the working substance in a closed system, we have by (1.16)

$$0 = p \, d\mathbf{V} - \delta(\mathbf{W}_{\text{by}})_{\text{closed, reversible}} \qquad (1.17)$$

However, even the internally reversible process is not generally encountered. The difference between the elastic work done by a closed system and the work done by the same system when the internal reversible restriction is removed will not equal zero, in general, but will have a definite numerical value:

$$0 \neq p \, d\mathbf{V} - \delta(\mathbf{W}_{\text{by}})_{\text{closed}} \qquad (1.18)$$

This difference that will exist in a closed system in the presence of a mechanical energy transfer or elastic work we define as the internal heat generated or, more simply, the *friction*.[1] Thus,

$$\delta F \equiv p \, d\mathbf{V} - \delta(\mathbf{W}_{\text{by}})_{\text{closed}} \qquad (1.19)$$

where the friction term is influenced by such factors within the system as the mechanical interference between moving parts, the shearing effect arising because of a nonstatic process involving a viscous fluid, fluid mixing, turbulence, and unrestrained expansions. All-inclusive as the friction term appears, however, it is not the criterion of reversibility because, even in the constant-volume,

---

[1]As is often true in engineering, the same symbol may be used to represent two or more concepts. In the case at hand, *F* can represent either *force* or *friction*. Since these concepts rarely occur in the same equation, the meaning of the symbol *F* normally will be clear from the context.

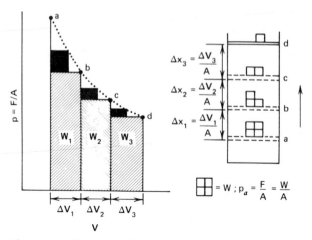

Figure 1.2 The reversible process as a limit. Imagine a weight, divided into four units, on a piston initially at rest at state *a*. By successively removing one unit of weight, with equilibrium established between each step, states *b*, *c*, and *d* result, where the actual works involved are

$$W_1 = F_1 \Delta x_1 = (\tfrac{3}{4} W) \left(\frac{\Delta V_1}{A} \right) = p_b \Delta V_1$$

$$W_2 = F_2 \Delta x_2 = (\tfrac{1}{2} W) \left(\frac{\Delta V_2}{A} \right) = p_c \Delta V_2$$

$$W_3 = F_3 \Delta x_3 = (\tfrac{1}{4} W) \left(\frac{\Delta V_3}{A} \right) = p_d \Delta V_3$$

as indicated by shaded areas on graph.

If the experiment is repeated, removing only one-half unit of weight per step, the darkened areas on the graph represent additional work involved.

If the experiment were repeated, removing an infinitesimal fraction of the weight per step, a plot of the states involved would approach a continuous curve as indicated by the dots from *a* to *d*. Such quasi-static changes of state represent a reversible process. Since the actual work approaches the area under the smooth curve, we note that the actual work approaches the reversible work as a limit.

closed-diathermic system in which *F* is necessarily zero, there may be irreversibilities in the presence of thermal energy transfer. These will be discussed more fully under second law considerations. Thus, the absence of friction is a necessary but not at all sufficient condition for reversibility.

As a generalization of experience, friction is a one-way street: either it is absent during a process, or it is positive, and friction involves happenings *within* system boundaries as opposed to work and heat, which are concerned with energy transfers *across* system boundaries in either direction. Like work and

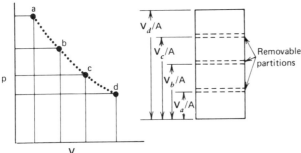

Figure 1.3   The irreversible process. Imagine a series of unrestrained expansions from initial equilibrium states, as indicated above by states *b, c,* and *d,* obtained by successively removing the partitions.

If the experiment were repeated, using a large number of partitions, a plot of the states involved would again appear to approach a continuous curve as indicated by the dots from *a* to *d*. However, such unrestrained expansions are highly irreversible.

The mathematical tendency to pass a smooth curve through the many state points must be resisted, since the actual work (*on* or *by* the system) is zero, and the series of states approaches no meaningful thermodynamic limit.

heat, friction is inherently a path function; hence, it is instructive to note that (1.19) also can be written as

$$dV = \frac{\delta F + (W_{by})_{closed}}{p} \tag{1.20}$$

where volume is inherently a point function. In other words, absolute pressure plays the role of an integrating factor in (1.20), mathematically transforming the inexact quantity, $(\delta F + \delta W)$, to one that is exact.

An important corollary of the first law and a useful form of the energy equation for a closed (nonflow) system can be obtained by combining (1.14) and (1.19) to obtain

$$\delta Q + \delta F = dU + p\, dV \tag{1.21}$$

Equation (1.21) brings together all the important concepts of thermodynamics so far discussed—namely, heat, friction, internal energy, and elastic work. Note that δF, in spite of its limitations, is the only term concerning irreversibility that must be considered in any of the energy equations. Equation (1.21) indicates that work can be converted, by means of the internal heat generated (that is friction), to produce the same thermal effects on the system as an external heat transfer. In keeping with this viewpoint, Joule stated, "The most frequent way in which limiting force (work) is converted into heat is by means of friction. . . ." [7].

1.5.3 General Energy

We have discussed the work done on or by a closed system and its relation to the nonflow energy equation. However, in gas dynamics we are interested in open systems, and we next inquire about the work involved and its relation to the energy equation for the more general open system under *steady flow* conditions—that is, when neither the mass nor the total energy of the working substance changes with time.

As already mentioned, work can be done on or by the working substance in any system only by boundary deformation. In a closed system, work crossing system boundaries is accounted for solely by friction and elastic work, as indicated by (1.19). In the more general system, however, additional forms of energy may be needed to account for work crossing system boundaries. The three energy terms that we will consider in connection with a moving fluid are flow work, kinetic energy, and potential energy. All of these are point functions.

Flow Work. A work term arising solely because the working substance crosses system boundaries. From fluid mechanics a change in flow work involves only the fluid pressure and volume at system boundaries:

$$dW_{flow} = d(pV) \tag{1.22}$$

[*Note:* in the nonflow system, this term may also exist, but it has no significance as a work term.]

Kinetic Energy. An energy term arising solely because the working substance exhibits directed motion with respect to the real boundaries of the system. From mechanics a change in kinetic energy involves only the fluid mass and its acceleration within a system boundaries:

$$d(K.E.) = d\left(\frac{mV^2}{2g_c}\right) \tag{1.23}$$

Potential Energy. An energy term arising solely because the working substance exhibits vertical displacement with respect to an arbitrary datum. From mechanics a change in potential energy involves only the fluid mass and its position within system boundaries:

$$d(P.E.) = \frac{d(mgZ)}{g_c} \tag{1.24}$$

Thus, the general equation for work done on the working substance is

$$\delta W_{on} = \delta(W_{on})_{closed} + dW_{flow} + d(K.E.) + d(P.E.) \tag{1.25}$$

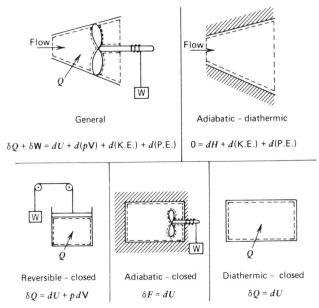

Figure 1.4   Thermodynamic system classifications.

General

$$\delta Q + \delta W = dU + d(pV) + d(K.E.) + d(P.E.)$$

Adiabatic – diathermic

$$0 = dH + d(K.E.) + d(P.E.)$$

Reversible – closed

$$\delta Q = dU + p\,dV$$

Adiabatic – closed

$$\delta F = dU$$

Diathermic – closed

$$\delta Q = dU$$

or, upon the substitution of (1.19), (1.22), (1.23), and (1.24) in (1.25), we get

$$\delta W_{on} = dF - p\,dV + d(pV) + d\left(\frac{mV^2}{2g_c}\right) + \frac{d(mgZ)}{g_c} \tag{1.26}$$

where any or all of the terms may be present in a given situation.

When (1.26), which represents a general accounting of mechanical energies, is combined with (1.21), which represents a general accounting of thermal energies, we obtain on a *per unit mass basis*

$$(\delta q_{added} + \delta w_{on})_{external\ effects} = \left[du + d(pv) + \frac{V\,dV}{g_c} + \frac{g}{g_c}dZ\right]_{internal\ effects} \tag{1.27}$$

where lowercase symbols q, w, u, and v signify, respectively: heat, work, internal energy, and volume per unit mass. Equation (1.27) is called, with good reason, the *steady flow general energy equation* since it applies equally well to reversible and irreversible processes within flow systems. No friction term appears in (1.27) (that is, internal irreversibilities in the presence of work transfer or elastic work are not recognized), simply because friction at the same time sets up counterbalancing work and heat terms, as shown by (1.21) and (1.26) (see Figure 1.4).

1.5.4 Second Law

The concepts of absolute temperature and entropy are clarified by the second law. In addition, the dual nature of friction (now a work effect, now a heat effect) and its unidirectionality (the one-way-street idea), as met in the first law corollaries, are clarified by the second law.

Note that the story of thermodynamics has several loose ends at this point. For instance, why did we not encounter an absolute temperature function? The analogous absolute pressure was introduced, and actually was seen to be essential to thermodynamics. And why did we not note a mathematical integrating factor for the inherent path function ($\delta Q + \delta F$) while we were doing so for the similar ($\delta W + \delta F$)? Recall, by the way, that absolute pressure was just such an integrating factor for the work and friction term. And whereas we observed that some processes (namely, the irreversible ones) could not be represented by continuous curves on property maps, we encountered no thermodynamic concept that would indicate that some processes might not even be possible! In other words, the first law and its corollaries aided us only with our bookkeeping accounts concerning energy in its various forms; they did not help us to judge which processes were useful or whether any limitations on the useful effect of heat existed.[2] However, experience has proven that:

For any adiabatic system, thermodynamic states exist that cannot be reached by any process from a given initial state.

This generalization of experience is the essence of what we will call the second law of thermodynamics, again following the general reasoning of Caratheodory [9].

The second law asserts the existence of two point functions of basic importance in thermodynamics—namely, the *entropy* and the *absolute temperature*—but the assertion is not at all obvious. The second law also ties up some of the loose ends by stating categorically that not all processes are possible. But although we are forewarned, we are not yet armed. We cannot tell by looking at the law just which states are inaccessible.

To be more specific, we first note that internal energy, being a property, can be expressed in terms of any other two independent properties such as p and V. Thus, we can rewrite (1.21) as

$$dU + p \, dV = N d\sigma \tag{1.28}$$

where N and σ are both functions of p and V alone. We can rewrite (1.21)

---

[2]As early as 1824, Carnot [8] introduced the cycle concept, with his famous reversible engine operating between two isotherms and two adiabats; suggested that the way to judge the merits of any heat engine was to compare the maximum work obtainable with the heat absorbed; anticipated the first law by claiming that the maximum work was equivalent to the net heat available; and noted that this efficiency could be a function of the two *empirical* temperatures only, independent of the working substance.

because we are assured mathematically that an integrating factor N exists for any two-variable linear differential equation; the resulting exact differential is then $d\sigma$.

It is a profound generalization of experience that if all parts of a system are temperature-coupled (that is, at a uniform empirical temperature), there always will be an integrating factor, which is necessarily a function of the empirical temperature and must have a fixed zero base—that is, an *absolute temperature*. Thus, we meet the missing absolute temperature function (with the conventional symbol T), and at the same time we identify it with the missing integrating factor N. Note that the absolute temperature plays the same role for the inexact $(\delta Q + \delta F)$ as absolute pressure does for $(\delta W + \delta F)$. The resulting exact differential $d\sigma$ we define to be the differential *entropy* (with the conventional symbol dS). Thus,

$$dS = \frac{\delta Q + \delta F}{T} \tag{1.29}$$

Alternatively, entropy can be defined as

$$dS = dS_{\substack{\text{transferred} \\ \text{across boundaries}}} + dS_{\substack{\text{produced} \\ \text{within boundaries}}} \tag{1.30}$$

where

$$dS_{\substack{\text{transferred} \\ \text{across boundaries}}} = \left(\frac{\delta Q}{T}\right)_{\substack{\text{evaluated} \\ \text{at boundaries}}} \tag{1.31}$$

The often quoted inequality first given by Clausius follows directly from (1.30) and (1.31). Thus,

$$dS \geqslant \frac{\delta Q}{T}_{\text{evaluated at boundaries}} \tag{1.32}$$

Neither (1.29) nor (1.30) is entirely satisfactory as a definition of entropy because the path of integration in the general irreversible process cannot be defined. However, since entropy is a point function, we must not overlook the important definition

$$dS = \left(\frac{\delta Q}{T}\right)_{\text{any reversible path}} \tag{1.33}$$

Equation (1.33) ensures that the entropy change for any process (reversible or not) can be determined readily by evaluating the entropy change for any reversible process or series of processes between the actual end states. Although

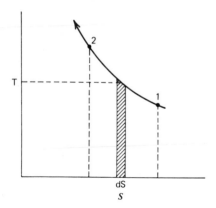

Figure 1.5 Area under TS curve is heat $\left[(Q_{added})_{reversible} = \int_{1}^{2} T\,dS \right]$

it is true that

$$\Delta S_{irreversible} = \Delta S_{reversible}$$

between the same end states, the implications are quite different. The irreversible entropy change includes irreparable entropy production, whereas the reversible entropy change represents entropy transfer only (for example, if a system undergoing a reversible process exhibits an entropy increase, its surroundings will exhibit a corresponding entropy decrease).

The very ease of computing ΔS, as indicated by (1.33), may cause us to lose sight of the irreversibilities that are involved in the usual process. To avoid this, entropy is best defined in combination as

$$dS = \frac{\delta Q + \delta F}{T} = dS_{transferred} + dS_{produced} = \left(\frac{\delta Q}{T} \right) \text{ any reversible path} \quad (1.34)$$

since (1.29), (1.30), and (1.33) are simply different viewpoints of the same concept. (See Figure 1.5.)

The entropy function, as given by (1.34), embodies the very concept we sought to indicate which processes are or are not possible. While the second law claims only that there will be inaccessible states in an adiabatic system, consideration of the entropy production indicates precisely which states are excluded. In other words, since $dS_{produced}$ can be positive or zero but cannot be negative because of the one-wayness of irreversibilities, the second law can be restated more specifically in terms of entropy as

In any adiabatic system all processes requiring a decrease in entropy are impossible,

or what amounts to the same thing

If a process is irreversible for any reason, entropy will be produced.

1.6   THE BASIC GAS DYNAMICS IDENTITY

A most important identity (that is, a statement that holds true for all working substances conforming to the laws of thermodynamics) is obtained by combining (1.21) and (1.29). It summarizes all the material of Section 1.5 and is known as the basic gas dynamics identity.

$$Tds = \delta q + \delta F = du + p\, dv \tag{1.35}$$

where all terms are expressed as energy per unit mass. Observe that the first law portion of (1.35) disclaims the production or destruction of energy, but admits the possibility of energy transformations only, while the second law portion of (1.35) admits the impossibility of entropy destruction, but claims that entropy can be produced freely. In effect, the first law says that no kind of energy is ever lost in any process, whereas the second law states that the opportunity to convert all the supplied heat energy to useful work is lost forever in any real process.

1.7   THE PERFECT GAS

The laws of thermodynamics are often applied in the study of fluid processes. However, the characteristics of real fluids are often so complicated that they preclude direct analysis by these laws. Hence, it is natural and necessary to seek a simplified fluid model that can be treated readily. A simplified macroscopic gas model will now be developed for this purpose.

1.7.1   The Boyle-Mariotte Law

In England in 1662, Boyle cautiously observed that over a limited pressure range the product of the pressure and volume of a fixed mass of a real gas was essentially a constant, independent of pressure level, under isothermal conditions. On the continent of Europe, Mariotte proclaimed this same observation in 1676. The Boyle-Mariotte law can be given as

$$(p\mathbf{V})_t = K_t \tag{1.36}$$

where the subscript t signifies that changes of state are allowed under conditions of constant temperature only. Thus, K_t indicates that although the isothermal $p\mathbf{V}$ product remains constant, its value changes as the temperature does. Temperature, of course, can be sensed by any empirical thermometer. We know today that Boyle's caution was quite in order, for no real gas satisfies (1.36) exactly.

1.7.2   The Charles—Gay–Lussac Law

Charles, in 1787, and Gay-Lussac, in 1802, found that equal volumes of real gases (for example, oxygen, nitrogen, hydrogen, carbon dioxide, and air) would expand the same amount for a given temperature increase under isobaric conditions. The Charles—Gay–Lussac law can be given as

$$\frac{1}{V_o}\left(\frac{V - V_o}{t - t_o}\right)_p = \alpha_{op} \tag{1.37}$$

where the subscript p signifies that changes of state are allowed under conditions of constant pressure only, the subscript o signifies that the variable is taken with respect to a definite reference state, and α_{op} indicates that although the isobaric cubical coefficient of expansion of any gas remains a constant, its value changes as the reference state or the pressure level changes. The symbol t represents temperature as measured on any empirical scale.

Similarly, when the volume of a given amount of any gas is held constant, the change in pressure is proportional to the change in temperature. Thus, the Charles—Gay–Lussac law can be given as

$$\frac{1}{p_o}\left(\frac{p - p_o}{t - t_o}\right)_v = \alpha_{ov}, \tag{1.38}$$

where the subscript v signifies that changes of state are allowed under conditions of constant volume only, and α_{ov} indicates that although the isochoric pressure coefficient of any gas remains constant, its value changes as the reference state or the volume changes. Today we know that no real gas follows the Charles—Gay–Lussac laws exactly.

1.7.3   Clapeyron's Equation of State

Clapeyron, in 1834, first combined the Boyle-Mariotte and Charles—Gay–Lussac laws to give the equation of state of a gas as

$$pv = \overline{R}\left(t - t_o + \frac{1}{\alpha_o}\right) \tag{1.39}$$

where $\overline{R}$ is a constant of integration, which can be evaluated at the reference state as

$$\overline{R} = p_o v_o \alpha_o \tag{1.40}$$

and where the parenthetical expression in (1.39) is known as *temperature from the zero of the air thermometer*. Note that the quantity $(t - t_o + 1/\alpha_o)$ is equivalent to expressing temperature on a new scale, whose zero is lower than that of the empirical scale of t by the quantity $(1/\alpha_o - t_o)$, but whose unit temperature interval (that is, degree) is the same as that of the empirical scale of t. Today we know that no real gas satisfies (1.39) exactly.

1.7.4   Regnault's Ideal Gas

Regnault, in 1845, found that the mean cubical coefficient of expansion for any real gas is approximately 1/273 per Celsius degree, in contrast to Gay–Lussac's evaluation of 1/267 per Celsius degree.

Regnault realized, however, that the cubical coefficients of expansion of all permanent gases are only approximately equal. For simplicity he proposed an imaginary substance that perfectly fulfilled all conditions of the Boyle-Mariotte and Charles—Gay–Lussac laws—that is, he defined an *ideal* gas whose thermodynamic state satisfied Clapeyron's equation of state. The equation of state of Regnault's ideal gas is

$$pv = \overline{R}\left(t - t_o + \frac{1}{\alpha}\right) \tag{1.41}$$

where the expression in parentheses represents temperature on the ideal-gas absolute-temperature scale. This is similar to the air-thermometer scale since its zero is lower than that of the empirical scale of t by the constant $(1/\alpha - t_o)$, and its degree is the same size as that of the empirical scale of t. Today we know that no real gas satisfies the requirements of Regnault's ideal gas exactly.

1.7.5   Kelvin's Ideal Gas

William Thomson (later Lord Kelvin), in 1848, recognized that Sadi Carnot's analysis, in 1824, of a reversible heat engine operating between two isotherms and two adiabats provided a basis for defining an absolute thermometric scale since the efficiency of the Carnot engine was only a function of the two empirical temperatures, independent of the working substance. His proposed *absolute thermodynamic temperature function* (θ) can be given in terms of the reversible Carnot heats as

$$\frac{\delta Q}{Q} = \frac{d\theta}{\theta} = \phi(t)dt \tag{1.42}$$

where θ is any arbitrary function of the empirical temperature t.

Kelvin adopted Joule's suggestion and patterned the new temperature function after temperature from the zero of the air thermometer. By further relating the fundamental temperature interval of his scale to that of the empirical scale (that is, by taking $\theta_{steam} - \theta_{ice} = t_{steam} - t_{ice}$), Kelvin succeeded in completely defining the absolute thermodynamic temperature scale. To experimentally realize temperatures on the θ scale, it was natural for Kelvin to turn to a gas thermometer:

$$\frac{\theta_2}{\theta_1} \simeq \left(\frac{p_2}{p_1}\right)_v \simeq \left(\frac{v_2}{v_1}\right)_p \tag{1.43}$$

The difference in the α_o factors for all real gases, however, means that no two gas thermometers can give the same temperature label to a common isotherm. Thus, although in theory Kelvin defined a thermodynamic temperature scale, independent of the thermometric substance, in effect he simply redefined an *ideal* gas whose thermodynamic state was now given by

$$pv = \overline{R}\theta \tag{1.44}$$

Today we know that no real gas follows (1.44) exactly.

1.7.6 Real Gas

In *real* gases it has been shown by all experimental data that absolute temperature is proportional not simply to the *pv* product, as in Kelvin's ideal gas, but to the limiting value of the *pv* product as *p* approaches zero along the respective isotherm. Thus,

$$\frac{T_2}{T_1} = \underset{p \to 0}{\text{limit}} \frac{(pv)_2}{(pv)_1} = \frac{(pv)_2^0}{(pv)_1^0} = \frac{\theta_2}{\theta_1} \tag{1.45}$$

where the superscript 0 indicates the zero pressure intercept. Equation (1.45) together with the relation $dT = dt$ serves to completely define absolute temperature today [10].

As engineering approximations, it has been found useful to define the following relations between empirical and absolute temperatures:

$$T(°R) = t(°F) + 460$$
$$t(K) \ = t(°C) + 273 \tag{1.46}$$

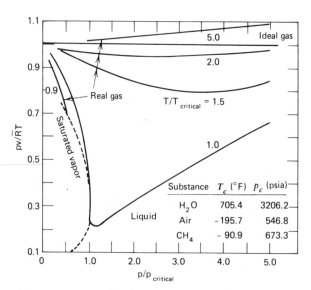

Figure 1.6 Generalized compressibility chart. This chart applies to any gas or gas mixture, and indicates departures from the ideal gas ($pv = \overline{R}T$) as a function of pressure and temperature, both referred to their critical values. At zero pressure, all gases act as the ideal gas, and again at the higher temperatures, with respect to the critical temperature, all gases approach the ideal gas.

Note that the ideal gas expression, as given by (1.44), serves as an increasingly exact relation for all real gases as the pressure approaches zero along the respective isotherm (see Figure 1.6). Thus, when we describe a real gas by (1.44), we imply that both the size of the molecules and the intermolecular forces are negligible. It follows that the transport properties such as viscosity and thermal conductivity, which depend on molecular size and interaction, likewise must be considered negligible. In reality, however, the gas flow need not be inviscid or adiabatic when applying (1.44), the ideal gas equation of state, as long as these effects do not cause the state of the gas to deviate appreciably from that represented by (1.44).

1.7.7 The Perfect Gas

It is often convenient to advance a step beyond (1.44) by defining the *perfect gas* of thermodynamics. The perfect gas has the same equation of state as the ideal gas with the additional simplifying assumption of constant specific heat capacities (see Figure 1.7). Some characteristic equations of the perfect gas are

$$pv = \overline{R}T$$

and

$$C_p = \text{constant}$$

along with

$$\frac{C_p}{C_v} = \gamma$$

$$C_p - C_v = \frac{\overline{R}}{J}$$

$$C_p = \frac{\gamma \overline{R}}{(\gamma - 1)J}$$ (1.47)

$$C_v = \frac{\overline{R}}{(\gamma - 1)J}$$

$$du = C_v dT = \frac{d(pv)}{(\gamma - 1)J}$$

$$dh = C_p dT = \frac{\gamma d(pv)}{(\gamma - 1)J}$$

In (1.47), γ is the ratio of specific heats, $\overline{R}$ is the specific gas constant, J is Joule's mechanical equivalent of heat (that is, ≈ 778 ft-lbf/Btu) for use in the U.S. Customary System, and h is the enthalpy of (1.7). Note that a bar is used over R to distinguish the gas constant $(\overline{R})$ from the important static-to-total pressure ratio (R) that is used so frequently in gas dynamics.

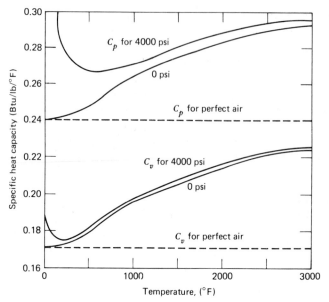

Figure 1.7 Comparison of specific heat capacities for air. At zero pressure, air acts essentially as an ideal gas (i.e., $C_p - C_v \approx$ constant). The higher the temperature, the more nearly this is true. Perfect air exhibits $C_p - C_v =$ constant. C_p and C_v for perfect air are based on $p = 0$ psi, $T = 0°F$.

EXAMPLE 1.2

Find the heat that must be transferred from the air in a tank of volume 100 ft³, initially at a pressure of 100 psia and a temperature of 100°F, if the temperature is to be reduced by 50°F.

(In terms of SI units, these same quantities can be given, via the conversion factors of Table 1.1, as:

$$\mathbf{V} = 2.832\text{m}^3, \ p = 689{,}480 \text{ pascals}, \ T_1 = 310.9 \text{ K}, \ T_2 = 283.1 \text{ K})$$

Solution:

Noting that specific volume (v) equals total volume ($\mathbf{V}$) divided by the mass (m), we find by (1.47)

$$m_{US} = \frac{p\mathbf{V}}{RT} = \frac{100 \text{ lbf}}{\text{in.}^2} \times \frac{144 \text{ in.}^2}{\text{ft}^2} \times 100 \text{ ft}^3 \times \frac{°\text{R-lbm}}{53.35 \text{ ft-lbf}}$$

$$\times \frac{1}{(100 + 460)°\text{R}} = 48.2 \text{ lbm}$$

and

$$m_{SI} = \frac{689{,}480 \text{ N}}{\text{m}^2} \times 2.832 \text{ m}^3 \times \frac{\text{kg-K}}{287.1 \text{ m-N}} \times \frac{1}{310.9 \text{ K}} = 21.87 \text{ kg}$$

By (1.21), $Q_{1,2} = U_2 - U_1$ since the volume of a tank is constant and, in this nonflow process, the loss term is zero. Hence, since by (1.47), $U_2 - U_1 = mC_v(T_2 - T_1)$, we have

$$Q_{US} = 48.2 \text{ lbm} \times 0.171 \frac{\text{Btu}}{\text{lbm-}^\circ\text{R}} \times (-50^\circ\text{R}) = -412.1 \text{ Btu}$$

and

$$Q_{SI} = 21.87 \text{ kg} \times 716 \frac{\text{m}-\text{N}}{\text{kg}-\text{K}} \times (-27.8 \text{ K}) = -435{,}318 \text{ Joules}$$

where the minus sign signifies that this amount of heat is transferred *out* of the air in the tank. Note that the gas constants used are from Table 1.2.

The consistency of these results can be seen by expressing one result in terms of the other (Table 1.1). Thus,

$$412.1 \text{ Btu}\left(\frac{1055.1 \text{ J}}{\text{Btu}}\right) = 435{,}000 \text{ J}$$

TABLE 1.2
NOMINAL VALUES OF SELECTED PROPERTIES FOR AIR

SYSTEM	GAS CONSTANT $\bar{R}$	CONSTANT PRESSURE SPECIFIC HEAT C_p	CONSTANT VOLUME SPECIFIC HEAT C_v	RATIO OF SPECIFIC HEATS γ
U.S. Customary	$53.35 \dfrac{\text{ft}-\text{lbf}}{\text{lbm}-^\circ\text{R}}$	$0.24 \dfrac{\text{Btu}}{\text{lbm}-^\circ\text{R}}$	$0.171 \dfrac{\text{Btu}}{\text{lbm}-^\circ\text{R}}$	1.4
S.I.	$287.1 \dfrac{\text{J}}{\text{kg}-\text{K}}$	$1{,}005 \dfrac{\text{J}}{\text{kg}-\text{K}}$	$716 \dfrac{\text{J}}{\text{kg}-\text{K}}$	1.4

1.8   GAS DYNAMICS PROCESSES

The laws of thermodynamics can be applied to real fluids and, with greater simplicity, to the perfect gas of thermodynamics, as the working substances undergo changes of state. The relations that permit the evaluation of such performance quantities as work and heat will now be developed.

The Polytropic Process.   The relation between p and v during an actual change of state may often be represented approximately by a member of the family

$$pv^n = K \text{ (a constant)} \tag{1.48}$$

It is conventional to let (1.48) exactly represent all changes of state that take place reversibly in any system and to call such processes polytropic. Curves representing these reversible changes of state are called polytropes.

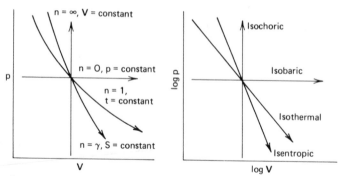

Figure 1.8 Rectifying several polytropic processes.

The exponent n in (1.48) is a constant whose value is determined by the nature of the process. The significance of n is seen by rectifying (1.48)—that is, by adjusting the scales of p and v so the polytropes plot as straight lines. Using the logarithm (to any base) of both sides of (1.48) will accomplish this, for note that

$$\log p = -n \log v + \log K \tag{1.49}$$

is in the form of a straight line ($y = Ax + B$), with the (1.49) counterparts of x, y, A, and B clearly apparent (see Figure 1.8). In particular, n represents the negative slope of the polytrope when expressed on a log-log basis. It follows from a consideration of (1.49) that whereas two given states may be joined by many different combinations of reversible processes, only one polytrope can connect given end states. Thus, polytropes are very special reversible changes of state.

Polytropic Processes for the Perfect Gas. Referring to (1.48) and (1.49) or to the differentiated form of (1.49)

$$\frac{dp}{p} = -n \frac{dv}{v} \tag{1.50}$$

we note the following simple reversible processes.

Isobaric. If we have a constant pressure process, then $dp = 0$; but from (1.50), since $dv \neq 0$, n must equal 0. Alternatively, if $n = 0$, this signifies a constant pressure process, which is represented on the pv diagram by a straight horizontal line (the log-log slope $= 0$).

Isochoric. If we have a constant volume process, then $dv = 0$; but from (1.50), since $dp \neq 0$, n must equal ∞. Alternatively, if $n = \infty$, this signifies a constant volume process, which is represented on the pv diagram by a straight vertical line (the log-log slope $= \infty$).

Isothermal. If we have a constant temperature process, then, for the perfect gas, pv = constant; and from (1.48), n must equal 1. Alternatively, if $n = 1$, this signifies a constant temperature process, which is represented on the pv diagram by an equilateral hyperbola (the log-log slope = -1).

Isentropic. If we have a process that is both adiabatic and reversible, we arbitrarily will denote this by setting $n = \gamma$ (the significance of γ is examined in Section 1.9). Alternatively, if $n = \gamma$, this signifies an insentropic process, which is represented on the pv diagram by a curve cutting across the isotherms (the log-log slope = $-\gamma$, with $\gamma > 1$).

pv-T Relation. For the perfect gas of (1.47) undergoing any reversible process described by (1.48), we obtain, by combination, the useful polytropic relations:

$$\frac{T_2}{T_1} = \left(\frac{p_2}{p_1}\right)^{(n-1)/n} = \left(\frac{v_1}{v_2}\right)^{n-1} \tag{1.51}$$

1.9 STAGNATION STATES

When a fluid is brought to rest adiabatically, the general energy equation of (1.27) becomes

$$0 = dh + \frac{V\,dV}{g_c} + \frac{g}{g_c}\,dz \tag{1.52}$$

It is convenient in gas dynamics to neglect the potential energy term in (1.52). This is justified by noting that the enthalpy and kinetic energy terms almost always dominate the energy balance. Thus, (1.52) becomes for a gas:

$$0 = dh + \frac{V\,dV}{g_c} \tag{1.53}$$

which, when integrated between static and total states, yields

$$0 = \int_s^t dh + \int_v^o \frac{V\,dV}{g_c}$$

or

$$h_t = h + \frac{V^2}{2g_c} \tag{1.54}$$

The *static* state means the undisturbed or free stream state, which is the actual state of the fluid. The *total* state means the state that results from stagnating the fluid by an isentropic process. The total term derives its name from the fact that it represents the sum of the static and dynamic terms, as seen in (1.54).

Since enthalpy and temperature are related through (1.47), it follows from (1.54) that

$$T_t = T + \frac{V^2}{2Jg_cC_p} \tag{1.55}$$

where the conventional units of C_p, the specific heat capacity at constant pressure, are British thermal units per pound mass per degree Rankine (Btu/lbm − °R).

The significance of γ can be seen by applying the first law of (1.21) to the perfect gas of (1.47) in an isentropic process. That is, by (1.21),

$$\delta q + \delta F = 0 = du + p \, dv$$

By (1.47),

$$p \, dv + v \, dp = \overline{R} \, dT$$
$$du = C_v \, dT$$
$$C_p = C_v + \overline{R}$$

Hence,

$$0 = \frac{C_v}{\overline{R}} (p \, dv + v \, dp) + p \, dv$$

or

$$0 = (C_v + \overline{R}) \, p \, dv + C_v v \, dp$$

or

$$0 = C_p \, p \, dv + C_v v \, dp$$

Dividing through by $(C_v pv)$, we have

$$0 = \left(\frac{C_p}{C_v}\right) \frac{dv}{v} + \frac{dp}{p}$$

that integrates to $pv^\gamma = K$ (a constant). But this relation is identical in form to (1.48), so it follows that $\gamma = n$ for an isentropic process of a perfect gas.

An important relation between pressure and temperature already has been given in (1.51) for the general polytropic process. This now can be expressed

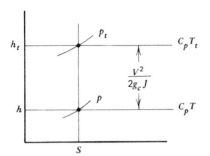

Figure 1.9 Various thermodynamic parameters.

in terms of an isentropic process between static and total states as

$$\frac{T_t}{T} = \left(\frac{p_t}{p}\right)^{(\gamma-1)/\gamma} \tag{1.56}$$

These concepts and terms involving the stagnation state are illustrated in Figure 1.9.

EXAMPLE 1.3

Air expands from a plenum chamber to the throat of a nozzle in an adiabatic process. Find the temperature of the air in the throat section in which the velocity is 1000 ft/sec if the air was initially at rest at 83°F.

(In terms of SI units, these same quantities are:

$$V_2 = 304.8 \text{ m/s}, \ T_1 = 301.5 \text{ K})$$

Solution

The velocity in a plenum chamber is essentially zero. Hence, by (1.55), the temperature in a plenum is the total temperature. Adiabatic flow implies that there is no heat transfer in the process. Therefore, the total temperature is conserved throughout the process. Applying (1.55) to the nozzle throat section, we have:

$$T_{2,\text{US}} = T_1 - \frac{V_2^2}{2Jg_cC_P} = (83+460) - \frac{1000^2}{2\times778\times32.174\times0.24} = 460°\text{R}$$

$$= 0°\text{F}$$

$$T_{2,\text{SI}} = T_1 - \frac{V_2^2}{2C_p} = 301.5 - \frac{304.8^2}{2\times1005} = 255.3\text{K} \qquad = -17.7°\text{C}$$

Note that the SI equation is simpler because in this system both the mechanical equivalant of heat (J_{US} = 778) and the proportionality constant (K_{US} = $1/g_c$) in Newton's second law are unity.

Observe the greatly decreased temperature of the gas resulting from this expansion process.

As a check on consistency, we can express one result in terms of the other. Thus,

$$°C = \frac{(°F - 32)}{1.8} = \frac{-32}{1.8} = -17.7°C$$

1.10 VISCOSITY

Because of its great importance in gas dynamics, we must next discuss and understand the concept of viscosity. Initially, Bernoulli and Euler, around 1750, worked with the *ideal, reversible* flow of thermodynamics, which coincides with the *potential* flow of mathematics and with the *loss-free* flow of hydraulics. However, such an approach fails to account for total pressure drops across duct and piping components, entropy-increasing processes, skin friction along pipe walls, unrestrained expansions across abrupt enlargements, irreversible mixing losses, and the like.

Ideal flow solutions are inadequate because all real fluids set up and transmit *tangential* as well as normal stresses (that is, shear as well as pressure stresses), especially in regions near solid boundaries. It is these viscosity-related tangential forces in gases that are overlooked by the ideal relations.

In 1827, Navier included for the first time a new term in the momentum equation to represent the hypothetical forces between adjacent molecules. This new term was taken as an unknown function of molecular spacing to which Navier attached no physical significance. By 1850, however, Stokes had replaced Navier's unknown function with the physically significant v, the kinematic viscosity.

It remained for Prandtl, in 1904, to advance the concept of a *boundary layer* to explain certain experimental observations. Briefly, if the flow in the main was well-described by the ideal Bernoulli-Euler relations and if the ideal relations broke down near solid boundaries, Prandtl would for purposes of analysis divide the flow into two parts. One part would concern a thin region adjacent to the solid boundary where, at large Reynolds Numbers, *all* the viscous effects are confined. The other part would include all the flow outside the boundary layer where, at large Reynolds Numbers, all viscous effects are to be ignored.

In the boundary layer region, the tangential velocities vary smoothly across the boundary layer, from zero at the walls to the ideal, potential velocity of the core flow. It is this sharp change in velocity with distance from the wall (that is, the large velocity gradient), rather than the magnitude of the velocity itself (which can be very small), that causes the shear stress to be so important.

In other words, since real fluids adhere to solid boundaries, a velocity gradient perpendicular to the flow direction is always present in real gas flow. This gradient sets up a sliding action between adjacent fluid layers. The continual energy interchange between these fluid layers, caused by the random motion of the gas molecules, links these layers and is the ultimate basis of viscosity. The viscosity (μ) or stickiness of the gas sets up a shear stress (τ) in the region of velocity gradient (dV/dy), as indicated by (1.9), that is

$$\tau = \mu \frac{dV}{dy} \tag{1.57}$$

The dynamic viscosity of most gases can be approximated by the Sutherland formula

$$\mu = \frac{C_1 g_c T^{3/2}}{T + C_2} \tag{1.58}$$

where the constants C_1 and C_2 are given in Table 1.3 for a few representative gases. The temperature in (1.58) is in °R, and the resulting viscosity is in 1bm/ft-sec. In practical gas dynamics, viscosity most often is determined by table, as a function of temperature, as given in Table 1.4. For air and water vapor, the Sutherland viscosities are compared with currently accepted values in Figure 1.10.

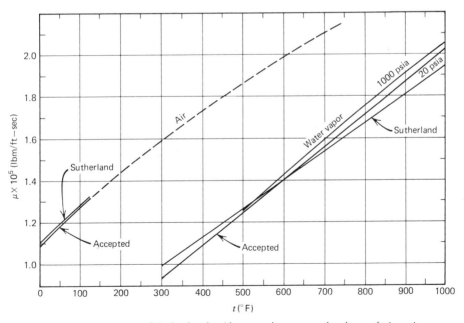

Figure 1.10 Comparison of Sutherland and currently accepted values of viscosity.

TABLE 1.3

*SUTHERLAND CONSTANTS FOR USE
IN (1.58)*

GAS	$C_1 \, (\times \, 10^8)$	C_2
Air	2.22	180
Oxygen	2.57	198
Nitrogen	2.16	184
Water vapor	2.85	1185
Carbon dioxide	2.42	420
Hydrogen	1.01	127
Methane	1.53	279

For now, it is enough to realize that we must cope with gas viscosity in gas dynamics work, that viscosity is responsible for most of the losses encountered in gas dynamics, that in the boundary layer all the flow losses are found, and that we will account for viscous effects mostly by empirical friction factors, as discussed next.

EXAMPLE 1.4

Find the viscosity by the Sutherland equation and compare it with the currently accepted value for:

A. Air at 100°F and 1 atmosphere.
B. Steam at 600°F and 500 psia.

Solution

A. Air By (1.58) and Table 1.3,

$$\mu_{\text{SUTH}} = \frac{2.22 \times 10^{-8} \times 32.174 \times 560^{1.5}}{560 + 180} = 1.279 \times 10^{-5} \text{ lbm/ft-sec}$$

whereas by Table 1.4a

$$\mu_{\text{ACCEPTED}} = 1.276 \times 10^{-5} \text{ lbm/ft-sec}$$

B. Steam By (1.58) and Table 1.3,

$$\mu_{\text{SUTH}} = \frac{2.85 \times 10^{-8} \times 32.174 \times 1060^{1.5}}{1060 + 1185} = 1.410 \times 10^{-5} \text{ lbm/ft-sec}$$

whereas by Table 1.4c

$$\mu_{\text{ACCEPTED}} = 1.416 \times 10^{-5} \text{ lbm/ft-sec}$$

TABLE 1.4a

VISCOSITY OF AIR IN US UNITS

t (°F)	μ (lbm/ft-sec) $\times$ 10^5 CONVENTIONAL[a]	SUTHERLAND[b]
0	1.086	1.101
20	1.125	1.138
40	1.159	1.174
60	1.206	1.210
80	1.242	1.245
100	1.276	1.279
120	1.293	1.313

[a]From [16], pg. 337.
[b]Equation (1.58).

TABLE 1.4b

VISCOSITY OF AIR IN SI UNITS

t (K)	μ $(N - s/m^2)$ $\times$ 10^7
200	132.5
250	159.6
300	184.6
350	208.2
400	230.1
450	250.7
500	270.1

TABLE 1.4c

VISCOSITY OF STEAM IN US UNITS

t (°F)	μ (lbm/ft-sec.) $\times$ 10^5 20 PSIA CONVENTIONAL[a]	SUTHERLAND[b]	1000 PSIA CONVENTIONAL[a]
300	0.933	0.988	—
400	1.094	1.131	—
500	1.255	1.272	—
600	1.416	1.410	1.415
700	1.544	1.545	1.609
800	1.705	1.677	1.770
900	1.866	1.807	1.898
1,000	2.027	1.934	2.059

[a]From ASME Steam Tables, 1967, pg. 280.
[b]Equation (1.58).

1.11 FRICTION

Whether we must deal with low speed gas flows where inertial effects are negligible and Σ forces ≈ 0 (that is, the laminar regime), or with high speed gas flows where inertial effects predominate and Σ forces $= Ma$ (that is, the turbulent regime), we still encounter losses in total pressure that can be described by the friction term (see Figure 1.11).

Briefly, for the adiabatic, workless flow of a gas, (1.21) and (1.27) combine to yield

$$0 = \delta F + \frac{dp}{\rho} + \frac{V\,dV}{g_c} \tag{1.59}$$

In this equation, δF represents the frictional head loss (in ft-lbf/1bm) that can be expressed in terms of a friction factor (f) as

$$\delta F = \left(f\frac{dx}{D}\right)\left(\frac{V^2}{2\,g_c}\right) \tag{1.60}$$

The friction factor of (1.60) has been well established, both theoretically and experimentally, for both smooth and rough pipes.

Laminar Flow Friction Factor. Although of limited use in gas dynamics, because laminar flow is rarely encountered in high speed gas flow, we give for completeness the simplest of the friction factors

$$f_L = \frac{64}{R_D} \tag{1.61}$$

where f_L is the laminar friction factor and R_D is the familiar Reynolds Number, based on the pipe diameter (D), and is defined as

$$R_D = \frac{\rho\,VD}{\mu} = \frac{VD}{\nu} \tag{1.62}$$

Smooth Pipe Friction Factor. Based on his boundary layer theory, Prandtl [11] obtained a theoretical expression for the friction factor of a smooth pipe, the numerical coefficients of which he adjusted slightly to agree with Nikuradse's experimental work [12]. In *rounded* form, for turbulent flow in smooth pipes, the Prandtl equation is

$$\frac{1}{\sqrt{f_s}} = 2\log\left(R_D\sqrt{f_s}\right) - 0.8 \tag{1.63}$$

where f_s is the friction factor for smooth pipes. It is important to note that the same f is used for both compressible and incompressible flows.

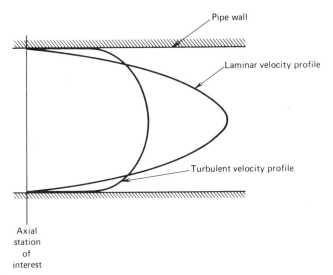

Figure 1.11 Laminar and turbulent velocity profiles in a pipe for the same volumetric average velocity.

Rough Pipe Friction Factor. Also based on Prandtl's boundary layer theory, von Karman [13] obtained a theoretical expression for the friction factor of a rough pipe (see Figure 1.12), the numerical coefficients of which he adjusted slightly to agree with Nikuradse's experimental work [14]. In *rounded* form, for turbulent flow in rough pipes, the von Karman equation is

$$\frac{1}{\sqrt{f_R}} = 2 \log\left(\frac{R}{e_s}\right) + 1.74 \tag{1.64}$$

The factor f_R in (1.64) is the friction factor for rough pipes, while R/e_s is the relative roughness of Nikuradse's artifically roughened pipes. R is the radius of the uncoated pipe and e_s is the diameter of the uncoated Gottingen sand used in the experiment.

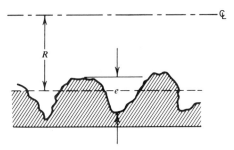

Figure 1.12 Greatly magnified sketch of a rough pipe wall.

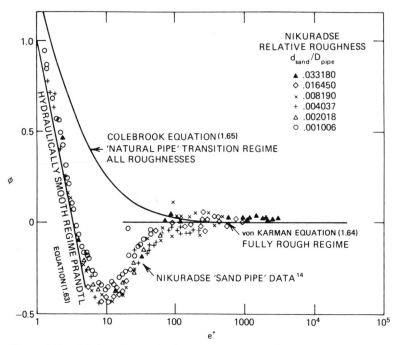

Figure 1.13 Friction factors in the transition region between smooth and rough pipes, in terms of the Colebrook coordinates.

Transition Between Smooth and Rough Pipes. To bridge the gap between the smooth pipe and the rough pipe characteristics, as given by (1.63) and (1.64), Colebrook [15], in 1938, developed an empirical function. He claimed it gave a transition curve that more closely agreed with *actual measurements* on most forms of naturally rough commercial pipes than the Nikuradse experiment indicated with artifically sand roughened pipes.

The Colebrook equation is

$$\frac{1}{\sqrt{f_T}} = 1.74 - 2\log\left(2\frac{e}{D} + \frac{18.7}{R_D\sqrt{f_T}}\right) \tag{1.65}$$

where f_T signifies the transition friction factor.

The difference between naturally and artificially roughened pipes in the transition region is clearly seen in Figures 1.13 and 1.14, where the Nikuradse data are shown on two different coordinate systems. The coordinates of Figure 1.13 need not concern us here (but see [16] for a detailed explanation), while those of Figure 1.14 are in common use today and owe their origin to Blasius [17].

Moody [18], in 1944, first presented a composite curve including the straight line friction factor curve (f_L) of (1.61); the smooth pipe turbulent friction factor curve (f_s) of (1.63); the various fully rough turbulent friction factor curves (f_R) of (1.64); and the transition friction factor (f_T) of (1.65).

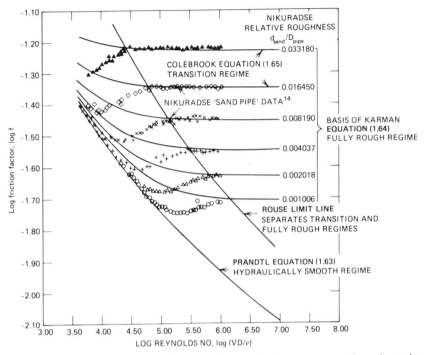

Figure 1.14 Friction factors in the transition region between smooth and rough pipes, in terms of the Blasius coordinates.

This information is organized in Figure 1.15 and is regarded with good reason as the *Moody plot*. Also shown on this plot is the Rouse limit line that separates the transition region from the fully rough region. In the critical zone, between the laminar and turbulent regimes, one can join the laminar line with the proper roughness curve by a straight line, with or without much reason.

Because the von Karman and Colebrook equations are based on Nikuradse's sand roughness scale, we are bound to express any pipe roughness on the Nikuradse scale as long as we continue to use either of these two equations for rough pipes. Moody [18] first gave the effective roughness of commercial pipes on the Nikuradse scale. His results for *new* pipes are given in Figure 1.16.

The best estimate of the *effective roughness* of a given pipe on the Nikuradse sand grain scale can be obtained by testing hydraulically a representative section of the pipe. The test should be run at a pipe Reynolds Number that exceeds the Rouse limit line. Then, in the fully rough regime, the relative roughness (e/D) that makes the von Karman equation (1.64) yield the experimentally determined f_R (obtained from pressure drop data) is the required effective relative roughness on the Nikuradse scale. Of course, it is this *effective roughness* that is to be used with the Moody plot.

Tables 1.5, 1.6, and 1.7 present numerical solutions to (1.63), (1.64), and (1.65), respectively, for convenience.

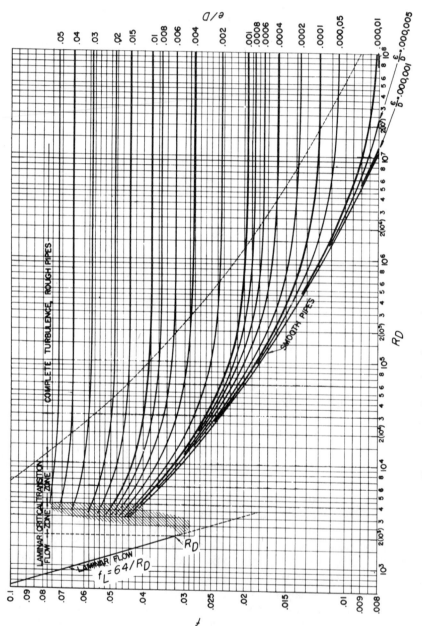

Figure 1.15 Complete friction factor map (after Moody [18]).

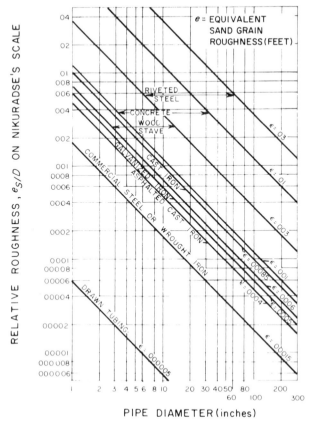

Figure 1.16 Commercial pipe roughness in terms of Nikuradse's sand grain scale (after Moody [18]).

EXAMPLE 1.5

Find the friction factor for a smooth pipe and for a pipe of $e/D = 0.001$, at a pipe Reynolds Number of 10^5, and compare these calculations with accepted table values.

Solution

A. **Smooth Pipe** By (1.63), a trial and error solution, to three decimals, yields $f_s = 0.018$ (guess 1 of 0.020 yields 0.018, guess 2 of 0.018 converges). Table 1.5 indicates $f_s = 0.01799$.

B. **Rough Pipe** According to Figure 1.15, the $e/D - R_D$ coordinates cross *below* the Rouse limit line, so that this pipe is not fully rough. Therefore, the transition equation (1.65) is used. A trial and error solution, to three decimals, yields $f_T = 0.022$ (guess 1 of 0.020 yields 0.022, guess 2 of 0.022 converges). Table 1.7 indicates $f_T = 0.02218$.

TABLE 1.5
SMOOTH PIPE FRICTION FACTOR BY
(1.63)

R_D	f_s
4×10^3	0.03992
5×10^3	0.03740
1×10^4	0.03089
2×10^4	0.02589
3×10^4	0.02349
4×10^4	0.02197
5×10^4	0.02090
1×10^5	0.01799
2×10^5	0.01564
3×10^5	0.01447
4×10^5	0.01371
5×10^5	0.01316
1×10^6	0.01165
2×10^6	0.01037
3×10^6	0.00972
4×10^6	0.00929
5×10^6	0.00898
1×10^7	0.00810

TABLE 1.6
ROUGH PIPE FRICTION FACTOR BY
(1.64)

e/D	R/e	f_R
1×10^{-5}	50,000	0.00806
5×10^{-5}	10,000	0.01054
1×10^{-4}	5,000	0.01198
2×10^{-4}	2,500	0.01372
4×10^{-4}	1,250	0.01589
6×10^{-4}	833	0.01740
1×10^{-3}	500	0.01963
2×10^{-3}	250	0.02341
4×10^{-3}	125	0.02840
6×10^{-3}	83	0.03210
1×10^{-2}	50	0.03788
3×10^{-2}	17	0.05713
5×10^{-2}	10	0.07149

TABLE 1.7
TRANSITION FRICTION FACTOR BY (1.65)

R_D \ e/D	1×10^{-5}	1×10^{-4}	1×10^{-3}	1×10^{-2}
		Transition friction factor, f_T		
5×10^3	0.03746	0.03756	0.03854	0.04728
1×10^4	0.03094	0.03108	0.03242	0.04313
5×10^4	0.02095	0.02127	0.02403	0.03907
1×10^5	0.01806	0.01853	0.02218	0.03848
5×10^5	0.01331	0.01444	0.02023	0.03800
1×10^6	0.01188	0.01344	0.01994	0.03794
5×10^6	0.00956	0.01234	0.01969	0.03789
1×10^7	0.00900	0.01216	0.01966	0.03789

1.12 CONCLUDING REMARKS

In this chapter we have reviewed some of the basic principles of thermo-dynamics including pertinent definitions, the laws of thermodynamics, and the basic gas dynamics identity. We have carefully defined the perfect gas, since that is the fluid we will be working with as we proceed into gas dynamics. The perturbations of viscosity and friction on the otherwise perfect gas have been reviewed since they will have practical bearing on the various gas dynamic analyses.

Even with this review behind us, it is still necessary to reexamine the conservation laws of mass, momentum, and energy in terms of a control volume, before we can properly approach the study of gas dynamics. This conservation material is dealt with in Chapter 2.

REFERENCES

1. N. A. Hall, *Thermodynamics of Fluid Flow*, Prentice-Hall, Englewood Cliffs, N.J., 1951, pp. 6–16.

2. F. Kreith and W. Z. Black, *Basic Heat Transfer*, Harper and Row, New York, 1980, Frontispiece.

3. R. P. Benedict, *Fundamentals of Pipe Flow*, Wiley, New York, 1980, pp. 67–68.

4. Ibid., pp. 68–80.

5. C. Caratheodory, "Investigations into the Foundations of Thermodynamics," *Math. Ann.*, Vol. 67, 1909, p. 355.

6. W. Thomson, "On the Dynamical Theory of Heat, With Numerical Results Deduced from Mr. Joule's Equivalent of a Thermal Unit, and M. Regnault's Observations in Steam," Part 2, *Trans. R. Soc. Edinb.*, March 1851.

7. J. P. Joule and W. Thomson, "On the Thermal Effects of Fluids in Motion," Part 2, *Phil. Trans. R. Soc. London,* Vol. 144, June 15, 1854, p. 350.

8. S. Carnot, *Reflections on the Motive Power of Fire,* Dover Publications, New York, 1960.

9. J. A. Goff, *Thermodynamic Notes,* 4th Ed., University of Pennsylvania Press, 1947.

10. R. P. Benedict, *Fundamentals of Temperature Pressure, and Flow Measurements,* 2nd Ed., Wiley, New York, 1977, p. 21.

11. L. Prandtl, "Neuere ergebnisse der turbulenzforschung," *Z. VDI,* Vol. 77, 1933, p. 105. Translated as "Recent Results of Turbulence Research."

12. J. Nikuradse, "Laws of Turbulent Flow in Smooth Pipes" (in German), *Forsch.-Arb. Ing.-Wesen,* No. 356, 1932.

13. T. von Karman, "Uber laminare und turbulente Reibung," *Z. Angew. Math. Mech.,* Vol. 1, 1921, p. 233. Translated as "On Laminar and Turbulent Friction," NACA TM 1092, 1946.

14. J. Nikuradse, "Laws of Flow in Rough Pipes" (in German), *Forsch.-Arb. Ing.-Wesen,* No. 361, 1933 (see also NACA TM 1292, 1950).

15. C. F. Colebrook, "Turbulent Flow in Pipes, with Particular Reference to the Transition Region Between the Smooth and Rough Pipe Laws," *J. Inst. Civil Eng.,* London, Vol. 11, 1938–1939, p. 133.

16. R. P. Benedict, *Fundamentals of Pipe Flow,* Wiley, New York, 1980, pp. 237–240.

17. P. R. H. Blasius, "Das Ähnlichkeitsgesetz bei Reibungsvorgangen in Flussigkeiten, *Phys. Z.,* Vol. 12, 1911, p. 1175. Translated as "The Law of Similarity Applied to Friction Phenomena."

18. L. F. Moody, "Friction Factors for Pipe Flow," *Trans. ASME,* November 1944, p. 676.

NOMENCLATURE

Roman

a	Acceleration
A	Area
C_p	Specific heat at constant pressure
C_v	Specific heat at constant volume
C_1, C_2	Sutherland viscosity constants
d	Exact differential
e	Absolute roughness
k	Thermal conductivity
K	Proportionality constant
f	Friction factor

F	Force, friction
g	Local gravitational acceleration
g_c	Gravitational constant
h	Specific enthalpy
J	Mechanical equivalent of heat
m	Mass
n	General polytropic exponent
p	Absolute static pressure
p_t	Absolute total pressure
$\dot{q}$	Rate of heat transfer
q	Heat transfered per unit mass
Q	Heat transferred
R	Pipe radius
$\overline{R}$	Specific gas constant
R_D	Pipe Reynolds Number
s	Specific entropy
S	Entropy
t	Empirical temperature
T	Absolute static temperature
T_t	Absolute total temperature
u	Specific internal energy
U	Internal energy
v	Specific volume
V	Directed fluid velocity
$\mathbf{V}$	Volume
w	Work per unit mass
$\dot{w}$	Rate of work
W	Weight
$\mathbf{W}$	Work
x	General displacement, usually in direction of flow
y	Displacement perpendicular to the flow
Z	Vertical displacement

Greek

α	Cubical coefficient of expansion of a gas
β	Angle
γ	Isentropic exponent, ratio of specific heats for a perfect gas
δ	Inexact differential
Δ	Finite difference
θ	Function of empirical temperature
μ	Dynamic viscosity
ν	Kinematic viscosity
ρ	Gas density
τ	Shear stress
ϕ	Function of

Subscripts

1	Axial station 1, 1 lb system
2	Axial station 2, 2 lb system
L	Laminar
p	Pressure
R	Rough
S	Smooth, sand
SI	International system
t	Temperature
T	Transition

PROBLEMS

1.1 A closed tank of 200 ft³ volume is initially charged with air at 50 psia and 150°F. How much heat must be transferred to this air for a final temperature of 300°F?

1.2 A closed tank of 100 m³ is charged with air at 345,000 pascals and 100°C. Find the heat transferred to this air to raise the temperature to 200°C.

1.3 Air expands from rest to the throat of a nozzle in an adiabatic process. Find the temperature in the throat where the velocity is 500 ft/sec if the air was initially at 90°F.

1.4 For an adiabatic process, find the air temperature at a point where the velocity is 350 m/s if the air was initially at rest at 15°C.

1.5 A. Find the thermal equivalent of the kinetic energy of a 1 lbm body moving at 500 ft/sec.

B. How much work would be required to bring this body to rest reversibly?

1.6 A. Convert the kinetic energy of a 1 kg body moving at 500 m/s to its thermal equivalent.

B. How much work would be required to bring this body to rest reversibly?

1.7 Find the velocity of air flowing at 10 lbm/sec through a 3 in. diameter pipe at a pressure of 100 psia and a temperature of −10°F.

1.8 Air flows through a 0.5 m diameter pipe at a pressure of 5,000 pascals and a temperature of 0°C at a flow rate of 5 kg/s. Find the velocity.

1.9 Express the given viscosities in lbm/ft-sec, slugs/ft-sec, and kilograms/meter-sec (use $g = g_c$).

A. 1.276×10^{-5} lbm/ft-sec.

B. 2.107×10^{-5} kg/m-s.

1.10 Find the Reynolds number for:

A. Air at atmospheric pressure and 80°F flowing at 1000 ft/sec in a 6 in. diameter pipe.

B. Saturated steam at 200 psia and 381.8°F (where v = 2.2873 ft³/ lbm) flowing at 30,000 lbm/h in a 3 in. diameter pipe.

1.11 Find the Reynolds number for air at atmospheric pressure and 300 K flowing at 500 m/s in a 0.1 m diameter pipe.

1.12 By means of appropriate equations calculate:

A. The friction factor of a smooth pipe at R_D = 2 × 10⁴.

B. The friction factor of a fully rough pipe if the relative roughness e/R = 0.0002.

C. The friction factor of a rough pipe if R_D = 5 × 10⁴ and e/D = 0.01.

1.13 By the Moody plot of Figure 1.15, determine the same f's of Problem 1.12.

1.14 Steam expands isentropically from 100 psia, 500°F to 1 atmosphere. Taking steam as a perfect gas at γ = 1.3, find the change in enthalpy.

2
CONSERVATION LAWS

2.1 GENERAL REMARKS

Several basic conservation concepts are relevant in gas dynamics. These physical concepts, embodied in several differential equations, will be developed next, including the principles of continuity, momentum, and energy.

More than one method of analysis is possible. We could work with a *fixed mass* as it moves with time within the system boundaries, or we could use the *control volume* that is a fixed region in space and consider the mass, momentum, and energy transfers as they cross the control volume boundaries. In the developments that follow, we will deal with the simpler case of a control volume fixed in space.

2.2 GENERAL CONSERVATION PRINCIPLE

Consider a differential control volume, dV, fixed in space and extent, and containing at a particular instant the fluid mass, dm. The various fluid and thermodynamic properties (for example, ρ, u, p) are specified at the *center* of the element of volume, where they are functions of time only (see Figure 2.1). However, all of these properties also may vary with position if they are considered at some position away from the center—at the surface of the control volume, for example. Thus, in general, each arbitrary property (P) is a function of both the time (t) and space (x, y, z) coordinates. At the center of the differential control volume, the space coordinates are fixed, and we can write

$$\left(\frac{dP}{dt}\right)_{x,\,y,\,z} = \frac{\partial P}{\partial t} \tag{2.1}$$

Whereas at the surfaces of the control volume (for a given time and with all second-order effects neglected), each arbitrary property can be expressed as

$$P \pm \frac{\partial P}{\partial x_k}\frac{dx_k}{2} \tag{2.2}$$

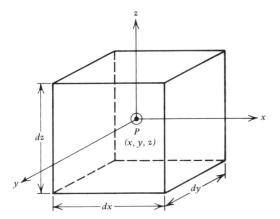

Figure 2.1   The control volume.

where the minus sign is used at the inlet surfaces and the plus sign at the outlet. The index, k, can be either 1, 2, or 3, depending on the specific coordinate being considered.

A general relation, patterned after the Reynolds Transport Theorem, can be given for any conserved quantity (N), in a flow field, as

The local rate of increase of N within volume + the net rate of efflux of N across surface of volume = the strength of sources of change of N.   (2.3)

The relation given by (2.3) embodies the general conservation principle and, in effect, states that the net rate of accumulation of N within the volume plus the net amount of N convected out of the volume in the same time must equal the total rate of change in N caused by the sources. The latter may occur by the spontaneous generation of N within the element, by the action of the resultant of all forces on the fluid within the element, or by changes in N caused by external energy or mass transfer to or from the fluid within the volume element.

2.3   CONSERVATION OF MASS

A basic premise of gas dynamics is that mass is one of the conserved quantities. Thus, we proceed to write a mass balance for the volume element $d\mathbf{V}$ in accordance with (2.3).

2.3.1   Local Rate of Increase of Mass Within Volume

Since a gas is deformable, both the mass and the density of the gas enclosed by the control volume may, in general, change with time. Since $m = \rho\mathbf{V}$, the rate of accumulation of mass can be expressed in terms of the rate of change of density as

$$\frac{\partial}{\partial t}(dm) = \frac{\partial}{\partial t}(\rho d\mathbf{V}) = \frac{\partial\rho}{\partial t}d\mathbf{V} \tag{2.4}$$

2.3.2   Net Rate of Efflux of Mass Across Surface of Volume

The mass per unit time convected across any particular surface may be expressed as the product of the appropriate density, velocity, and area terms. Thus, the net difference between the mass per unit time leaving the volume element and that entering it is

$$\left[\left(\rho + \frac{\partial \rho}{\partial x_i}\frac{dx_i}{2}\right)\left(u_i + \frac{\partial u_i}{\partial x_i}\frac{dx_i}{2}\right)dA_j\right]_{\text{out}}$$

$$-\left[\left(\rho - \frac{\partial \rho}{\partial x_i}\frac{dx_i}{2}\right)\left(u_i - \frac{\partial u_i}{\partial x_i}\frac{dx_i}{2}\right)dA_j\right]_{\text{in}} = \frac{\partial}{\partial x_i}(\rho u_i)\, dV \qquad (2.5)$$

Note that higher order terms are neglected in (2.5).

Also in (2.5), the index i indicates a summation operation, whereas the subscript j indicates perpendicularity to the direction of the term under consideration. When expanded, the final form of (2.5) is to be interpreted as

$$\left[\frac{\partial}{\partial x}(\rho u_1) + \frac{\partial}{\partial y}(\rho u_2) + \frac{\partial}{\partial z}(\rho u_3)\right]dV$$

2.3.3   Strength of Sources of Change of Mass

In gas dynamics, we consider a flow field having no points where mass is spontaneously introduced or removed; that is, we consider a flow with no sources or sinks.

2.3.4   Summation

Applying (2.3), we have via (2.4) and (2.5)

$$\frac{\partial \rho}{\partial t} + \frac{\partial}{\partial x_i}(\rho u_i) = 0 \qquad (2.6)$$

that mathematically expresses the principle of conservation of mass and is usually called the *continuity equation*.

In expanded form, (2.6) is

$$\frac{\partial \rho}{\partial t} + \frac{\partial}{\partial x}(\rho u_1) + \frac{\partial}{\partial y}(\rho u_2) + \frac{\partial}{\partial z}(\rho u_3) = 0 \qquad (2.7)$$

where ρ is the gas density; u_1, u_2, u_3, are the velocity components in the three mutually perpendicular directions, x, y, z; and t is the time.

In the steady state, since there can be no accumulation of mass within the element (that is, $\partial \rho / \partial t = 0$), the conservation of mass is achieved by a balance of the convected quantities alone. The continuity equation then reduces to

$$\frac{\partial}{\partial x_i}(\rho u_i) = 0 \tag{2.8}$$

2.3.5 One-Dimensional Steady Flow

For the one-dimensional, steady flow of gas dynamics, we have from (2.5)

$$\frac{\partial}{\partial x}(\rho u_1 dx\, dy\, dz) = 0 \tag{2.9}$$

or, more simply,

$$\dot{m} = \rho\, VA = \text{a constant} \tag{2.10}$$

where, for a given system, the constant $\dot{m}$ is called the mass flow rate, and V is the volumetric average velocity.

The various forms of the continuity equation for steady flow are summarized in Table 2.1.

TABLE 2.1
SUMMARY OF VARIOUS FORMS OF THE STEADY FLOW CONTINUITY EQUATION

SITUATION	CONTINUITY EQUATION
General	$\dfrac{\partial}{\partial x_i}(\rho u_i) = 0$
Three-dimensional	$\dfrac{\partial}{\partial x}(\rho u_1) + \dfrac{\partial}{\partial y}(\rho u_2) + \dfrac{\partial}{\partial z}(\rho u_3) = 0$
One-dimensional	$\dfrac{\partial}{\partial x}(\rho u_1) = 0$
or	$\dot{m} = \rho AV = \text{a constant (mass flow rate)}$

2.4 CONSERVATION OF MOMENTUM

Another premise that is basic to gas dynamics is the idea that the total momentum of any system may change only under the action of forces. We thus proceed to write a momentum-force balance on the fluid within the control volume according to (2.3).

2.4.1 Local Rate of Increase of Momentum Within Volume

The momentum of the fluid enclosed by the volume element may change with time since mass and velocity are both functions of time. The rate of accumulation of momentum may be expressed in terms of (1.1) as

$$\frac{1}{g_c}\frac{\partial}{\partial t}(dmu_k) = \frac{1}{g_c}\frac{\partial}{\partial t}(\rho\,dVu_k) = \frac{1}{g_c}\frac{\partial}{\partial t}(\rho u_k)\,dV \tag{2.11}$$

where the index k can be either 1, 2, or 3, and indicates the various components of momentum under consideration.

2.4.2 Net Rate of Efflux of Momentum Across Surface of Volume

The momentum per unit time convected across any particular surface may be expressed as the product of the appropriate mass per unit time and velocity terms. Thus, the net difference between the momentum per unit time leaving the volume element and that entering it is

$$\frac{1}{g_c}\left[\left(\rho + \frac{\partial\rho}{\partial x_i}\frac{dx_i}{2}\right)\left(u_i + \frac{\partial u_i}{\partial x_i}\frac{dx_i}{2}\right)dA_j\left(u_k + \frac{\partial u_k}{\partial x_i}\frac{dx_i}{2}\right)\right]_{\text{out}}$$

$$-\frac{1}{g_c}\left[\left(\rho - \frac{\partial\rho}{\partial x_i}\frac{dx_i}{2}\right)\left(u_i - \frac{\partial u_i}{\partial x_i}\frac{dx_i}{2}\right)dA_j\left(u_k - \frac{\partial u_k}{\partial x_i}\frac{dx_i}{2}\right)\right]_{\text{in}}$$

$$=\frac{1}{g_c}\frac{\partial}{\partial x_i}(\rho u_i u_k)\,dV \tag{2.12}$$

where the index i indicates a summation of terms at a particular k, which consistently indicates the component under consideration. The expanded form of the right-hand side of (2.12) is

$$\frac{1}{g_c}\left[\frac{\partial}{\partial x}(\rho u_1 u_1) + \frac{\partial}{\partial y}(\rho u_2 u_1) + \frac{\partial}{\partial z}(\rho u_3 u_1)\right]dV \text{ in the } k = 1 \text{ direction,}$$

$$\frac{1}{g_c}\left[\frac{\partial}{\partial x}(\rho u_1 u_2) + \frac{\partial}{\partial y}(\rho u_2 u_2) + \frac{\partial}{\partial z}(\rho u_3 u_2)\right]dV \text{ in the } k = 2 \text{ direction,}$$

$$\frac{1}{g_c}\left[\frac{\partial}{\partial x}(\rho u_1 u_3) + \frac{\partial}{\partial y}(\rho u_2 u_3) + \frac{\partial}{\partial z}(\rho u_3 u_3)\right]dV \text{ in the } k = 3 \text{ direction.}$$

2.4.3 Strength of Sources of Change of Momentum

In the absence of viscous shearing stresses, as in the *ideal* gas dynamics under discussion here, we will consider only forces arising from internal normal stresses (that is, pressures), and those arising because the fluid within the element is in an external conserved force field such as the earth's gravitational field.

The net difference between the *pressure forces* acting on the inlet and the

Thus, (2.17) reduces to

$$0 = -\frac{g_c}{\rho}\frac{\partial p}{\partial x} \tag{2.19}$$

For steady, one-dimensional, horizontal, *variable area* gas dynamics (2.17) can be written as

$$0 + u_1\frac{\partial u_1}{\partial x}(\rho d\mathbf{V}) = -g_c\frac{\partial p}{\partial x}d\mathbf{V} - 0 \tag{2.20}$$

which indicates that a pressure gradient and a velocity gradient are to be expected under these conditions.

In the more familiar form of an elementary force balance, (2.20) becomes

$$g_c(p_1A_1 - p_2A_2) = (\rho AV)(V_2 - V_1) \tag{2.21}$$

where the symbols may be clarified by reference to Figure 2.2

The various forms of the momentum equation for the steady flow of an *inviscid* fluid are summarized in Table 2.2.

TABLE 2.2
SUMMARY OF VARIOUS FORMS OF THE MOMENTUM EQUATION FOR THE STEADY FLOW OF AN INVISCID FLUID

SITUATION	MOMENTUM EQUATION
General	$u_i\dfrac{\partial u_k}{\partial x_i} = -\dfrac{g_c}{\rho}\dfrac{\partial p}{\partial x_k} - g\dfrac{\partial Z}{\partial x_k}$
Three-dimensional x direction $k=1$ $i = 1, 2, 3$	$u_1\dfrac{\partial u_1}{\partial x} + u_2\dfrac{\partial u_1}{\partial y} + u_3\dfrac{\partial u_1}{\partial z} = -\dfrac{g_c}{\rho}\dfrac{\partial p}{\partial x} - g\dfrac{\partial Z}{\partial x}$
One-dimensional x direction $k = i = 1$	$u_1\dfrac{\partial u_1}{\partial x} = -\dfrac{g_c}{\rho}\dfrac{\partial p}{\partial x} - g\dfrac{\partial Z}{\partial x}$
One-dimensional horizontal	$u_1\dfrac{\partial u_1}{\partial x}(\rho\, d\mathbf{V}) = -g_c\dfrac{\partial p}{\partial x}d\mathbf{V}$
or	$g_c(p_1A_1 - p_2A_2) = (\rho AV)(V_2 - V_1)$

2.5   CONSERVATION OF ENERGY

A third basic premise involved in gas dynamics is the concept that the total energy of any isolated system must be conserved. For the more general case, where external energy transfers are involved, we can write an energy balance on the fluid in the volume element of Figure 2.1 according to the relations of (2.3).

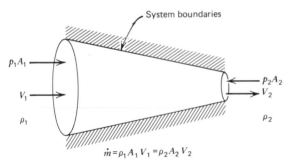

Figure 2.2 Notation for a one-dimensional force balance.

2.5.1 Local Rate of Increase of Energy Within Volume

The total energy of the fluid enclosed by the volume is composed of the internal energy of the fluid mass and the kinetic and potential energies of the fluid continuum. In general, each of these can change with time. Thus, the rate of accumulation of fluid energy can be expressed as

$$\frac{\partial}{\partial t}\left(\rho e + \frac{\rho V^2}{2g_c} + \frac{\rho g Z}{g_c}\right) dV \tag{2.22}$$

where e^1 is the internal energy per unit mass, V is the directed resultant velocity of the fluid continuum (that is, $V = iu_1 + ju_2 + ku_3$, where u_1, u_2, u_3 are the x, y, z components of V, and i, j, k in this relation are unit vectors), and Z is the vertical distance above some arbitrary horizontal datum where the potential energy is assumed to be zero.

2.5.2 Net Rate of Efflux of Fluid Energy Across Surface of Volume

The fluid energy per unit time convected across any particular surface may be expressed as the product of the appropriate terms for fluid energy per unit mass per unit time. Thus, the net difference between values of fluid energy per unit time leaving and entering the volume element is

$$\left[\left(e + \frac{\partial e}{\partial x_i}\frac{dx_i}{2}\right) + \frac{1}{2g_c}\left(V^2 + \frac{\partial V^2}{\partial x_i}\frac{dx_i}{2}\right) + \frac{g}{g_c}\left(Z + \frac{\partial Z}{\partial x_i}\frac{dx_i}{2}\right)\right]$$

$$\times \left[\left(\rho + \frac{\partial \rho}{\partial x_i}\frac{dx_i}{2}\right)\left(u_i + \frac{\partial u_i}{\partial x_i}\frac{dx_i}{2}\right) dA_j\right]_{\text{out}}$$

$$-\left[\left(e - \frac{\partial e}{\partial x_i}\frac{dx_i}{2}\right) + \frac{1}{2g_c}\left(V^2 - \frac{\partial V^2}{\partial x_i}\frac{dx_i}{2}\right) + \frac{g}{g_c}\left(Z - \frac{\partial Z}{\partial x_i}\frac{dx_i}{2}\right)\right] \tag{2.23}$$

$$\times \left[\left(\rho - \frac{\partial \rho}{\partial x_i}\frac{dx_i}{2}\right)\left(u_i - \frac{\partial u_i}{\partial x_i}\frac{dx_i}{2}\right) dA_j\right]_{\text{in}} = \frac{\partial}{\partial x_i}\left[\left(e + \frac{V^2}{2g_c} + \frac{g}{g_c}Z\right)(\rho u_i)\right] dV$$

---

[1]In this section only, e is used for internal energy instead of the usual u to avoid confusion with the x component of velocity that is also u.

2.5.3   **Strength of Sources of Change of Fluid Energy**

We here consider the net rate of internal pressure-volume work done on the fluid, the net rate of transfer of work out of the fluid by boundary deformation (that is, by external paddle wheel type work), and the net rate of heat transfer into the fluid from external sources.

The net difference between the pressure-volume work done on the fluid at the inlet surfaces and that done at the outlet surfaces in a unit of time is

$$
\left[\left(p - \frac{\partial p}{\partial x_i} \frac{dx_i}{2} \right) \left(u_i \frac{\partial u_i}{\partial x_i} \frac{dx_i}{2} \right) dA_j \right]_{\text{inlet surfaces}}
$$

$$
- \left[\left(p + \frac{\partial p}{\partial x_i} \frac{dx_i}{2} \right) \left(u_i + \frac{\partial u_i}{\partial x_i} \frac{dx_i}{2} \right) dA_j \right]_{\text{outlet surfaces}}
$$

$$
= - \frac{\partial}{\partial x_i} (pu_i) d\mathbf{V} \tag{2.24}
$$

where the minus sign indicates that pressure-volume work is done by the fluid.

We represent the net rate of transfer of external work by boundary deformation by the term $\delta \mathbf{W}$, while the net rate of heat transfer from external sources is simply δQ.

2.5.4   **Summation**

Applying (2.3), we obtain via (2.22), (2.23), and (2.24)

$$
\frac{\partial}{\partial t} \left(\rho e + \frac{\rho V^2}{2g_c} + \frac{\rho g Z}{g_c} \right) d\mathbf{V} + \frac{\partial}{\partial x_i} \left[\left(e + \frac{V^2}{2g_c} + \frac{g Z}{g_c} \right) (\rho u_i) \right] d\mathbf{V}
$$

$$
= - \frac{\partial}{\partial x_i} (pu_i) \, d\mathbf{V} + \delta \dot{\mathbf{W}} + \delta \dot{Q} \tag{2.25}
$$

which expresses the principle of conservation of energy and is usually called the *general energy equation.*

In expanded form (2.25) is

$$
\frac{\partial}{\partial t} \left[\rho e + \frac{\rho V^2}{2g_c} + \frac{\rho g Z}{g_c} \right] d\mathbf{V} + \frac{\partial}{\partial x} \left[\left(e + \frac{V^2}{2g_c} + \frac{g Z}{g_c} \right) (\rho u_1) \right] d\mathbf{V}
$$

$$
+ \frac{\partial}{\partial y} \left[\left(e + \frac{V^2}{2g_c} + \frac{g Z}{g_c} \right) (\rho u_2) \right] d\mathbf{V}
$$

$$
+ \frac{\partial}{\partial z} \left[\left(e + \frac{V^2}{2g_c} + \frac{g Z}{g_c} \right) (\rho u_3) \right] d\mathbf{V}
$$

$$
= - \left[\frac{\partial}{\partial x} (pu_1) + \frac{\partial}{\partial y} (pu_2) + \frac{\partial}{\partial z} (pu_3) \right] d\mathbf{V} + \delta \dot{\mathbf{W}} + \delta \dot{Q} \tag{2.26}
$$

2.5.5 One-Dimensional Steady Flow

In the steady state there can be no accumulation of fluid energy within the element—that is, $\partial/\partial t(\rho e + \rho V^2/2g_c + \rho gZ/g_c) = 0$. Then, by separating internal and external effects and by using continuity as given by (2.8), the general energy equation of (2.25) becomes in the steady state

$$(\delta\dot{Q} + \delta\dot{W})_{external} = (\rho u_i dA_j)\frac{\partial}{\partial x_i}\left[e + \frac{p}{\rho} + \frac{V^2}{2g_c} + \frac{g}{g_c}Z\right]dx_{i\;internal} \qquad (2.27)$$

Equation (2.27) can be expressed in the familiar thermodynamic form of energy per unit mass by dividing through by the mass flow rate $\dot{m}$ of (2.10). Thus,

$$\delta q + \delta w = de + p\,dv + v\,dp + \frac{V\,dV}{g_c} + \frac{g}{g_c}dZ \qquad (2.28)$$

where each term has the conventional units of foot-pounds force per pound mass, and $v = 1/\rho$ and represents the specific volume of the fluid. Equation (2.28) is seen to be identical to (1.27).

The various forms of the energy equation for steady flow are summarized in Table 2.3.

TABLE 2.3
SUMMARY OF VARIOUS FORMS OF THE STEADY FLOW ENERGY EQUATION

SITUATION	ENERGY EQUATION
General	$\dfrac{\partial}{\partial x_i}\left[\left(e + \dfrac{V^2}{2g_c} + \dfrac{g}{g_c}Z\right)(\rho u_i)\right]dV = -\dfrac{\partial}{\partial x_i}(pu_i)dV + \delta\dot{W} + \delta\dot{Q}$
Three-dimensional	$\dfrac{\partial}{\partial x}\left[\left(e + \dfrac{V^2}{2g_c} + \dfrac{g}{g_c}Z\right)(\rho u_1)\right]dV + \dfrac{\partial}{\partial y}\left[\left(e + \dfrac{V^2}{2g_c} + \dfrac{g}{g_c}Z\right)(\rho u_2)\right]dV$
	$+\dfrac{\partial}{\partial z}\left[\left(e + \dfrac{V^2}{2g_c} + \dfrac{g}{g_c}Z\right)(\rho u_3)\right]dV$
	$= -\left[\dfrac{\partial}{\partial x}(pu_1) + \dfrac{\partial}{\partial y}(pu_2) + \dfrac{\partial}{\partial z}(pu_3)\right]dV + \delta\dot{W} + \delta\dot{Q}$
One-dimensional	$\delta q + \delta w = de + p\,dv + v\,dp + \dfrac{V\,dV}{g_c} + \dfrac{g}{g_c}dZ$

2.6 CONCLUDING REMARKS

In this chapter we have reviewed the basic conservation laws of mass, momentum, and energy. Starting from a general conservation principle, (2.3), we proceeded to apply this to the mass, momentum, and energy balances of a differential control volume. For one-dimensional, steady flow, gas dynamics the conservation of mass analysis led us to the continuity equation of (2.10), namely

$$\dot{m} = \rho V A = \text{constant}$$

Under these same conditions and in the absence of viscous shearing stresses, the conservation of momentum analysis led us to the simplified force blance of (2.21), namely

$$p_1 A_1 - p_2 A_2 = \frac{\dot{m}}{g_c}(V_2 - V_1)$$

Finally, again for the one-dimensional steady flow of a perfect gas, but now with the restriction of zero viscosity removed, the conservation of energy analysis led us to the general energy equation of (2.28), namely

$$\delta q + \delta w = de + p \, dv + v \, dp + \frac{V \, dV}{g_c}$$

The potential energy term is considered negligible in most gas dynamics analyses.

With these conservation principles understood, as summarized by Tables 2.1, 2.2, and 2.3, we are in a better position to undertake the study of gas dynamics. We begin in Chapter 3 with the basic compressible concept of the Mach number.

REFERENCES

1. R. P. Benedict, "Analog Simulation," *Electro-Technol.*, Science and Engineering Series 60, December 1963, p. 73.

2. R. P. Benedict, *Fundamentals of Pipe Flow*, Wiley, New York, 1980, pp. 3–19.

3. R. M. Rotty, *Introduction to Gas Dynamics*, Wiley, New York, 1962, pp. 24–41.

NOMENCLATURE

Roman

a	Acceleration
A	Area
e	Internal energy per pound mass
f	Function
g	Local gravity
g_c	Gravitational constant
m	Mass
N	Conserved quantity
p	Pressure

P	Arbitrary property
P.E.	Potential energy
q	Heat transferred per unit mass
$\dot{Q}$	Rate of heat transfer
Q	Heat
t	Time
u	Velocity component
v	Specific volume
V	Resultant velocity
V	Volume
w	Work per unit mass
$\dot{w}$	Rate of work
W	Work
x, y, z	Cartesian coordinates
Z	Vertical height

Greek

ρ Fluid density

Mathematical Symbols

d Total derivative
∂ Partial derivative

Subscripts

1, 2, 3	In x, y, z directions
i, k	Indices, generally 1 to 3 (i signifies a summation process, while k signifies the particular component under consideration)
j	Geometric subscript signifying perpendicularity to the component or term under consideration

PROBLEMS

2.1 The average velocity of air flowing in a 12-in. diameter pipe is 500 ft/sec at a pressure of 20 psia and a temperature of 100°F. Find the average velocity where the diameter is reduced to 8 in., the pressure is 15 psia, and the temperature is 50°F.

2.2 What will be the velocity in a 1/6 m diameter section of a pipe where the pressure is 75,000 pascals and the temperature is 30°C if the velocity of air flowing in a 1/3 m diameter section of the same pipe is 100 m/s at a pressure of 120,000 pascals and a temperature of 50°C?

2.3 Air flows through a constant area pipe with negligible losses.

    A. If inlet conditions are p_1 = 80 psia, p_{t1} = 100 psia, T_1 = 560°R, and V_1 = 665.5 ft/sec, find the inlet T_t.
    B. If V_2 = 846 ft/sec, find the static pressure, p_2.
    C. If p_{t2} = 96.4 psia, find the heat transferred per pound mass.

2.4 Air flows through a constant area duct without loss.

    A. Find the inlet total temperature if p_1 = 350,000 pascals, p_{t1} = 400,000 pascals, T_1 = 333K, and V_1 = 161.3 m/s.
    B. If V_2 = 246 m/s, find the static pressure, p_2.
    C. If p_{t2} = 379,100 pascals, find the heat transferred per kilogram.

2.5 Air flows isothermally (that is, at T = constant) in a horizontal pipe of constant diameter. At one axial location the pressure is 200 psia and the average velocity is 150 ft/sec. Further downstream, the pressure is reduced to 100 psia. How much heat must be transferred to the pipe?

2.6 Find the amount of heat transfer involved in an isothermal flow of air in a uniform diameter pipe from an initial pressure of 1,400,000 pascals and an initial velocity of 50 m/s to a final pressure of 700,000 pascals.

2.7 Air at 2000°R enters a turbine at a mass flow rate of 2 lbm/sec. The air expands and leaves at 1000°R. Assuming the flow is adiabatic and that the inlet and exit velocities are equal, find the horsepower developed by the turbine.

3
MACH NUMBER

3.1 VELOCITY OF SOUND

Whenever a gas, in motion or at rest, is disturbed slightly, small pressure waves will be set up that will travel through the gas at a finite velocity, designated by the arbitrary symbol, a. Such waves are propagated by the elastic properties (that is, by the density variations) of the gas. The propagation velocity (a) is finite because wave transmission is retarded by the inertia of the gas elements. The small pressure wave can be visualized as a surface, moving perpendicular to the system boundaries, across which a small change of state takes place.

Propagation of the small pressure wave can be considered in two ways. According to one viewpoint, the boundaries are fixed and the wave front moves at the velocity $V_w = a + V$, where V is the initial uniform velocity of the gas (see Figure 3.1a). Observe the discontinuity in pressure across the wave front and the necessary change in gas velocity behind the wave.

From a more convenient viewpoint, we can imagine ourselves traveling with the wave. Now, the wave front appears fixed, and the gas is seen moving relative to the wave (see Figure 3.1b). This is equivalent to imposing a uniform velocity $-V_w$ on the entire fluid system. From the right, the gas appears to approach the fixed wave front at the wave propagation velocity, a. From the left, the gas appears to leave the fixed wave front at the net velocity, $a - dV$.

Experimental work on the transmission of sound waves in a gas confirms that the change in state across a small pressure wave is essentially isentropic. Specifically, this means that the flow is reversible and adiabatic.

Applying the conservation principles of mass and momentum, across the constant area pressure wave, we can obtain a useful expression for the propagation velocity of the small disturbance.

Continuity. From (2.10) we have

$$\rho a = (\rho + d\rho)(a - dV)$$

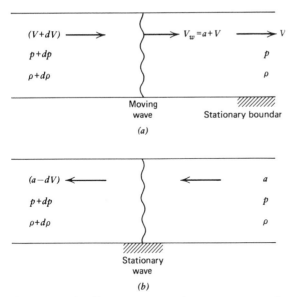

Figure 3.1   Small pressure wave in constant area pipe. (a) Fixed boundaries. (b) Fixed wave front.

or, ignoring second order terms, we obtain

$$dV = \frac{ad\rho}{\rho} \tag{3.1}$$

Momentum.   From (2.21), for the reversible case, we have

$$p - (p + dp) = \frac{\rho a\,(-dV)}{g_c}$$

or

$$dV = \frac{g_c dp}{a\rho} \tag{3.2}$$

When dV is eliminated between (3.1) and (3.2), the following results:

$$a^2 = g_c\left(\frac{\partial p}{\partial \rho}\right)_s \tag{3.3}$$

where partials and the subscript s have been used to indicate that changes in pressure with density have been considered at constant entropy only. Such changes would be different if a process other than isentropic was considered.

When we differentiate the isentropic form of (1.48), namely $p = C\rho^\gamma$, we obtain for the perfect gas

$$\left(\frac{\partial p}{\partial \rho}\right)_s = \frac{\gamma p}{\rho} \tag{3.4}$$

Combining (3.3) and (3.4), we have

$$a^2 = \frac{\gamma g_c p}{\rho} \tag{3.5}$$

and if the perfect gas equation of state of (1.47) is used, there results finally

$$a = \sqrt{\gamma g_c \overline{R} T} \tag{3.6}$$

Equation (3.6) represents alternatively: the propagation velocity of a weak pressure wave, the velocity of sound in the gas, the sonic velocity, and the acoustic velocity (this latter accounts for the symbol a).

Although we have treated the plane wave only, it is interesting to note that the spherical wave travels at the same velocity.

The acoustic velocity is, of course, of primary importance in gas dynamics.

The derivation of (3.6) is based on Laplace's assumption of 1816 that the rarefactions and compressions of air accompanying the passage of a sound wave take place with no heat transfer (and with no losses). Laplace reviewed Newton's isothermal evaluation[1] of the velocity of sound in air, that is

$$a^2_{\text{newton}} = g_c \left(\frac{\partial p}{\partial \rho}\right)_{t=c} = g_c \frac{p}{\rho} \tag{3.7}$$

and stated it more correctly as (3.3). Equations (3.3) and (3.7) lead to acoustic velocities that differ for air by the factor $\sqrt{1.4}$, or by about 18%.

Much of this material has been reviewed in references [1 through 5] given at the end of this chapter.

EXAMPLE 3.1

Estimate the distance to an observed lightening flash if the accompanying thunder is heard 4 seconds later and the air temperature is 80°F (26.67°C).

Solution

Since light travels at an extremely high velocity, we can assume we will see a lightening flash almost instantaneously.

By (3.6), we have

$$a_{\text{US}} = \sqrt{\gamma g_c \overline{R}} \sqrt{T} = \sqrt{1.4 \times 32.174 \times 53.35} \sqrt{(80+460)}$$

---

[1]"The velocities of pulses propagated in an elastic fluid are in a ratio compounded of the square root of the ratio of the elastic force directly, and the square root of the ratio of the density inversely." Isaac Newton, 1687.

$$a_{US} = 49.02 \sqrt{540} = 1139 \text{ ft/sec}$$

In SI, the constant g_c is not required and we have

$$a_{SI} = \sqrt{\gamma \overline{R}} \sqrt{T} = \sqrt{1.4 \times 287.1} \sqrt{(26.67 + 273.15)}$$

$$a_{SI} = 20.05 \sqrt{300} = 347.2 \text{ m/s}$$

The constants in (3.6) are encountered so frequently in gas dynamics that we have separated them from the absolute static temperature. For air, in the US system, the square root of these constants is closely 49. In SI, we have closely 20.

From the relation, distance = rate × time, we obtain

$$L_{US} = 1139 \times 4 = 4556 \text{ ft}$$

$$L_{SI} = 347.2 \times 4 = 1389 \text{ m}$$

As a check on consistency, we can express one result in terms of the other. Thus,

$$4556 \text{ ft} \left(\frac{0.3048 \text{ m}}{\text{ft}} \right) = 1389 \text{ m}$$

3.2   MACH NUMBER

The continuity equation of (2.10) can be differentiated logarithmically to yield

$$\frac{dA}{A} = -\frac{dV}{V} - \frac{d\rho}{\rho}$$

or, upon rearrangement,

$$\frac{dA}{A} = -\frac{dV}{V} \left[1 + \left(\frac{V^2}{V dV} \right) \frac{d\rho}{\rho} \right]$$

When this equation is combined with the general energy equation of (1.27) or (2.28), which for an isentropic-workless process takes the form $\rho V dV = -g_c dp$, we have

$$\frac{dA}{A} = \frac{dV}{V} \left[\frac{V^2}{g_c (\partial p / \partial \rho)_s} - 1 \right] = \frac{dV}{V} \left[\left(\frac{V}{a} \right)^2 - 1 \right] \tag{3.8}$$

the quantity $g_c (\partial p / \partial \rho)_s$ being recognized from (3.3) as the square of the acoustic velocity in a gas. Thus, in (3.8), the quantity $(V/a)^2$ is seen to be critical with respect to unity. That is, as long as $(V/a)^2$ is less than one, the area must decrease

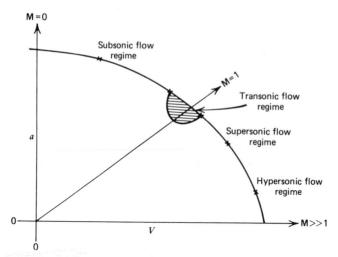

Figure 3.2   Relations and zones involving gas velocity (*V*) and acoustic velocity (*a*).

for the velocity to increase (this is the subsonic nozzle). Conversely, velocity can increase only if the area increases when $(V/a)^2$ exceeds one (this we will see later is the supersonic nozzle). And, of course, when $(V/a)^2$ just equals one, we have a critical flow situation that requires the minimum flow area (called the throat section of a nozzle). Later, in Chapter 5, this relationship between the flow area and the critical flow situation is considered in greater detail.

The velocity ratio (V/a) is so important in gas dynamics that it has a special name, the Mach number (**M**), after the Viennese physicist, Ernst Mach. Thus,

$$\mathbf{M} \equiv \frac{V}{a} \tag{3.9}$$

Note that, according to Figure 3.2, if $\mathbf{M} < 1$, we speak of the subsonic regime; if $\mathbf{M} > 1$, we speak of the supersonic regime; while the condition $\mathbf{M} = 1$ signifies a *critical* flow situation.

3.3   THE MACH ANGLE

In a gas at rest, small pressure pulses from a stationary disturbance are propagated uniformly in all directions at the speed of sound, much as ripples spread on the surface of still water (see Figure 3.3*a*).

When the gas is moving at subsonic speeds, the small pressure pulses from a stationary disturbance still propagate in all directions at the speed of sound, but the wave fronts are no longer symmetrical (see Figure 3.3*b*). That is, the wave fronts are swept downstream by the gas velocity.

However, when the gas is moving at supersonic speeds, the gas particles are moving faster than the signal waves. This means that the small pressure pulses from a stationary disturbance can propagate only in the direction of flow.

They cannot advance upstream. Thus, all pressure pulses are confined to a cone trailing downstream of and having its apex at the source of the disturbance (see Figure 3.3c). Outside this cone of action is the so-called zone of silence signifying that in this region no signals propagate to indicate the presence of a disturbance.

The half angle (θ) at the apex in Figure 3.3c is known as the Mach angle. From geometry, it is given by

$$\sin \theta = \frac{at}{Vt} = \frac{1}{M} \tag{3.10}$$

Equation (3.10) indicates that the Mach angle (θ) is that angle whose sine is 1/**M**.

Experimentally, the Mach angle is often the best means of estimating the Mach number of a supersonic flow. When a pinlike probe is placed in a supersonic stream, the resulting Mach lines form a two-dimensional cone made visible by shadowgraph, or by other optical techniques. From these Mach lines, the Mach angle and hence the Mach number can be determined.

EXAMPLE 3.2

Estimate the velocity of the air leaving a supersonic nozzle, if the Mach angle is measured to be 30°, and the air temperature is taken to be 40°F.

Solution

The Mach number is, from (3.10),

$$\mathbf{M} = \frac{1}{\sin 30°} = \frac{1}{0.5} = 2$$

The acoustic velocity is from (3.6) and Example 3.1

$$a = 49 \sqrt{(40 + 460)} = 1096 \text{ ft/sec}$$

Hence, from (3.9), the air velocity is

$$V = 2 \times 1096 = 2192 \text{ ft/sec}$$

3.4   MACH NUMBER EQUATIONS

The total to static temperature relation of (1.55) can be written in terms of the Mach number as follows. In

$$T_t = T + \frac{V^2}{2Jg_cC_p}$$

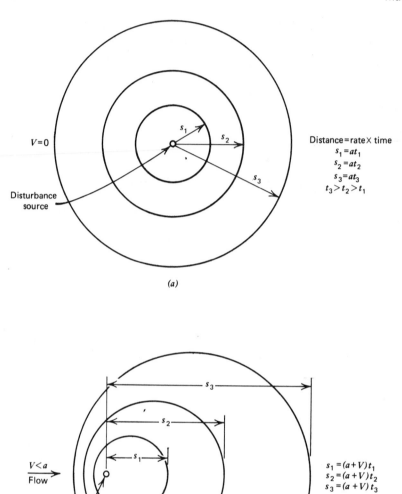

(a)

(b)

Figure 3.3 Wave patterns at various gas velocities. *(a)* Wave fronts in a stationary gas. *(b)* Wave fronts in a subsonic gas flow. *(c)* Wave fronts in a supersonic gas flow. Conical surface forming the locus of all wave fronts is called a Mach wave. Half angle (θ) at apex is termed the Mach angle.

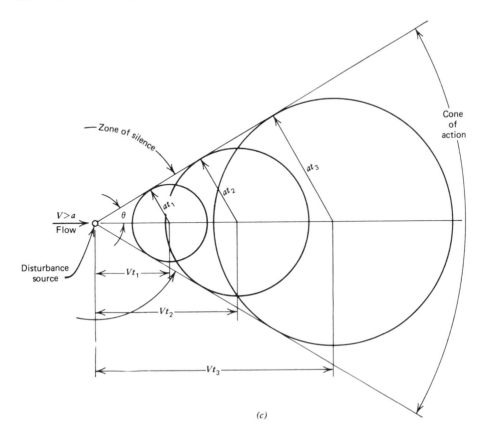

Cone
of
action

—Zone of silence—

at_3

at_2

at_1

$V > a$
Flow

θ

Disturbance
source

Vt_1

Vt_2

Vt_3

(c)

the specific heat is replaced by the perfect gas relation of (1.47), namely

$$C_p = \frac{\gamma \overline{R}}{(\gamma - 1)J}$$

When the resulting expression is divided through by the static temperature, we obtain

$$\frac{T_t}{T} = 1 + \frac{\gamma - 1}{2}\left(\frac{V^2}{\gamma g_c \overline{R} T}\right) \qquad (3.11)$$

Applying (3.6) and (3.9) to (3.11) yields

$$\frac{T_t}{T} = 1 + \frac{\gamma - 1}{2}\mathbf{M}^2 \qquad (3.12)$$

From the isentropic relation (1.56), the pressure ratio likewise can be given in terms of the Mach number as

$$\frac{p_t}{p} = \left(1 + \frac{\gamma - 1}{2}\mathbf{M}^2\right)^{\gamma/(\gamma-1)}$$ (3.13)

Note that (3.13), solved in terms of the Mach number, yields the useful relation

$$\mathbf{M} = \left\{\frac{2}{\gamma - 1}\left[\left(\frac{p}{p_t}\right)^{(1-\gamma)/\gamma} - 1\right]\right\}^{1/2}$$ (3.14)

It is easy to see that once the pressure ratio (p/p_t) at a state point is determined, by measurements or by design, the Mach number also is uniquely defined via (3.14). Conversely, if the Mach number is specified at a state point, we immediately know the pressure ratio (p/p_t) and the temperature ratio (T/T_t) at the same point. These relations, (3.12), (3.13), and (3.14), ensure that tables can be drawn up with any one of these three dimensionless ratios as the independent variable. It follows that the other two dependent variables are uniquely defined.

EXAMPLE 3.3

Find the static pressure and temperature of air ($\gamma = 1.4$) at a point where the Mach number is 1.5, the total pressure is 50 psia, and the total temperature is 500°F.

Solution

By (3.12) and (3.13), we have

$$\frac{T_t}{T} = 1 + \frac{0.4}{2}(1.5)^2 = 1.45$$

and

$$\frac{p_t}{p} = (1.45)^{1.4/0.4} = 3.671$$

Noting the importance of working with absolute values of temperature and pressure, we have

$$T = \frac{(500 + 460)}{1.45} = 662°R = 202°F$$

and

$$p = \frac{50}{3.671} = 13.62 \text{ psia}$$

Another relation that is usefully expressed in terms of the Mach number is the mass flow rate of (2.10). The density in the expression ($\dot{m} = \rho A V$) is first replaced by the perfect gas equation of state ($\rho = p/\overline{R}T$) to yield

$$\dot{m} = \frac{pAV}{\overline{R}T}$$

Introducing the acoustic velocity of (3.6) and the Mach number of (3.9), we obtain

$$\dot{m} = \frac{pA\mathbf{M}}{\sqrt{\dfrac{\overline{R}T}{\gamma g_c}}} \tag{3.15}$$

This is often rearranged to the dimensionless *static* flow number

$$\left(\frac{\dot{m}}{Ap}\right)\sqrt{\frac{\overline{R}T}{g_c}} = \sqrt{\gamma}\,\mathbf{M} \tag{3.16}$$

that, through (3.14), can also be given as

$$\left(\frac{\dot{m}}{Ap}\right)\sqrt{\frac{\overline{R}T}{g_c}} = \left\{\left(\frac{2\gamma}{\gamma-1}\right)\left[\left(\frac{p}{p_t}\right)^{(1-\gamma)/\gamma} - 1\right]\right\}^{1/2} \tag{3.17}$$

Note for the constant flow per unit area case that (3.15) can be rearranged to the useful form

$$\frac{p\mathbf{M}}{\sqrt{T}} = \text{constant} \tag{3.18}$$

Finally, when (3.12) is introduced in (3.16), we obtain the dimensionless *total* flow number

$$\left(\frac{\dot{m}}{Ap_t}\right)\sqrt{\frac{\overline{R}T_t}{g_c}} = \frac{\mathbf{M}\sqrt{\gamma}}{\left(1 + \dfrac{\gamma-1}{2}\mathbf{M}^2\right)^{(\gamma+1)/2(\gamma-1)}} \tag{3.19}$$

Alternatively, when (1.56) is introduced in (3.17), we get

$$\left(\frac{\dot{m}}{Ap_t}\right)\sqrt{\frac{\overline{R}T_t}{g_c}} = \left\{\left(\frac{2\gamma}{\gamma-1}\right)\left[\left(\frac{p}{p_t}\right)^{2/\gamma} - \left(\frac{p}{p_t}\right)^{(\gamma+1)/\gamma}\right]\right\}^{1/2} \tag{3.20}$$

EXAMPLE 3.4

Find the Mach number for air flowing through a 4-in. diameter duct at 5 lbm/sec when the temperature is 50°F and the pressure is 15 psia.

(In terms of SI units, these same qualities are: $D = 0.1016$ m, $\dot{m} = 2.268$ kg/s, $T = 10°C$, and $p = 103{,}422$ pascals.)

Solution

By (3.16),

$$\mathbf{M}_{US} = \left(\frac{\dot{m}}{Ap}\right)\sqrt{\frac{RT}{\gamma g_c}}$$

$$= \frac{5 \text{ lbm}}{\text{sec}} \times \frac{4}{\pi(16)\text{in}^2} \times \frac{\text{in.}^2}{15 \text{ lbf}}\sqrt{\frac{53.35 \text{ ft-lbf} \times (50 + 460)°\text{R}}{°\text{R-lbm} \times 1.4 \times 32.174 \dfrac{\text{ft-lbm}}{\text{lbf-sec}^2}}} = 0.652$$

In SI, the constant g_c is not required, and we have

$$\mathbf{M}_{SI} = 2.268 \times \frac{4}{\pi(0.1016)^2} \times \frac{1}{103{,}422}\sqrt{\frac{287.1 \times 283}{1.4}} = 0.652$$

3.5 CONCLUDING REMARKS

We have seen that in a subsonic flow the presence of a small disturbance in a gas is signaled throughout the gas by a wave traveling at the local velocity of sound in the gas. However, if the gas particles are moving at a velocity greater than the acoustic velocity, no signaling upstream of a disturbance is possible. Furthermore, abrupt changes in pressure, density, and velocity are to be expected in a supersonic flow field.

Measuring the Mach angle is one technique for determining the Mach number in a supersonic flow according to the relation, $\sin \theta = 1/\mathbf{M}$.

Several important equations, in terms of the Mach number, were developed in terms of the static to total temperature and pressure ratios, and in terms of the mass flow rate. These equations, namely (3.12), (3.13), and (3.16), will prove useful throughout the remainder of our study.

REFERENCES

1. N. A. Hall, *Thermodynamics of Fluid Flow*, Prentice-Hall, Englewood Cliffs, N.J., 1951, pp. 70–76.

2. R. C. Binder, *Fluid Mechanics*, Fourth Ed., Prentice-Hall, Englewood Cliffs, N.J., 1962, pp. 221–228.

3. R. M. Rotty, *Introduction to Gas Dynamics*, Wiley, New York, 1962, pp. 42–59.

4. F. Cheers, *Elements of Compressible Flow*, Wiley, New York, 1963, pp. 40–63.
5. R. P. Benedict, *Fundamentals of Pipe Flow*, Wiley, New York, 1980, pp. 91–92.

NOMENCLATURE

Roman

a	Acoustic velocity
A	Area
C_p	Specific heat at constant pressure
g_c	Gravitational constant
J	Mechanical equivalent of heat
$\dot{m}$	Mass flow rate
$\mathbf{M}$	Mach number
p	Absolute static pressure
p_t	Absolute total pressure
$\overline{R}$	Specific gas constant
T	Absolute static temperature
T_t	Absolute total temperature
V	Directed fluid velocity
V_w	Wave front velocity

Greek

γ	Isentropic exponent
θ	Mach angle
ρ	Gas density

Math Symbols

d	Total derivative
∂	Partial derivative

Subscripts

S	At contant entropy

PROBLEMS

3.1 Air at 100°F flows at a Mach number of 2. Find the velocity and the Mach angle.

3.2 Find the velocity and the Mach angle if air flows at a Mach number of 2.5 at a temperature of 50°C.

3.3 In terms of the U.S. Customary System, express the maximum velocity that can occur in the throat of a nozzle in terms of the total temperature (note that the maximum Mach number is 1).

3.4 Find an expression for the maximum velocity that can occur at the throat of a nozzle in terms of the total temperature, using the S.I. system of units.

3.5 Air flows at a mass flow rate of 2 lbm/sec through a 3-in. diameter pipe when the total temperature is 80°F. Find the Mach number, the velocity, and the total pressure at a point where the static pressure is 10 psia.

3.6 Find the Mach number, the velocity, and the total pressure at a point where the static pressure is 50,000 pascals when air flows at a mass flow rate of 1 kg/s through a 0.1 m diameter pipe and the total temperature is 50°C.

3.7 At one plane in an adiabatic nozzle, air flows at 1,000 ft/sec at a static temperature of 100°F. Find the air temperature at another plane where the Mach number is 2.

3.8 Air flows adiabatically through a nozzle at 500 m/s at a plane where the static temperature is 70°C. Find the temperature at another plane in the nozzle where the Mach number is 1.5.

3.9 Air flows isentropically at $T_t = 100°F, p_t = 20$ psia. Find the velocities at planes where the pressures are: $p_1 = 15$ psia, $p_2 = 10$ psia.

3.10 Air flows isentropically through a piping system having the total conditions, $T_t = 100°C$ and $p_t = 125,000$ pascals. Find the velocities where the pressures are: $p_1 = 100,000$ pascals and $p_2 = 50,000$ pascals.

4
GENERALIZED GAS DYNAMICS EQUATION

4.1 GENERALIZED GAS DYNAMICS EQUATION

As we have reviewed the fundamentals of gas dynamics in Chapter 1, the conservation laws in Chapter 2, and the Mach number in Chapter 3, it is now appropriate for us to here develop *a generalized flow equation* that will apply to any and all gas dynamics processes [1–4].

Five basic equations are invoked. These are:

Continuity (2.10).

General energy (1.53).

Basic gas dynamics identity (1.35).

Polytrope (1.48).

Perfect gas equation of state (1.47).

The first equation (2.10), expressing the conservation of mass principle, applies to any process. It is only natural, therefore, that it be used as the basis of the generalized gas dynamics equation. The next three equations, (1.53), (1.35), and (1.48), are applied in this development only between static and total states at a point, rather than between any two points in the flow path. So they too will be independent of the actual gas dynamics process involved.

The last equation, (1.47), simply describes the fluid we are working with and is completely independent of the process. Thus, the generalized continuity expression we arrive at truly will apply to any and all flow processes.

The one-dimensional steady flow continuity equation of (2.10) is first written between any two arbitrary stations in the flow as

$$\dot{m} = \rho_1 A_1 V_1 = \rho_2 A_2 V_2 \tag{4.1}$$

A general expression for the density (ρ), as required in (4.1), can be obtained as follows. First, we note that an isentropic process always links the static and total states at a point, as discussed in Section 1.9. Thus, by applying the isentropic form of (1.48), namely

$$\frac{p}{\rho^\gamma} = K \tag{4.2}$$

between both static and total states, we obtain

$$\rho = \rho_t \left(\frac{p}{p_t}\right)^{1/\gamma} \tag{4.3}$$

A general expression for the velocity (V), as required in (4.1), can be obtained as follows. For an adiabatic-workless process, the general energy equation, (1.53), becomes

$$0 = du + p \, dv + v \, dp + \frac{V \, dV}{g_c} \tag{4.4}$$

For an isentropic process, the basic gas dynamics identity of (1.35) becomes

$$0 = du + p \, dv \tag{4.5}$$

Thus, energy for the isentropic process between static and total states at a point is simply

$$0 = \frac{dp}{\rho} + \frac{V \, dV}{g_c} \tag{4.6}$$

It is necessary to express density in terms of pressure before (4.6) can be integrated. Such an expression can be obtained by differentiating (4.2) to obtain

$$dp = K\gamma\rho^{\gamma-1} \, d\rho \tag{4.7}$$

Equation (4.6) can be integrated between static and total states, once the dp of (4.6) is replaced by that of (4.7). That is,

$$0 = K\gamma \int_\rho^{\rho_t} \rho^{\gamma-2} \, d\rho + \int_V^o \frac{V \, dV}{g_c}$$

to yield

$$V = \left[\left(\frac{2\gamma g_c}{\gamma-1}\right)\left(\frac{p_t}{\rho_t} - \frac{p}{\rho}\right)\right]^{1/2} \tag{4.8}$$

Combining (4.3) and (4.8) according to (4.1) we get

$$\rho_{t1}\left(\frac{p_1}{p_{t1}}\right)^{1/\gamma} A_1\left(\frac{p_{t1}}{\rho_{t1}} - \frac{p_1}{\rho_1}\right)^{1/2} = \rho_{t2}\left(\frac{p_2}{p_{t2}}\right)^{1/\gamma} A_2\left(\frac{p_{t2}}{\rho_{t2}} - \frac{p_2}{\rho_2}\right)^{1/2} \tag{4.9}$$

Equation (4.9) can be simplified by introducing the static and total forms of the perfect gas equation of state of (1.47), namely

$$\frac{p}{\rho} = \bar{R}T \tag{4.10}$$

and

$$\frac{p_t}{\rho_t} = \bar{R}\,T_t \tag{4.11}$$

After some algebraic manipulations we obtain

$$\left(\frac{T_{t2}}{T_{t1}}\right)^{1/2}\left(\frac{p_{t1}}{p_{t2}}\right)\left(\frac{A_1}{A_2}\right)\left[\left(\frac{p_1}{p_{t1}}\right)^{2/\gamma} - \left(\frac{p_1}{p_{t1}}\right)^{(\gamma+1)/\gamma}\right]^{1/2} = \left[\left(\frac{p_2}{p_{t2}}\right)^{2/\gamma} - \left(\frac{p_2}{p_{t2}}\right)^{(\gamma+1)/\gamma}\right]^{1/2} \tag{4.12}$$

For convenience, (4.12) can be written

$$\left(\frac{T_{t2}}{T_{t1}}\right)^{1/2}\left(\frac{p_{t1}}{p_{t2}}\right)\left(\frac{A_1}{A_2}\right)\mathbf{P}_1 = \mathbf{P}_2 \tag{4.13}$$

where **P** is the pressure ratio function of (4.12), namely

$$\mathbf{P} = \left[\left(\frac{p}{p_t}\right)^{2/\gamma} - \left(\frac{p}{p_t}\right)^{(\gamma+1)/\gamma}\right]^{1/2} \tag{4.14}$$

Although equations (4.12) and (4.13) represent an entirely general gas dynamics equation, we have not yet arrived at a normalized form of this equation. By *generalized*, of course, we mean that (4.12) and (4.13) apply to all gas dynamics processes, and that each term in these equations is dimensionless (that is, a pure number). By *normalized*, we mean that the pressure ratio function in the generalized equation should vary only between 0 and 1. That this is not now the case can be seen by calculating values of **P** in (4.14) for various values of $R = p/p_t$. Such values are given in Table 4.1. Thus, as R takes on values from 0 to 1, **P** takes on values from 0 to a maximum value and then back to 0.

4.2 NORMALIZED GAS DYNAMICS FUNCTION

When we divide the **P** of (4.14) by its maximum value ($\mathbf{P}_*$), we achieve normalization, for then $\mathbf{P}/\mathbf{P}_*$ will necessarily vary from 0 to 1 as p/p_t varies from 0 to 1. And, in fact, $\mathbf{P}/\mathbf{P}_*$ will maximize when $\mathbf{P} = \mathbf{P}_*$.

TABLE 4.1
*THE PRESSURE FUNCTION **P** IN TERMS OF R (FOR $\gamma = 1.4$)*

R	P	P/P$_*$
1	0	0
0.9	0.15972	0.61715
0.8	0.21191	0.81880
0.7	0.24126	0.93222
0.6	0.25585	0.98858
0.52828	0.25880	1
0.5	0.25835	0.99825
0.4	0.24942	0.96375
0.3	0.22830	0.88214
0.2	0.19232	0.74311
0.1	0.13405	0.51795
0	0	0

By the usual means of calculus, **P** is maximized by taking the derivative of **P** (or **P**^{2}) with respect to p/p_t, and by then setting the result to 0. Thus,

$$\frac{\partial \mathbf{P}^2}{\partial (p/p_t)} = \frac{\partial \mathbf{P}^2}{\partial R} = \frac{\partial}{\partial R}(R^{2/\gamma} - R^{(\gamma+1)/\gamma}) = 0$$

where R represents the static to total pressure ratio; it will be used for convenience throughout this study. We obtain the following result:

$$\left(\frac{2}{\gamma}\right) R_*^{(2-\gamma)/\gamma} - \left(\frac{\gamma+1}{\gamma}\right) R_*^{1/\gamma} = 0$$

where the subscript $*$ here signifies the R that will maximize **P**. Upon reduction

$$R_* = \left(\frac{2}{\gamma+1}\right)^{\gamma/(\gamma-1)} \tag{4.15}$$

Later equation (4.15) will be shown to take on added significance as the isentropic critical pressure ratio, where the critical Mach number of unity occurs. For now, R_* represents that static to total pressure ratio where the function **P** maximizes (see again Table 4.1).

Applying (4.15) in (4.14), we get

$$\mathbf{P}_* = \left[\left(\frac{2}{\gamma+1}\right)^{2/(\gamma-1)} \left(\frac{\gamma-1}{\gamma+1}\right)\right]^{1/2} \tag{4.16}$$

Making use of this $\mathbf{P}_*$ in (4.13) yields

$$\left(\frac{T_{t2}}{T_{t1}}\right)^{1/2} \left(\frac{p_{t1}}{p_{t2}}\right)\left(\frac{A_1}{A_2}\right)\frac{\mathbf{P}_1}{\mathbf{P}_*} = \frac{\mathbf{P}_2}{\mathbf{P}_*} \tag{4.17}$$

For added convenience, we replace $\mathbf{P}/\mathbf{P}_*$ by the single symbol Γ to obtain finally

$$\left(\frac{T_{t2}}{T_{t1}}\right)^{1/2} \left(\frac{p_{t1}}{p_{t2}}\right)\left(\frac{A_1}{A_2}\right)\Gamma_1 = \Gamma_2 \tag{4.18}$$

Equation (4.18) is the required generalized gas dynamics equation, and Γ in (4.18) is the required normalized gas dynamics function.

Specifically, Γ can be given in terms of the pressure ratio (R) as

$$\Gamma = \left[\frac{R^{2/\gamma} - R^{(\gamma+1)/\gamma}}{\left(\dfrac{2}{\gamma+1}\right)^{2/(\gamma-1)}\left(\dfrac{\gamma-1}{\gamma+1}\right)}\right]^{1/2} \tag{4.19}$$

and in terms of the Mach number as

$$\Gamma = \frac{\mathbf{M}}{\left[\left(\dfrac{2}{\gamma+1}\right)\left(1 + \dfrac{\gamma-1}{2}\mathbf{M}^2\right)\right]^{(\gamma+1)/2(\gamma-1)}} \tag{4.20}$$

Note that we could also obtain the normalized gas dynamics function (Γ) from another viewpoint. We first define a state point flow number (α) as

$$\alpha = \left(\frac{\dot{m}}{Ap_t}\right)\sqrt{\frac{\overline{R}T_t}{g_c}} \tag{4.21}$$

and, from the total flow number of (3.20), we know

$$\alpha = \left[\left(\frac{2\gamma}{\gamma-1}\right)(R^{2/\gamma} - R^{(\gamma+1)/\gamma})\right]^{1/2} \tag{4.22}$$

Then, we can define an isentropic critical flow number (α_*), based on the flow that yields a Mach number of unity, as

$$\alpha_* = \left(\frac{\dot{m}_*}{Ap_t}\right)\sqrt{\frac{\overline{R}T_t}{g_c}} \tag{4.23}$$

which can also be given in terms of (3.20) and (4.15) as

$$\alpha_* = \left[\gamma \left(\frac{2}{\gamma + 1} \right)^{(\gamma + 1)/(\gamma - 1)} \right]^{1/2} \tag{4.24}$$

Note for future reference that for $\gamma = 1.4$, $\alpha_* = 0.68473$; while for $\gamma = 1.3$, $\alpha_* = 0.66726$.

The ratios α/α_*, $\dot{m}/\dot{m}_*$, and P/P_* are all seen to equal Γ, the generalized normalized gas dynamics function, via (3.20), (4.14), (4.15), (4.21), (4.22), (4.23), and (4.24). That is,

$$\Gamma = \frac{\alpha}{\alpha_*} = \frac{\dot{m}}{\dot{m}_*} = \frac{P}{P_*} \tag{4.25}$$

Some of the attributes of the Γ function are:

1. Γ varies between 0 and 1 for all gas dynamics processes.
2. Γ is a function of p/p_t or of M only.
3. Multiplying Γ_1 by $(T_{t2}/T_{t1})^{1/2} (p_{t1}/p_{t2}) (A_1/A_2)$ yields Γ_2 and, therefore, p_2/p_{t2}; and M_2 for any process.

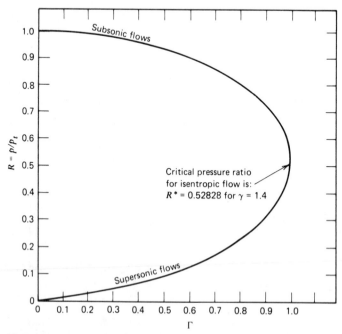

Figure 4.1 Generalized gas dynamics plot ($\gamma = 1.4$).

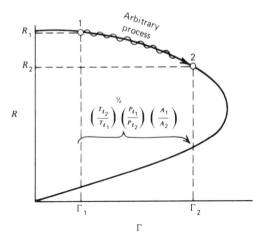

Figure 4.2   Arbitrary gas dynamics process on the Γ–R plot.

4.3   GENERALIZED GAS DYNAMICS PLOT

Γ is plotted as a function of R in Figure 4.1. Note that Γ maximizes at 1 when $R = R_*$, as expected. Note further that a plot of $\dot{m}/\dot{m}_*$, $\mathbf{P}/\mathbf{P}_*$, or α/α_* versus R would yield an identical plot according to (4.25). However, the added significance of the Γ–R plot is that it applies to any and all gas dynamics processes and that the multipliers required to go from one state to another are clearly spelled out in the Γ formulation of (4.18).

An arbitrary process is pictured on the Γ–R plot as shown in Figure 4.2.

4.4   THE DIMENSIONLESS MULTIPLIERS

The dimensionless multipliers called for in (4.18) are not always easy to come by. It is no mean feat to arrive at good estimates of the total pressure drop across a flow element or to predict the total temperature change accompanying a heat transfer process. Thus, we will not detail engineering approaches toward judicious choices for these multipliers until later chapters. For now, given (T_{t2}/T_{t1}), (p_{t1}/p_{t2}), and (A_1/A_2), we can solve any one-dimensional steady flow gas dynamics problem between any two arbitrary points by means of (4.18).

EXAMPLE 4.1

Find the pressure ratio (R_2) if air, initially at $R_1 = 0.9$, is heated from 100 to 200°F, while its total pressure decreases from 20 to 18 psia, and the pipe area decreases by a factor of 1.1.

(In terms of SI units these same quantities are: $T_1 = 37.8°C$, $T_2 = 93.3°C$, $p_{t1} = 137,896$ pascals, and $p_{t2} = 124,106$ pascals.)

Solution

By 4.25 and Table 4.1, $\Gamma_1 = 0.61715$.
By (4.18),

$$\Gamma_2 \atop US = \left(\frac{660}{560}\right)^{1/2} \left(\frac{20}{18}\right) (1.1)(0.61715) = 0.8189$$

$$\Gamma_2 \atop SI = \left(\frac{93.3 + 273.2}{37.8 + 273.2}\right)^{1/2} \left(\frac{137,896}{124,106}\right) (1.1)(0.61715) = 0.8189$$

By (4.19) or Table 4.1, $R_2 \approx 0.8$.

EXAMPLE 4.2

Air flows from a 3-in. pipe in which the static pressure is 40 psia and the total pressure is 50 psia to a 4-in. pipe in which the Mach number is 0.6. Find the static pressure in the 4-in. pipe if the total temperature drops during the flow process from 1000 to 500°F.

(In SI units, these same quantities are: $D_1 = 0.0762$ m, $p_1 = 275,792$ pascals, $p_{t1} = 344,740$ pascals, $D_2 = 0.1016$ m, $T_{t1} = 537.8°C$, and $T_{t2} = 260°C$.)

Solution

At the inlet pressure ratio of

$$R_1 = \frac{p_1}{p_{t1}} = 0.8$$

we have by (4.25) and Table 4.1, $\Gamma_1 = 0.81880$.
At a Mach number of $M_2 = 0.6$, we have by (4.20), $\Gamma_2 = 0.84161$.
By (4.18),

$$p_{t2} = p_{t1} \left(\frac{\Gamma_1}{\Gamma_2}\right)\left(\frac{T_{t2}}{T_{t1}}\right)^{1/2}\left(\frac{A_1}{A_2}\right)$$

$$p_{t2} \atop US = 50 \text{ psia} \left(\frac{0.81880}{0.84161}\right)\left(\frac{960}{1460}\right)^{1/2}\left(\frac{3}{4}\right)^2 = 22.188 \text{ psia}$$

$$p_{t2} \atop SI = 344,740 \left(\frac{0.81880}{0.84161}\right)\left(\frac{260 + 273}{537.8 + 273}\right)^{1/2}\left(\frac{0.0762}{0.1016}\right)^2 = 152,985 \text{ pascals}$$

By (4.19),

$$R_2 = 0.78400$$

and

$$p_2 = p_{t2} R_2 = 22.188 \text{ psia} \times 0.784 = 17.395 \text{ psia}$$
$$\text{US}$$

and

$$p_2 = 152{,}985 \times 0.784 = 119{,}940 \text{ pascals}$$
$$\text{SI}$$

As a check on consistency, we can express one result in terms of the other. Thus,

$$17.395 \text{ psia} \left(\frac{6894.8 \text{ pascals}}{\text{psia}} \right) = 119{,}935 \text{ pascals}$$

4.5 CONCLUDING REMARKS

In this chapter we have accomplished a significant task. We have developed a generalized gas dynamics equation that can be applied to any and all flow processes. Thus, we will have ample reason to use (4.18) over and over again. Not only does the Γ equation hold for all gas dynamics problems, but it displays and forces us to decide upon values for three very important dimensionless multipliers: namely, T_{t2}/T_{t1}, p_{t1}/p_{t2}, and A_1/A_2. Given these multipliers, we are in a position to solve any one-dimensional steady flow gas dynamics problem between any two arbitrary stations in the flow path.

We are now prepared to consider the several simplified gas dynamics processes, armed with (4.18).

REFERENCES

1. R. P. Benedict and W. G. Steltz, *Handbook of Generalized Gas Dynamics,* Plenum Press, New York, 1966, pp. 1–4.

2. R. P. Benedict, *Fundamentals of Pipe Flow,* Wiley, New York, 1980, pp. 314–318.

3. R. R. Jamison and D. L. Mordell, "The Compressible Flow of Fluids in Ducts," Aeronautical Research Council Reports and Memoranda, R&M 2031, March, 1945.

4. A. H. Shapiro and W. R. Hawthorne, "The Mechanics and Thermodynamics of Steady One-Dimensional Gas Flow," *J. App. Mechanics,* December, 1947, pp. A-317 to A-336.

NOMENCLATURE
Roman

A	Area
g_c	Gravitational constant

$\dot{m}$ Mass flow rate
$\dot{m}_*$ Maximum value of $\dot{m}$
M   Mach number
p Absolute static pressure
p_t Absolute total pressure
P   Pressure ratio function
$\mathbf{P}_*$ Maximum value of P
R Static to total pressure ratio
R_* Value of R that maximizes **P**
$\overline{R}$ Specific gas constant
T Absolute static temperature
T_t Absolute total temperature
V Directed fluid velocity

Greek

α Flow number
α_* Isentropic critical flow number
γ Isentropic exponent
Γ Normalized gas dynamics function
ρ Static gas density
ρ_t Total gas density

PROBLEMS

4.1 Air flows subsonically with loss and heat transfer through a convergent passage whose area ratio (A_1/A_2) is 2, such that the total pressure ratio (p_{t1}/p_{t2}) is 1.09138, the total temperature ratio (T_{t2}/T_{t1}) is 1.2, and the inlet pressure ratio (R_1) is 0.98. Find the exit Mach number.

4.2 Find the total temperature rise necessary to accelerate air from a Mach number of 0.2 to 0.5 in a constant area passage if the total pressure drops from 50 to 40 psia.

4.3 Air flows in a constant area passage from a Mach number of 0.1 to a Mach number of 0.4. Find the total temperature rise that must occur if the total pressure drops from 400,000 pascals to 300,000 pascals.

4.4 Show by differentiation that the pressure ratio that maximizes the normalized gas dynamics function (Γ) is

$$R_{\text{MAX}} = [2/(\gamma + 1)]^{\gamma/(\gamma - 1)}$$

4.5 Find the velocity of air at a point if the static pressure is measured at 20 psia, the total pressure is 30 psia, and the total temperature is 580°R.

4.6 At a point in a pipe, the following measurements are available: p = 150,000 pascals, p_t = 200,000 pascals, and T_t = 330K. Find the air velocity at this point.

4.7 Find the pressure ratio at a downstream point in a constant diameter pipe if the upstream air pressures are, p_1 = 95 psia, p_{t1} = 100 psia, the total temperature rises between the upstream and downstream stations from 700 to 800°R, and the downstream total pressure measures at 90 psia.

4.8 Find the Mach number at 2 if air flows in a constant area passage such that p_1 = 50,000 pascals, p_{t1} = 60,000 pascals, the total temperature rises between 1 and 2 from 50 to 80°C, while the total pressure at 2 is 50,000 pascals.

4.9 Air flows adiabatically through a piping system made up of a 6-in. diameter pipe connected to an 8-in. diameter pipe. The static pressure in the smaller pipe is 24 psia and the total pressure is 30 psia. The Mach number in the larger pipe is 0.4. Find the static pressure in the 8-in. pipe.

4.10 An adiabatic flow of air takes place in a 1-meter diameter pipe. If the inlet static pressure is 90 psia, the inlet total pressure is 100 psia, and the exit Mach number is 0.6, find the exit total pressure.

5
ISENTROPIC FLOW

5.1 ISENTROPIC FLOW EQUATION

By isentropic flow we mean that there is no change in entropy in the process. From the second law of (1.29), we further limit the isentropic process to one that is both adiabatic and reversible. This at once ensures, for the perfect gas, that both the total temperature and the total pressure are conserved. Stated differently, there can be no change in total temperature in the absence of heat transfer, nor can there be a change in total pressure in the absence of losses [1–3].

On an h–S diagram, the isentropic process for a perfect gas plots as shown in Figure 5.1. On the generalized R–Γ diagram the isentropic process plots, as do all processes, as shown in Figure 4.2.

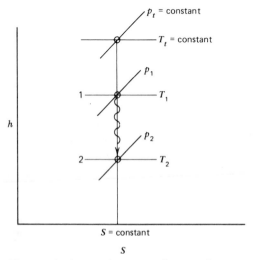

Figure 5.1 Isentropic process for a perfect gas.

From the generalized gas dynamics equation of (4.18), the isentropic conditions of p_t = constant and T_t = constant require

$$\left(\frac{A_1}{A_2}\right)\Gamma_1 = \Gamma_2 \tag{5.1}$$

5.2 ISENTROPIC CRITICAL STATE

In isentropic flow, the critical state (designated by the subscript *) is where $\mathbf{M}_* = 1$ and where R_* is given by (4.15)—that is,

$$R_* = \left(\frac{2}{\gamma + 1}\right)^{\gamma/(\gamma - 1)} \tag{5.2}$$

For $\gamma = 1.4$, $R_* = 0.52828$, and for $\gamma = 1.3$, $R_* = 0.54573$.

We already have seen in Section 3.2 that in a variable area problem, this critical state can occur only at the minimum flow area. When the Mach number is 1 at this throat, we say that in this device the critical flow rate $\dot{m}_*$ exists.

Also, as discussed in Section 3.2, for isentropic flow we know that as long as the Mach number is less than 1, the area must decrease for the gas velocity to increase (this is the subsonic nozzle). And the velocity can increase only if the area increases when $\mathbf{M}$ exceeds 1 (this is the supersonic nozzle).

Figure 5.2 illustrates these same ideas for both the nozzle (whose purpose is to accelerate the gas at the expense of a static pressure drop) and the diffuser (whose purpose is to decelerate the gas with a gain in static pressure).

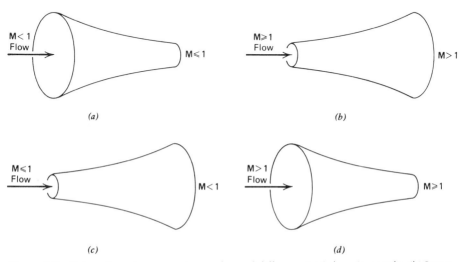

Figure 5.2 Subsonic and supersonic nozzles and diffusers. *(a)* Subsonic nozzle. *(b)* Supersonic nozzle. *(c)* Subsonic diffuser. *(d)* Supersonic diffuser.

The role of Γ, the normalized gas dynamics function, can be seen more clearly in the isentropic process if state 1 is taken to be a general state point, and if state 2 is taken to be the isentropic critical state point. Then, (5.1) becomes

$$\left(\frac{A}{A_*}\right)\Gamma = \Gamma_* = 1$$

or

$$\Gamma_{\text{isentropic}} = \frac{A_*}{A} \tag{5.3}$$

Thus, Γ, which previously was given by (4.25) in terms of α/α_*, $\dot{m}/\dot{m}_*$, and P/P_*, is now seen to also represent the area ratio, A_*/A.

As a consequence of (5.1) and (5.3), we obtain the useful isentropic identity

$$\left(\frac{A_1}{A_2}\right)\left(\frac{A_*}{A_1}\right) = \left(\frac{A_*}{A_2}\right) \tag{5.4}$$

and based on the Γ formulations of (4.19) and (4.20), it further follows from (5.1), (5.3), and (5.4) that

$$\frac{A_*}{A} = \left[\frac{R^{2/\gamma} - R^{(\gamma + 1)/\gamma}}{\left(\frac{2}{\gamma + 1}\right)^{2/(\gamma - 1)}\left(\frac{\gamma - 1}{\gamma + 1}\right)}\right]^{1/2} \tag{5.5}$$

and in terms of the Mach number

$$\frac{A_*}{A} = \frac{M}{\left[\left(\frac{2}{\gamma + 1}\right)\left(1 + \frac{\gamma - 1}{2}M^2\right)\right]^{(\gamma + 1)/2(\gamma - 1)}} \tag{5.6}$$

TABLE 5.1

GENERALIZED ISENTROPIC GAS DYNAMICS TABLE ($\gamma = 1.4$)

PRESSURE RATIO, p/p_t	TEMPERATURE RATIO, T/T_t	MACH NUMBER M	GENERALIZED FUNCTION Γ
1.00000	1.00000	0	0
0.98000	0.99424	0.17013	0.28894
0.96000	0.98840	0.24220	0.40412
0.94000	0.98248	0.29863	0.48938
0.92000	0.97646	0.34720	0.55858
0.90000	0.97035	0.39090	0.61715

PRESSURE RATIO, p/p_t	TEMPERATURE RATIO, T/T_t	MACH NUMBER M	GENERALIZED FUNCTION Γ
0.88000	0.96414	0.43127	0.66789
0.86000	0.95782	0.46922	0.71249
0.84000	0.95141	0.50536	0.75203
0.82000	0.94488	0.54009	0.78729
0.80000	0.93823	0.57372	0.81880
0.78000	0.93147	0.60650	0.84701
0.76000	0.92458	0.63862	0.87222
0.74000	0.91757	0.67022	0.89469
0.72000	0.91041	0.70144	0.91464
0.70000	0.90311	0.73239	0.93222
0.68000	0.89566	0.76318	0.94756
0.66000	0.88806	0.79389	0.96079
0.64000	0.88028	0.82461	0.97199
0.62000	0.87234	0.85542	0.98123
0.60000	0.86420	0.88639	0.98858
0.58000	0.85587	0.91761	0.09409
0.56000	0.84733	0.94914	0.99778
0.54000	0.83857	0.98107	0.99970
0.52828	0.83333	1.00000	1.00000
0.52000	0.82958	1.01348	0.99985
0.50000	0.82034	1.04645	0.99825
0.48000	0.81082	1.08008	0.99490
0.46000	0.80102	1.11446	0.98979
0.44000	0.79091	1.14969	0.98291
0.42000	0.78047	1.18591	0.97424
0.40000	0.76967	1.22324	0.96375
0.38000	0.75847	1.26183	0.95139
0.36000	0.74684	1.30186	0.93712
0.34000	0.73475	1.34353	0.92088
0.32000	0.72213	1.38707	0.90258
0.30000	0.70893	1.43277	0.88214
0.28000	0.69510	1.48096	0.85945
0.26000	0.68053	1.53205	0.83438
0.24000	0.66515	1.58655	0.80677
0.22000	0.64882	1.64510	0.77642
0.20000	0.63139	1.70853	0.74311
0.18000	0.61266	1.77795	0.70652
0.16000	0.59239	1.85484	0.66630
0.14000	0.57021	1.94130	0.62194
0.12000	0.54564	2.04046	0.57280
0.10000	0.51795	2.15719	0.51795
0.08000	0.48596	2.29978	0.45606
0.06000	0.44761	2.48403	0.38495
0.04000	0.39865	2.74634	0.30066
0.02000	0.32703	3.20769	0.19386
0.	0.	∞	0.

Apparently to provide a complete solution to any isentropic gas dynamics problem, we need only tabulate the dimensionless quantities R, $\mathbf{M}$, T/T_t, and Γ. These quantities are given in brief form in Table 5.1.

EXAMPLE 5.1

If air flows subsonically and isentropically through a convergent nozzle that has an inlet area of 25 in.^{2} and a throat area of 6 in.^{2}, find the maximum velocity at the inlet where the temperature is 80°F.

(In terms of SI units, these same quantities are: $A_1 = 0.01613$ m^2, $A_2 = 0.00387$ m^2, $T_1 = 26.7$°C.)

Solution

The maximum velocity anywhere in the system will occur when the throat velocity is a maximum, that is, when $\mathbf{M}_2 = 1$. But at this limiting condition, $A_*/A_2 = \Gamma_2 = 1$ (see Table 5.1).
By (5.3) and (5.4),

$$\Gamma_1 \underset{\text{US}}{=} \frac{A_*}{A_1} = \left(\frac{A_*}{A_2}\right)\left(\frac{A_2}{A_1}\right) = (1)\left(\frac{6}{25}\right) = 0.24$$

and

$$\Gamma_1 \underset{\text{SI}}{=} (1)\left(\frac{0.00387}{0.01613}\right) = 0.24$$

By (4.20), or by Table 5.1, we obtain $\mathbf{M}_1 = 0.14054$.
Hence, by (3.9),

$$(V_1)\text{max} \underset{\text{US}}{=} \mathbf{M}_1 a_1 = 0.14054 \times 49.02 \sqrt{540} = 160 \text{ ft/sec}$$

and

$$(V_1)\text{max} \underset{\text{SI}}{=} 0.14054 \times 20.05 \sqrt{(26.7 + 273.2)} = 48.8 \text{ m/s}$$

As a check on consistency, we can express one result in terms of the other. Thus,

$$160 \frac{\text{ft}}{\text{sec}} \left(\frac{0.3048 \text{ m}}{\text{ft}}\right) = 48.8 \text{ m/s}$$

EXAMPLE 5.2

Find the difference in static pressure between the inlet and exit for an isentropic process across a reducer ($D_1 = 12$ in., $D_2 = 6$ in.), if air flows at 10 lbm/sec at an inlet pressure of 20 psia, and at an inlet temperature of 80°F.

(In terms of SI units, these same quantities are: $D_1 = 0.3048$ m, $D_2 = 0.1524$ m, $\dot{m} = 4.536$ kg/s, $p_1 = 137,896$ pascals, $T_1 = 27.6$°C.)

Solution

It is evident from the generalized gas dynamics equation that to find conditions at 2, we must first know Γ_1. To obtain Γ_1 by Table 5.1, we must have either R_1, M_1, or T_1/T_t.

Of these three table entries, the easiest to obtain appears to be M_1. By (2.10),

$$V_1 \underset{US}{=} \frac{\dot{m}}{\rho_1 A_1} = \frac{\dot{m}\overline{R}T_1}{p_1 A_1} = \frac{10 \times 53.35 \times 540}{20 \times \dfrac{\pi(12)^2}{4}} = 127.4 \text{ ft/sec}$$

and

$$V_1 \underset{SI}{=} \frac{4.536 \times 287.1 \times 300.8}{137{,}896 \times \dfrac{\pi(0.3048)^2}{4}} = 38.93 \text{ m/s}$$

By (3.6)

$$a_1 \underset{US}{=} 49.02 \sqrt{540} = 1139.1 \text{ ft/sec}$$

and

$$a_1 \underset{SI}{=} 20.05 \sqrt{300.8} = 347.7 \text{ m/s}$$

By (3.9),

$$\mathbf{M}_1 = V_1/a_1 = 0.11184$$

By Table 5.1 or by (4.20), $\Gamma_1 = 0.19176$. By (4.18), $\Gamma_2 = \Gamma_1 (A_1/A_2) = 0.76704$. By Table 5.1 or by (4.19), $R_2 = 0.83176$. But,

$$p_1 - p_2 = \Delta p = p_t (R_1 - R_2) = p_1 \left(1 - \frac{R_2}{R_1}\right) \tag{5.7}$$

so to find the required pressure drop, it is necessary to determine R_1. This is an easy matter by Table 5.1 or by (3.13), given the inlet Mach number. $R_1 = 0.99130$ results.

By (5.7)

$$\Delta p \underset{US}{=} 20 \left(1 - \frac{0.83176}{0.99130}\right) = 3.2188 \text{ psi}$$

and

$$\Delta p \underset{SI}{=} 137{,}896 \left(1 - \frac{0.83176}{0.99130}\right) = 22{,}193 \text{ pascals}$$

As a check on consistency, one result can be expressed in terms of the other. Thus,

$$3.2188 \text{ psi} \left(\frac{6894.8 \text{ pascals}}{\text{psi}} \right) = 22{,}193 \text{ pascals}$$

5.3 CONVERGENT-DIVERGENT NOZZLE

The geometric flow element shown in Figure 5.3 features a converging inlet section, a minimum area (throat), and a diverging exit section. To understand the isentropic flow through this device, it is helpful to consider several cases as indicated by *A, B, C,* and *D* in Figure 5.3.

A. Where $p_{exit} = p_{inlet}$, there will be no flow.
B. As p_{exit} is reduced, the gas accelerates to some minimum pressure in the throat and then diffuses back subsonically to p_{exit}.

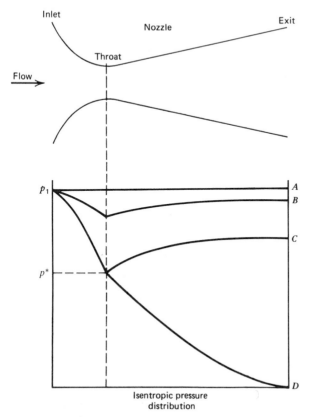

Figure 5.3 The convergent-divergent nozzle.

C. Eventually as p_{exit} is lowered, the gas will just accelerate to a Mach number of 1 in the throat. This we call the critical exit pressure, and the throat pressure will be p_*. Beyond the throat the gas will diffuse subsonically back to the given p_{exit}.

If p_{exit} is reduced beyond this critical exit pressure, its effect will not be communicated upstream through the throat because the gas is now moving there at the acoustic velocity, that is, at the velocity of propagation of a pressure wave (see Section 3.1). No matter how low p_{exit} becomes, the throat pressure will remain at p_* and the flow rate will remain at the choking flow rate, $\dot{m}_*$; the nozzle is said to be choked.

D. Only one other isentropic flow condition is possible in the convergent-divergent nozzle. This is when p_{exit} is low enough to cause completely supersonic flow of the gas, beyond the throat. Such would then be the design exit pressure of the supersonic nozzle.

Exit pressures between C and D and beyond D are treated in Chapter 9 on the normal shock process.

EXAMPLE 5.3
Air flows isentropically from a plenum inlet, where the pressure is 15 psia and the temperature is 70°F, through a convergent-divergent nozzle having a throat area of 1 ft². Find the flow rate and the area at a point where the Mach number is 2.5.

Solution
Since $M_2 > 1$, it follows that the Mach number at the throat (where $dA/A = 0$) is 1. Thus, $T_{inlet} = T_t = 70 + 460 = 530°R$, and $p_{inlet} = p_t = 15$ psia.

By (4.15) $R_* = 0.52828$ and $p_* = 7.92$ psia. By Table 5.1, $(T/T_t)_* = 0.83333$ and $T_* = 441.7°R$. By (3.9), $V_* = (1) a_* = 49.02 \sqrt{441.7} = 1030.2$ ft/sec. Thus,

$$\dot{m} = \rho_* A_* V_* = \frac{p_* A_* V_*}{R T_*} = 49.86 \text{ lbm/sec}$$

By Table 5.1, $\Gamma_2 = A_*/A_2 = f(M_2) = 0.37926$, and since $A_* = 1$ ft², it follows that $A_2 = 2.6367$ ft².

5.4 APPLICATIONS
The generalized isentropic flow equation (5.1) can be used to solve most but not all isentropic gas dynamics problems. For example, the simple but

realistic case of flow from an inlet plenum causes some concern. Here, $A_2/A_1 \sim 0$, and (5.1) becomes useless. In such cases, it is convenient to revert back to the total or static flow numbers for a solution.

EXAMPLE 5.4

Air flows isentropically from a plenum inlet (station 1) through a reducer to station 2. Find the required flow area at 2 for $\dot{m} = 1$ lbm/sec, if $p_1 = 20$ psia, $T_1 = 80°F$, and $p_2 = 15$ psia.

Solution

For a plenum inlet $p_1 = p_t$. In isentropic flow, p_t and T_t are constants.
Then, $R_2 = p_2/p_t = p_2/p_1 = 15/20 = 0.75$. By Table 5.1 or (4.19), $\Gamma_2 = 0.88378$. By (4.24), $\alpha_2 = \alpha_* \Gamma_2 = 0.68473 \times 0.88378 = 0.60515$.
Alternatively, from the total flow number of (3.20) and (4.22),

$$\alpha_2 = \left[\left(\frac{2\gamma}{\gamma - 1} \right) \left(R_2^{2/\gamma} - R_2^{(\gamma + 1)/\gamma} \right) \right]^{1/2} = 0.60516$$

In either case, solving (3.20) or (4.14) for A_2 yields

$$A_2 = \left(\frac{\dot{m}}{p_t} \right) \left(\frac{\overline{R} T_t}{g_c} \right)^{1/2} \left(\frac{1}{\alpha_2} \right) = 2.47238 \text{ in.}^2$$

The static flow number of (3.17) also can be used to determine A_2 once the static temperature at 2 is found.
Table 5.1 yields for $\Gamma_2 = 0.88378$, $T_2/T_t = 0.92109$, and hence, $T_2 = 0.92109 \times 540 = 497.3886°R$.
By (3.17),

$$\left[\left(\frac{2\gamma}{\gamma - 1} \right) \left(R_2^{(1 - \gamma)/\gamma} - 1 \right) \right]^{1/2} = 0.7743846$$

Solving (3.17) for A_2 yields

$$A_2 = \left(\frac{\dot{m}}{p_2} \right) \left(\frac{\overline{R} T_2}{g_c} \right)^{1/2} \left(\frac{1}{0.7743846} \right) = 2.47238 \text{ in.}^2$$

that, of course, checks the total flow number solution.

Total pressure is always related isentropically to the static pressure at a given state point. A useful expression for the total pressure can be obtained from the total flow number of (3.20) by squaring both sides of this equation and rearranging slightly to obtain

$$\left(\frac{\dot{m}}{Ap}\right)^2 \left(\frac{\overline{R}T_t}{g_c}\right) = \left(\frac{2\gamma}{\gamma - 1}\right)(R^{2(1-\gamma)/\gamma} - R^{(1-\gamma)/\gamma}) \tag{5.8}$$

This is seen to be a simple quadratic of the form

$$X^2 - X - C = 0$$

where

$$X = R^{(1-\gamma)/\gamma}$$

and

$$C = \left(\frac{\gamma - 1}{2\gamma}\right)\left(\frac{\dot{m}}{Ap}\right)^2 \left(\frac{\overline{R}T_t}{g_c}\right)$$

Solving by the usual $X = 1/2 \pm \sqrt{1/4 + C}$, we obtain on substitution

$$p_t = p\left[\frac{1}{2} + \sqrt{\frac{1}{4} + \left(\frac{\gamma - 1}{2\gamma}\right)\left(\frac{\dot{m}}{Ap}\right)^2 \left(\frac{\overline{R}T_t}{g_c}\right)}\right]^{\gamma/(\gamma-1)} \tag{5.9}$$

Equation (5.9) is especially useful for determining the effective total pressure across a passage when it is not convenient or practical to install and traverse the pipe with a Pitot tube.

EXAMPLE 5.5
Air flows at 5 lbm/sec through a 6-in. duct. Find the total pressure where the static pressure is 20 psia and the total temperature is 80°F.

Solution
By (5.9),

$$p_t = 20\left[\frac{1}{2} + \sqrt{\frac{1}{4} + \left(\frac{0.4}{2.8}\right)\left(\frac{5}{36\pi/4 \times 20}\right)^2 \left(\frac{53.35 \times 540}{32.174}\right)}\right]^{1.4/0.4} = 20.7 \text{ psia}$$

EXAMPLE 5.6
If air flows isentropically through an area ratio of $A_2/A_1 = 0.8$ from an initial Mach number of 0.4, find the exit Mach number.

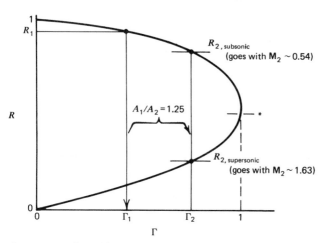

Figure 5.4 The multivalued Γ function.

Solution

By (4.20) or Table 5.1, $\Gamma_1 = 0.62888$. By (5.1), $\Gamma_2 = (A_1/A_2)\Gamma_1 = 0.62888/$
$0.8 = 0.78610$. By (4.20) or Table 5.1, $M_2 = 0.53888$.

This result unfortunately involved an assumption on our part. Both Γ and
M are multivalued functions (see, for example, Figure 4.1). Thus, we always
must make a choice regarding whether or not a throat (a minimum area) exists
between stations 1 and 2. The result, $M_2 = 0.53888$, presumes that no such
throat exists and that the flow remains subsonic throughout. On the other hand,
if we assume a throat between 1 and 2, the same Γ_2 of 0.78610 would then be
interpreted, again by Table 5.1 or (4.20), as requiring a M_2 of 1.62654. These
results are clarified by Figure 5.4.

5.5 CONCLUDING REMARKS

Although no real gas dynamics process is truly isentropic, the isentropic
process is worthy of study, serving as the simplest case in gas dynamics. For
example, the nozzle flow from the inlet to the throat often can be approximated
by an isentropic process, while many pipe flows can be estimated as roughly
isentropic. All in all, isentropic flow serves as a useful standard, representing
ideal compressible flow.

In this chapter, we have applied the generalized gas dynamics equation of
(4.18) to the simplest of the processes—that is, the isentropic process—and
found it entirely satisfactory in the form of (5.1), namely

$$\left(\frac{A_1}{A_2}\right)\Gamma_1 = \Gamma_2$$

We defined the isentropic critical state as characterized by (5.2), namely

$$R_* = \left(\frac{2}{\gamma + 1}\right)^{\gamma/(\gamma - 1)}$$

We provided the first of many gas dynamics tables (Table 5.1). Such tables aid us in obtaining rapid numerical solutions to the various simplified processes. Finally, we discussed the convergent-divergent nozzle in terms of its isentropic modes of operation.

REFERENCES

1. R. P. Benedict and W. G. Steltz, *Handbook of Generalized Gas Dynamics*, Plenum Press, New York, 1966, pp. 1–4.
2. R. P. Benedict, *Fundamentals of Pipe Flow*, Wiley, New York, 1980, pp. 314–318.
3 R. M. Rotty, *Introduction to Gas Dynamics*, Wiley, New York, 1962, pp. 181–186.

NOMENCLATURE

Roman

a	Acoustic velocity
A	Area
g_c	Gravitational constant
h	Specific enthalpy
$\dot{m}$	Mass rate of flow
$\mathbf{M}$	Mach number
p	Absolute pressure
$\mathbf{P}$	Pressure ratio function
R	Static to total pressure ratio
$\overline{R}$	Specific gas constant
S	Entropy
T	Absolute temperature
V	Directed fluid velocity

Greek

α	Isentropic flow number
γ	Isentropic exponent
Γ	Normalized gas dynamics function
Δ	Finite difference
ρ	Fluid density

Subscripts

1, 2   Axial stations
*   Critical state
t Total

PROBLEMS

5.1 Air flows adiabatically and without loss from a plenum at 100 psia and 300°F, through a convergent nozzle of throat area 5 in², to an exhaust chamber at 80 psia. Find T, V, **M**, and $\dot{m}$ at the nozzle exit.

5.2 Air flows isentropically through a converging nozzle from a plenum inlet at 800,000 pascals and 150°C. The exit area is 0.001 m² where the pressure is 608,000 pascals. Find T, V, **M**, and $\dot{m}$ at the nozzle exit.

5.3 An isentropic diffuser of area ratio 3 accepts air at the following inlet conditions: $\mathbf{M}_1 = 0.5$, $p_1 = 20$ psia, $T_1 = 100°F$. Find $\mathbf{M}_2, p_2$, and T_2 at the exit.

5.4 Air flows isentropically from $A_1 = 0.5$ m² to $A_2 = 1$ m² from $\mathbf{M}_1 = 0.4$, $p_1 = 150,000$ pascals, and $T_1 = 50°C$. Find $\mathbf{M}_2, p_2$, and T_2.

5.5 Air flows through a pipe of 20 in.² cross-sectional area at $p = 15$ psia, $T = 0°F$, and $\mathbf{M} = 2$. Find the flow rate and the minimum area that would pass this same flow.

5.6 Find the flow rate of air and the minimum area that would pass this same flow if $p = 100,000$ pascals, $T = 0°C$, and $\mathbf{M} = 1.5$ in a pipe of 0.01 m² cross-sectional area.

5.7 Air flows subsonically and isentropically through a convergent nozzle having an inlet area of 30 in.² and a throat area of 10 in.². Find the maximum velocity at the inlet where the temperature is 100°F.

5.8 A convergent nozzle has an inlet area of 1 m² and a throat area of 0.2 m². If air flows isentropically and subsonically from the inlet where the temperature is 50°C, find the maximum velocity that could occur at the inlet.

5.9 Air flows isentropically through a 2-in. diameter pipe at a Mach number of 0.5. Find the Mach number in a section where the diameter is 5 in.

5.10 Air flows isentropically from a plenum inlet at $p_1 = 50$ psia and $T_1 = 100°F$. Find the flow area required to pass 2 lbm/sec at a station downstream where the pressure is 40 psia.

5.11 Air flows isentropically from a plenum inlet where the pressure is 30 psia and the temperature is 80°F, through a convergent-divergent nozzle of throat area 0.5 ft². Find the flow rate and the area at a point where the Mach number is 2.

5.12 A heavily insulated convergent-divergent nozzle has choked air flow passing through it with negligible losses. For inlet conditions of $\mathbf{M}_1 = 0.1$,

T_t = 100°F, and p_t = 50 psia, find the exit conditions of $\mathbf{M}_2$, T_2, and p_2 if A_1/A_2 = 4.9498.

5.13 Air flows isentropically through a *C–D* nozzle. Plenum inlet conditions are 2,000,000 pascals and 50°C. The nozzle exit pressure is 200,000 pascals and the throat area is 0.2 m². Find the mass flow rate and the nozzle exit area.

5.14 A *C–D* nozzle discharges air at atmospheric pressure. The inlet area is 1 ft² where the pressure is 100 psia, the temperature is 200°F, and the Mach number is 0.2. For isentropic flow, find the flow rate, the throat area, and the exit area.

5.15 A *C–D* nozzle operates isentropically at an exit Mach number of 2 and an exit area of 2 ft². For plenum inlet pressure and temperature of 500 psia and 500°R, respectively, find the maximum exit pressure to choke the nozzle and the flow rate at this condition.

6
ADIABATIC FLOW AND THE LOSS COEFFICIENT

6.1 ADIABATIC FLOW EQUATION

By *adiabatic* flow we mean that there is no heat transfer in the process. In general, this ensures that the total enthalpy remains constant. For the perfect gas, the adiabatic restriction further ensures that the total temperature also remains constant.

On an h–S diagram, a general adiabatic process for a perfect gas is shown in Figure 6.1. On the generalized R–Γ diagram, the adiabatic process plots, as do all processes, as shown in Figure 4.2.

From the generalized gas dynamics equation of (4.18), the adiabatic condition of $T_t =$ constant requires

$$\left(\frac{P_{t1}}{P_{t2}}\right)\left(\frac{A_1}{A_2}\right)\Gamma_1 = \Gamma_2 \tag{6.1}$$

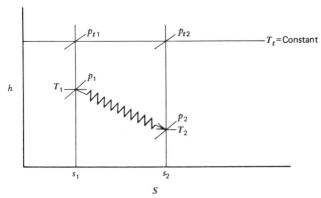

Figure 6.1 General adiabatic process for a perfect gas.

Equation (6.1) also can be written in terms of the isentropic Γ of (5.3) (that is, $\Gamma_{isen} = A_*/A$) as

$$p_{t1}A_1(A_*/A_1) = p_{t2}A_2(A_{*2}/A_2)$$

to yield the sometimes useful expression

$$p_{t1}A_{*1} = p_{t2}A_{*2} \tag{6.2}$$

For an isentropic process, $A_{*1} = A_{*2}$ but in a general adiabatic process, A_{*X} represents the area (real or imaginary) that would yield a Mach number and a Γ value of unity, starting from the given M_X and the given Γ_X. This concept will be illustrated in Example 6.4.

6.2   ADIABATIC ENTROPY CHANGE

A general expression for the entropy increase that accompanies the general adiabatic process (as shown in Figure 6.1) can be obtained as follows. Energy, for the workless-adiabatic case, yields through (1.53) and (1.54)

$$o = dh + \frac{V\,dV}{g_c} = dh_t \tag{6.3}$$

Entropy, via the basic gas dynamics identity of (1.35) and the enthalpy definitions of (1.7) and (1.54), can be given as

$$ds = \frac{dh - v\,dp}{T} = \frac{dh_t - v_t\,dp_t}{T_t} \tag{6.4}$$

When (6.3) and (6.4) are combined, we obtain

$$ds = -\frac{dp_t}{\rho_t T_t} \tag{6.5}$$

If we recall the perfect gas equation of state of (1.47) and its equivalent

$$\frac{p_t}{\rho_t} = \overline{R}T_t$$

equation (6.5) also can be given as

$$ds = -\frac{\overline{R}}{J}\frac{dp_t}{p_t} \tag{6.6}$$

that integrates to the required expression for the entropy increase in a general adiabatic process, namely

$$s_2 - s_1 = \frac{\overline{R}}{J} \ln\left(\frac{p_{t1}}{p_{t2}}\right) \tag{6.7}$$

EXAMPLE 6.1

Find the entropy increase when air flows adiabatically at a total temperature of 800°R from an initial total pressure of 75 psia to a static state in which $p_2 = 50$ psia and $T_2 = 728.9°R$.

(In terms of SI units, these same quantities are: $T_t = 444.3$ K, $p_t = 517$, 110 pascals, $p_2 = 344{,}740$ pascals, $T_2 = 404.8$ K.)

Solution

At

$$\left(\frac{T_2}{T_t}\right)_{US} = \frac{728.9}{800} = 0.91113 \quad \text{or} \quad \left(\frac{T_2}{T_t}\right)_{SI} = \frac{404.8}{444.3}$$

we have by (1.56) or by Table 5.1,

$$\frac{p_2}{p_{t2}} = 0.722$$

Then, by (6.7),

$$\Delta s_{US} = \frac{\overline{R}}{J} \ln\left(\frac{p_{t1}/p_2}{p_{t2}/p_2}\right) = \frac{53.35}{788} \ln\left(\frac{0.722 \times 75}{50}\right) = 0.00547 \frac{\text{Btu}}{\text{lbm-°R}}$$

and

$$\Delta s_{SI} = \overline{R} \ln\left(\frac{R_2}{R_{21}}\right) = 287.1 \ln\left(\frac{0.722 \times 517, 110}{344{,}740}\right) = 22.892 \frac{\text{Joules}}{\text{kg-K}}$$

As a check on consistency, we can express one result in terms of the other. Thus,

$$0.00547 \frac{\text{Btu}}{\text{lbm-°R}} \left(\frac{4187 \text{ J/kg-K}}{\text{Btu/lbm-°R}}\right) = 22.9 \frac{\text{J}}{\text{kg-K}}$$

6.3 ADIABATIC CRITICAL STATE

In adiabatic flow, the critical state (designated by *) occurs when $\mathbf{M}_* = 1$ and R_* is given by (4.15) and (5.2) as

$$R_{*\text{ ADIABATIC}} = \left(\frac{2}{\gamma + 1}\right)^{\gamma/(\gamma-1)} \tag{6.8}$$

The role of Γ, the normalized gas dynamics function, can be seen more clearly in the adiabatic process if state 1 is taken as a general state point, and if state 2 is regarded as the adiabatic critical state point. Then, (6.1) becomes

$$\left(\frac{p_t}{p_{t*}}\right)\left(\frac{A}{A_*}\right)\Gamma = \Gamma_* = 1$$

or

$$\Gamma_{\text{ADIABATIC}} = \left(\frac{p_{t*}}{p_t}\right)\left(\frac{A_*}{A}\right) \tag{6.9}$$

Thus, Γ that previously was given by (4.25) in terms of α/α_*, $\dot{m}/\dot{m}_*$, and P/P_* and by (5.3) in terms of A_*/A for isentropic flow is now seen to also represent $(p_{t*}/p_t)(A_*/A)$.

6.4 FANNO FLOW

A special type of adiabatic flow in which the flow area remains constant has been called Fanno[1] flow. Under these adiabatic constant area restrictions, the generalized gas dynamics equation of (4.18) and the adiabatic equation of (6.1) reduce to

$$\left(\frac{p_{t1}}{p_{t2}}\right)\Gamma_1 = \Gamma_2 \tag{6.10}$$

Patterned after (6.9), Γ in a Fanno process becomes

$$\Gamma_{\text{FANNO}} = \frac{p_{t*}}{p_t} \tag{6.11}$$

As a consequence of (6.10) and (6.11), we obtain the useful Fanno identity

$$\left(\frac{p_{t1}}{p_{t2}}\right)\left(\frac{p_{t*}}{p_{t1}}\right) = \left(\frac{p_{t*}}{p_{t2}}\right) \tag{6.12}$$

Since Γ of (4.18) is a generalized function that applies equally well to any flow process, it follows from (4.19), (4.20), and (6.11) that

---

[1]So named after a student who first described this type of flow in his thesis at the Eidgen. Techn. Hochschule in 1904.

$$\left(\frac{p_{t*}}{p_t}\right)_{\text{FANNO}} = \left[\frac{R^{2/\gamma} - R^{(\gamma+1)/\gamma}}{\left(\frac{2}{\gamma+1}\right)^{2/(\gamma-1)}\left(\frac{\gamma-1}{\gamma+1}\right)}\right]^{1/2} \tag{6.13}$$

and in terms of the Mach number

$$\left(\frac{p_{t*}}{p_t}\right)_{\text{FANNO}} = \frac{M}{\left[\left(\frac{2}{\gamma+1}\right)\left(1 + \frac{\gamma-1}{2}M^2\right)\right]^{(\gamma+1)/2(\gamma-1)}} \tag{6.14}$$

We cannot fail to note the identity between Γ, $(A_*/A)_{\text{ISENTROPIC}}$ and $(p_{t*}/p_t)_{\text{FANNO}}$ by comparing (4.19) and (4.20) with (5.5) and (5.6) and with (6.13) and (6.14), although this common bond has not always been recognized in the literature.

Evidently, to solve any Fanno problem in gas dynamics, which includes adiabatic flow with losses in a constant area channel, we need only tabulate the dimensionless quantities R, M, T/T_t, and Γ. These quantities already have been given in Table 5.1.

However, even the *variable area* adiabatic flow with losses can be treated by applying (6.1) directly. This general adiabatic flow process is called a Fanno-type process and is depicted in Figure 6.2 on a *h–S* diagram. The constant flow per unit area lines are known as Fanno lines.[2]

Since Fanno lines are not straight lines on the *h–S* plot, it follows that if a frictional process proceeds far enough, changes in state would occur more rapidly than changes in entropy until a point is reached along the Fanno line where there is no further increase in entropy. This, of course, marks the critical state where S_*, M_*, and Γ_* are all maximized and R_* is given by (6.8).

Since we already have seen in Chapter 5 that area variations alone can cause isentropic changes of state, and in Fanno flow that total pressure decreases alone can result in entropy production, we come to the interesting conclusion that we may deal with the combined effects of viscous losses and area variations separately [1, 2]. That is, a viscous flow problem involving variable area may be reduced to one of constant area by simply altering the inlet static conditions to conform with the isentropic change of state required by the area ratio, A_1/A_2. From this revised initial state, we proceed to consider the losses as in a constant area process, that is as Fanno flow.

Thus, the general adiabatic flow process can be handled in two steps.

1. One first accounts for the area change to obtain the isentropic flow function at the revised initial state (Γ_1'), that is,

---

[2] "This Fanno condition line tells nothing about the lengths of the distance traveled, but it represents the locus of all conditions possible in a conduit of constant friction factor and the given flow rate per unit area," Aurel Stodola, 1945.

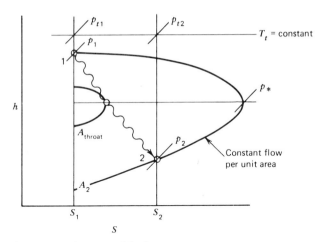

Figure 6.2 Compressible Fanno-type process.

$$\left(\frac{A_1}{A_2}\right)\Gamma_1 = \Gamma_1' \tag{6.15}$$

2. Then one completes the operation by accounting for the total pressure loss to obtain the flow function at the final state, that is,

$$\left(\frac{p_{t1}}{p_{t2}}\right)\Gamma_1' = \Gamma_2 \tag{6.16}$$

EXAMPLE 6.2

Air flows adiabatically in a constant area duct from an initial Mach number of 0.25. Find the Mach number downstream where the entropy increase is 0.03 Btu/lbm-°R.

Solution

This is a Fanno problem because it involves constant area adiabatic flow with losses.

At $M_1 = 0.25$, Table 5.1 yields $\Gamma_1 = 0.41620$.
By (6.7),

$$p_{t1}/p_{t2} = e^{J\Delta S/\bar{R}} = e^{778 \times 0.03/53.35} = 1.54881$$

By (6.10), $(p_{t1}/p_{t2})\,\Gamma_1 = \Gamma_2 = 1.54881 \times 0.41620 = 0.64462$. From Table 5.1, interpolated, $M_2 = 0.41243$.

EXAMPLE 6.3

For the same initial conditions as given in Example 6.2, find the exit Mach number if $A_2/A_1 = 1.35$.

Solution

We previously found (p_{t1}/p_{t2}) $\Gamma_1 = 0.64462$. Thus, by (6.1), $(A_1/A_2)\, 0.64462 = \Gamma_2 = 0.47750$. From Table 5.1, interpolated, $M_2 = 0.29057$.

However, this solution presumes no throat exists between stations 1 and 2, that is, the flow was wholly subsonic. If a throat existed, M_2 would be obtained by interpolation in the supersonic portion of Table 5.1 to yield $M_2 = 2.24884$.

EXAMPLE 6.4

Air flows in an adiabatic process with loss. If $T_1 = 100°F$, $p_1 = 30$ psia, $T_2 = 75°F$, $T_{t2}, = 125°F$, and $p_2 = 15$ psia, find A_2 if $A_1 = 10$ in.^{2}

(In terms of SI units, these same quantities are: $T_1 = 310.9$ K, $T_2 = 297$ K, $T_{t2} = 324.8$ K, $p_1 = 206{,}844$ pascals, $p_2 = 103{,}422$ pascals, $A_1 = 0.006452$ m^2.)

Solution

From

$$\frac{T_2}{T_{t2}} = \frac{535}{585} = \frac{297}{324.8} = 0.9145$$

we obtain by table or equation

$$\Gamma_2 = 0.90349 \quad \text{and} \quad R_2 = 0.73147$$

Then

$$P_{t2} \underset{\text{US}}{=} \frac{p_2}{R_2} = \frac{15}{0.73147} = 20.50 \text{ psia}$$

and

$$P_{t2} \underset{\text{SI}}{=} \frac{103{,}422}{0.73147} = 141{,}389 \text{ pascals}$$

Similarly, from

$$\frac{T_1}{T_{t1}} = \frac{560}{585} = \frac{310.9}{324.8} = 0.9572$$

we obtain $\Gamma_1 = 0.71619$ and $R_1 = 0.85822$, where $T_{t1} = T_{t2}$. Then,

$$P_{t1} \underset{\text{US}}{=} \frac{p_1}{R_1} = \frac{30}{0.85822} = 34.96 \text{ psia}$$

and

$$p_{r1 \atop \text{SI}} = \frac{206{,}844}{0.85822} = 241{,}015 \text{ pascals}$$

By the two-step method of (6.15) and (6.16),

$$\Gamma_1' = \frac{\Gamma_2}{p_{r1}/p_{r2}} = \frac{0.90349}{34.96/20.50} = \frac{0.90349}{241{,}015/141{,}389} = 0.53$$

and

$$\frac{A_2}{A_1} = \frac{\Gamma_1}{\Gamma_1'} = \frac{0.71619}{0.53} = 1.3513$$

Alternatively, by (6.2),

$$\frac{A_{*2}}{A_{*1}} = \frac{p_{r1}}{p_{r2}} = \frac{34.96}{20.50} = 1.705$$

By algebra,

$$\frac{A_2}{A_1} = \frac{A_2}{A_{*2}} \times \frac{A_{*1}}{A_1} \times \frac{A_{*2}}{A_{*1}} = \frac{1}{\Gamma_2} \times \Gamma_1 \times \frac{p_{r1}}{p_{r2}}$$

or

$$\frac{A_2}{A_1} = \frac{0.71619}{0.90349} \times 1.705 = 1.3515$$

which checks the two-step method closely. By either method,

$$A_2 \atop \text{US} = A_1 \times \frac{A_2}{A_1} = 10 \times 1.3514 = 13.514 \text{ in.}^2$$

and

$$A_2 \atop \text{SI} = 0.006452 \text{ m}^2 \times 1.3514 = 0.008719 \text{ m}^2.$$

As a check on consistency, we can express one result in terms of the other. Thus,

$$13.514 \text{ in.}^2 \left(\frac{6.452 \times 10^{-4} \text{ m}^2}{\text{in.}^2} \right) = 0.008719 \text{ m}^2$$

It is interesting to note in this adiabatic flow with loss that $A_{*1} \neq A_{*2}$, for note:

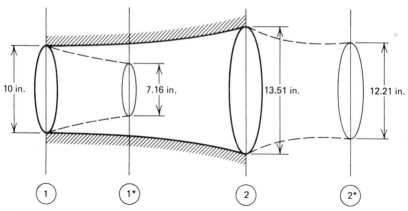

Figure 6.3   Geometric relations of Example 6.4.

$$A_{*1} = A_1\Gamma_1 = 10 \times 0.71619 = 7.1619 \text{ in.}^2$$

and

$$A_{*2} = A_2\Gamma_2 = 13.514 \times 0.90349 = 12.2098 \text{ in.}^2$$

Figure 6.3 clarifies these geometric relations.

6.5   ADIABATIC NOZZLE FLOW WITH LOSS

As discussed in Section 5.3, we can handle the isentropic flow in a convergent-divergent nozzle. We now consider the effects of loss on this same
problem.

When losses are involved, we can no longer claim that $A_* = A_{\text{THROAT}}$.
Instead, we must simply apply the general adiabatic relations, (6.1) and (6.9),
to obtain a solution.

EXAMPLE 6.5

Air flows adiabatically through a convergent-divergent nozzle that can be
described, geometrically, by the following: $A_1/A_{\text{THROAT}} = 5$, $A_2/A_{\text{THROAT}} = 1.75$,
and $A_{\text{THROAT}} = 1 \text{ ft}^2$. If $p_1 = 15$ psia, $T_1 = 70°F$, and $\mathbf{M}_1 = 0.1$, find the flow
rate and the exit Mach number when the total pressure loss is 5 psi.

Solution

By Table 5.1, at $\mathbf{M}_1 = 0.1$, $p_1/p_{t1} = 0.99303$, $\Gamma_1 = 0.17177$. Thus,
$p_{t1} = 15/0.99303 = 15.1$ psia, and $p_{t2} = 10.1$ psia. Note that while Γ_1
always equals $(A_*/A_1)_{\text{ISEN}} = 0.17177$, $(A_*/A_1)_{\text{ISEN}}$ does not always equal
$(A_{\text{THROAT}}/A_1)_{\text{ACTUAL}} = 0.2$. These quantities will not be equal in the presence
of losses. This same observation has been cited in the text concerning (6.2)
and in Example 6.4.

By the continuity expression of (2.10),

$$\dot{m} = \rho_1 A_1 V_1 = \frac{p_1 A_1 \mathbf{M}_1 \times 49.02 \sqrt{T_1}}{\bar{R} T_1}$$

$$\dot{m} = \frac{15 \times 144 \times 5 \times 0.1 \times 49.02}{53.35 \times \sqrt{530}} = 43.1 \text{ lbm/sec}$$

By the general adiabatic relation of (6.1),

$$\left(\frac{15.1}{10.1}\right)\left(\frac{5}{1.75}\right) 0.17177 = \Gamma_2 = 0.73373$$

Assuming that the nozzle is choked at the throat and that the exit flow is supersonic, we obtain from Table 5.1, interpolated, $\mathbf{M}_2 = 1.73$.

6.6 ADIABATIC LOSS COEFFICIENT

Although A_1/A_2 may be obvious from the given geometry of a flow system, there is no assurance that the total pressure ratio, as required in (6.1), will be available.

We could insist on total pressure measurements at inlet and exit stations in the flow system. Alternatively, we could apply the total pressure equation (5.8) to deduce total pressures from static pressure measurements and the flow rate. But there will be cases, such as encountered in design work or analysis work, where none of these measurements would be available.

To help estimate the total pressure ratio, we next introduce the adiabatic loss coefficient.

6.6.1 Generalized Loss Coefficient

In general (that is, not restricted to an adiabatic process), the steady flow general energy equation of (1.27) combined with the first law of thermodynamics of (1.21) yields, in the absence of external work,

$$0 = \delta F + \frac{dp}{\rho} + \frac{V\, dV}{g_c} \tag{6.17}$$

This is the one-dimensional energy equation with losses (δF) and applies to real gas flow with or without heat transfer.

The loss term can be further delineated by a modified Darcy-Weisbach equation of the form

$$\delta F = \left(f \frac{dx}{D}\right) \frac{V^2}{2g_c} \tag{6.18}$$

The quantity (fdx/D) represents the number of velocity heads, $V^2/2g_c$, lost in the flow process and is called the compressible loss coefficient, that is,

$$dK = f\frac{dx}{D} \tag{6.19}$$

In (6.19), f is the conventional friction factor that was extensively discussed in Section 1.11. We take f to be independent of length. In fact, if it is not, an average value of f over the length should be used.

Combining (6.17), (6.18), and (6.19), we obtain

$$dK = \frac{-2g_c dp}{\rho V^2} - 2\frac{dV}{V} \tag{6.20}$$

To further particularize the loss coefficient, it is necessary to specify the thermodynamic flow process involved. There will be different loss coefficients for different flow processes. In this chapter, our interest is the adiabatic process.

6.6.2 Adiabatic Loss Coefficient

In (6.20), density can be replaced, according to continuity, by $\rho = \dot{m}/AV$. It is further convenient to introduce here the state point total flow number (α) of (4.21) as

$$\alpha = \left(\frac{\dot{m}}{Ap_t}\right)\left(\frac{p_t}{\rho_t g_c}\right)^{1/2} \tag{6.21}$$

where $\overline{R}T_t$ has been replaced by p_t/ρ_t. Hence, α is a constant for a given area and total pressure. This flow number also can be given in terms of the static to total pressure ratio ($R = p/p_t$) as in (4.22) as

$$\alpha = \left[\left(\frac{2\gamma}{\gamma - 1}\right)(R^{2/\gamma} - R^{(\gamma+1)/\gamma})\right]^{1/2} \tag{6.22}$$

The remaining variable to be replaced in (6.20) is the velocity (V). Using the general compressible relation of (4.8), namely

$$V^2 = \left(\frac{2g_c\gamma}{\gamma - 1}\right)\left(\frac{p_t}{\rho_t} - \frac{p}{\rho}\right) \tag{6.23}$$

we obtain the quadratic

$$V^2 + \left(\frac{2g_c\gamma}{\gamma - 1}\right)\left(\frac{pA}{\dot{m}}\right)V - \left(\frac{2g_c\gamma}{\gamma - 1}\right)\frac{p_t}{\rho_t} = 0 \tag{6.24}$$

that has the real solution

$$V = \frac{2(p_t/\rho_t g_c)^{1/2}}{[(R/\alpha)^2 + 2(\gamma - 1)/\gamma]^{1/2} + R/\alpha} \tag{6.25}$$

Combining these expressions according to (6.20), we obtain

$$dK = -\frac{1}{\alpha}\left\{\left[\left(\frac{R}{\alpha}\right)^2 + \frac{2(\gamma - 1)}{\gamma}\right]^{1/2} + \frac{R}{\alpha}\right\} dR - 2\frac{dV}{V} \tag{6.26}$$

that can be integrated between any two stations in the flow passage by using the general form

$$\int (ax^2 + b)^{1/2} dx = \frac{x}{2}(ax^2 + b)^{1/2} + \frac{b}{2\sqrt{a}} \ln \left[(ax^2 + b)^{1/2} + x\sqrt{a}\right] \tag{6.27}$$

It is important to note, in connection with the integration, that the quantity p_t/ρ_t, as given by the perfect gas relation of (4.11), is a constant for the adiabatic case under consideration here. There results [2]

$$(K_{adi})_{1,\,2} = \frac{1}{2}\left(\frac{R}{\alpha}\right)\left[\left(\frac{R}{\alpha}\right)^2 + \frac{2(\gamma - 1)}{\gamma}\right]^{1/2}\Bigg|_2^1 + \frac{1}{2}\left(\frac{R}{\alpha}\right)^2\Bigg|_2^1$$

$$- \left(\frac{\gamma + 1}{\gamma}\right) \ln \left\{\left(\frac{R}{\alpha}\right)^2 + \frac{2(\gamma - 1)}{\gamma}\right]^{1/2} + \frac{R}{\alpha}\right\}\Bigg|_2^1 \tag{6.28}$$

where for the upper limit R takes on the value $R_1 = p_1/p_{t1}$, a point pressure ratio, while for the lower limit we have $R_{21} = p_2/p_{t1}$, a *hybrid* pressure ratio; that is, both pressure ratios are based on the same (inlet) total pressure.

The term K_{adi} of (6.28) maximizes to K^*_{adi} when R_{21} is evaluated at the critical state (that is, where the flow maximizes), as given in terms of the initial pressure ratio by

$$(R_{21})^*_{adi} = \frac{2R_1^{1/\gamma}\left[1 - R_1^{(\gamma - 1)/\gamma}\right]^{1/2}}{[(\gamma - 1)(\gamma - 1)]^{1/2}} \tag{6.29}$$

The significance of K^*_{adi} is that it indicates the maximum length of the flow passage possible for the given inlet pressure ratio, R_1.

In terms of the Mach number, this same adiabatic loss coefficient can be given [3] as

$$(K_{adi})_{1,\,2} = \frac{1}{\gamma}\left(\frac{1}{M_1^2} - \frac{1}{M_2^2}\right) + \left(\frac{\gamma + 1}{2\gamma}\right) \ln \left\{\frac{M_1^2}{M_2^2}\left[\frac{2 + (\gamma - 1)M_2^2}{2 + (\gamma - 1)M_1^2}\right]\right\} \tag{6.30}$$

that attains the maximum value, when $M_2 = 1$, of

$$(K_{adi})_{1, *} = \frac{1}{\gamma}\left(\frac{1}{M_1^2} - 1\right) + \left(\frac{\gamma + 1}{2\gamma}\right)\ln\left[\frac{(\gamma + 1)M_1^2}{2 + (\gamma - 1)M_1^2}\right] \tag{6.31}$$

EXAMPLE 6.6

Find the adiabatic compressible loss coefficient if the pressure ratios, $R_1 = 0.9$ and $R_{21} = 0.76504$, are determined experimentally in air at $\gamma = 1.4$.

Solution
By (6.22),

$$\alpha = \left[\left(\frac{2 \times 1.4}{0.4}\right)\left((0.9)^{2/1.4} - (0.9)^{2.4/1.4}\right)\right]^{1/2} = 0.422581$$

By (6.28),

$$(K_{adi})_{1, 2} = \frac{1}{2}\left(\frac{R_1}{\alpha}\right)\left[\left(\frac{R_1}{\alpha}\right)^2 + \frac{2(\gamma - 1)}{\gamma}\right]^{1/2} + \frac{1}{2}\left(\frac{R_1}{\alpha}\right)^2$$

$$- \left(\frac{\gamma + 1}{\gamma}\right)\ln\left\{\left[\left(\frac{R_1}{\alpha}\right)^2 + \frac{2(\gamma - 1)}{\gamma}\right]^{1/2} + \frac{R_1}{\alpha}\right\}$$

$$- \frac{1}{2}\left(\frac{R_{21}}{\alpha}\right)\left[\left(\frac{R_{21}}{\alpha}\right)^2 + \frac{2(\gamma - 1)}{\gamma}\right]^{1/2} - \frac{1}{2}\left(\frac{R_{21}}{\alpha}\right)^2$$

$$+ \left(\frac{\gamma + 1}{\gamma}\right)\ln\left\{\left[\left(\frac{R_{21}}{\alpha}\right)^2 + \frac{2(\gamma - 1)}{\alpha}\right]^{1/2} + \frac{R_{21}}{\alpha}\right\}$$

$$= \left(\frac{0.9}{2 \times 0.422581}\right)\left[\left(\frac{0.9}{0.422581}\right)^2 + \frac{2 \times 0.4}{1.4}\right]^{1/2 \cdot}$$

$$+ 2.267958 - 2.535881$$

$$- \left(\frac{0.76504}{2 \times 0.4222581}\right)\left[\left(\frac{0.76504}{0.422581}\right)^2 + 0.5714286\right]^{1/2}$$

$$- 1.6387713 + 2.276021$$

$$= 1.000014$$

EXAMPLE 6.7

With the same conditions as in Example 6.6, find the adiabatic loss coefficient by the Mach number formulation of (6.30) if $R_2 = p_2/p_{t2}$ is given by 0.866362.

Solution

From (3.14) on Table 5.1, $M_1 = 0.390901$ and $M_2 = 0.457373$.
From (6.30),

$$(K_{adi})_{1,\,2} = \frac{1}{1.4}\left(\frac{1}{0.390901^2} - \frac{1}{0.457373^2}\right)$$

$$+ \frac{2.4}{2.8}\ln\left[\frac{0.390901^2}{0.457373^2}\left(\frac{2 + 0.4 \times 0.457373^2}{2 + 0.4 \times 0.390901^2}\right)\right]$$

$$= 1.26000503 + 0.85714286 \ln\left(\frac{0.318393177}{0.431166117}\right)$$

$$= 1.000114$$

that closely checks the previous result.

EXAMPLE 6.8

For the same inlet conditions as in Examples 6.6 and 6.7, find the maximum K_{adi} possible by the pressure ratio and Mach number formulations.

Solution

By (6.29),

$$(R_{21})_{adi}^* = \frac{2 \times 0.9^{1/1.4} \times (1 - 0.9^{0.4/1.4})^{1/2}}{(2.4 \times 0.4)^{1/2}} = 0.3260282$$

By (6.28), using the results of Example 6.6 for the upper limit of integration, we have

$$(K_{adi})_{1,\,*} = 2.406579 + 2.267958 - 2.535881$$

$$- 0.4166664 - 0.29761883 + 1.0561227$$

$$= 2.480494$$

By (6.31),

$$(K_{adi})_{1,\,*} = \frac{1}{1.4}(6.5443489 - 1) + 0.85714286 \ln\left(\frac{2.4 \times 0.15280359}{2 + 0.4 \times 0.15280359}\right)$$

$$= 2.480492$$

that closely checks the previous result.

6.7   APPLICATIONS OF K_{adi}

6.7.1 K_{adi} and the Total Pressure Ratio

The whole purpose of introducing the loss coefficient, K_{adi}, was to aid in estimating p_{t1}/p_{t2}. Therefore, we must determine a relationship between K_{adi} and the total pressure ratio (TPR). The means for obtaining one of these factors in terms of the other involves an iterative solution.

We first recall that any area change can be accounted for by an isentropic process, so the general adiabatic problem always reduces to a constant area adiabatic (that is, FANNO) solution for TPR.

Both the pressure ratio and Mach number approaches must be considered.

By the pressure ratio method, we obtain α, the flow number, via (6.22). Then, for any estimate of K_{adi} we can obtain R_{21}, iteratively, from (6.28). However,

$$\text{TPR}_A = \frac{R_2}{R_{21}} \tag{6.32}$$

and

$$(\text{TPR}_B)_{\text{FANNO}} = \left\{ \left(\frac{R_2}{R_1} \right)^{2/\gamma} \left[\frac{1 - R_2^{(\gamma - 1)/\gamma}}{1 - R_1^{(\gamma - 1)/\gamma}} \right] \right\}^{1/2} \tag{6.33}$$

When these alternative forms, (6.32) and (6.33), for TPR converge within required accuracy limits, we obtain both R_2 and TPR [4].

By the Mach number method, we obtain M_2, iteratively, from (6.30), for any estimate of K_{adi}, given M_1. The two Mach numbers, of course, lead unambiguously to R_1 and R_2 via (3.13). Then, by applying (6.32) and (6.33), we can obtain R_{21} and TPR.

The Mach number form of (6.33) is

$$\text{TPR}_{\text{FANNO}} = \frac{M_2}{M_1} \left[\frac{2 + (\gamma - 1) M_1^2}{2 + (\gamma - 1) M_2^2} \right]^{(\gamma + 1)/2 (\gamma - 1)} \tag{6.34}$$

For the usual constant area duct, K_{adi} is formed readily from (6.19) as

$$K_{adi} = f \frac{L}{D} \tag{6.35}$$

For the many other flow elements that could be encountered, such as nozzles, diffusers, orifices, abrupt enlargements and contractions, valves, inlets, exits, reducers, and screens, to name a few, several texts [5, 6] are available to aid in forming estimates of K_{adi}.

EXAMPLE 6.9

For a constant area adiabatic flow of air from $R_1 = 0.9$, through a loss device that can be characterized by $K_{adi} = 2$, find the exit Mach number and the total pressure loss.

Solution

By (6.22), $\alpha_1 = 0.42258$. By (6.28), $R_{21} = 0.57222$. To find R_{21} it is necessary to apply an iterative solution (see Figure 6.4) as follows.

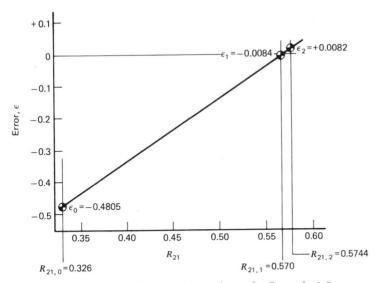

Figure 6.4 Newton-Raphson iterative scheme for Example 6.9.

1. A first guess at R_{21}'s value is made. This is called $R_{21,0}$ to indicate an initial guess. A good first guess is the lower limiting value, R_{21}^*, of (6.29). Thus, $R_{21,0} = 0.326$.

2. Since Example 6.6 had the same inlet pressure ratio, the upper limit value already has been calculated so we have

$$K = 2.138656 - \left[\frac{1}{2}\left(\frac{R_{21}}{\alpha} \right) \left\{ \left(\frac{R_{21}}{\alpha} \right)^2 + \frac{2(\gamma - 1)}{\gamma} 1 \right\}^{1/2} \right.$$
$$\left. + \frac{1}{2}\left(\frac{R_{21}}{\alpha} \right)^2 - \left(\frac{\gamma + 1}{\gamma} \right) \ln \left[\left\{ \left(\frac{R_{21}}{\alpha} \right)^2 + \frac{2(\gamma - 1)}{\gamma} \right\}^{1/2} + \frac{R_{21}}{\alpha} \right] \right]$$

3. Evaluating this equation at $R_{21,0}$, we get $K_0 = 2.480494$.

4. Thus, $R_{21,0}$ leads to an error of

$$\epsilon_0 = K - K_0 = -0.480494$$

5. A second guess of R_{21} is made arbitrarily, say $R_{21,1} = 0.57$. By similar calculations $K_1 = 2.008438$ and $\epsilon_1 = -0.008438$.

6. With two guesses arrived at, the third need not be arbitrary. A straight line interpolation between the first and second guesses (called the Newton-Raphson Method) is made according to the relation

$$R_{21,2} = R_{21,1} - \epsilon_1 \left(\frac{R_{21,0} - R_{21,1}}{\epsilon_0 - \epsilon_1} \right)$$

This yields $R_{21,2} = 0.574362$.

7. A further calculation can be made using this R_{21} value that leads to $K_2 = 1.991767$ and $\epsilon_2 = + 0.008232$. Eventually, R_{21} converges on 0.57222.

Determining TPR and M_2 remains. By (6.32) and (6.33), iteratively once more, we find TPR $= 1.36727$ and $R_2 = 0.78238$. Thus, the loss in total pressure can be characterized by $p_{t1}/p_{t2} = 1.36727$.

By (3.14) or Table 5.1, for the given R_2, $M_2 = 0.60264$.

EXAMPLE 6.10
Complete Example 6.9 in terms of the Mach number formulations.

Solution
By (3.14), $M_1 = 0.390901$. By (6.30), $M_2 = 0.60264$.

Note that to obtain M_2, it is necessary to apply an iterative solution, as explained in Example 6.9.

To make things easier, since we have already done Example 6.9, the first guess of the exit Mach number might as well be $M_{2,0} = 0.60264$. By (6.30), this leads immediately to $K_0 = 2.0$, which shows zero error, and hence M_2 as guessed is correct.

With M_2, known, it is a simple matter to find R_2, via (3.13) or Table 5.1, as 0.78238.

The solution for TPR is straightforward through (6.33) since both R_1 and R_2 are available.

6.7.2 K_{adi} and the Critical State

Still another use of K_{adi} can be given. For every pressure ratio (R) or Mach number (M), we have seen that it is possible to generate (and hence to tabulate) K_{adi}^*, the loss coefficient from any given state to the critical state. In Example 6.8, K_{adi}^* was so determined by the pressure ratio and the Mach number formulations of (6.28), (6.29), and (6.31).

As illustrated in Figure 6.5 and the relation

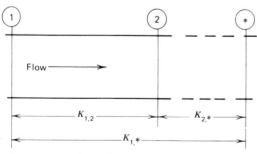

Figure 6.5 Relation between the various loss coefficients in a pipe.

$$K_{1, *} = K_{1, 2} + K_{2, *} \tag{6.36}$$

it follows that the simple algebraic addition of any two of the three terms involved in (6.36) leads immediately to the third term. Thus, the tabular values of $K_{x, *}$ plus (6.36) provide another solution to Fanno problems.

Note that the critical state (*) need not be located in the flow system. It may be an imaginary state that is located beyond the piping system exit. This is depicted by the dotted lines in Figure 6.5.

EXAMPLE 6.11

Air flows adiabatically through a 10-in. duct of 200 ft. length with an average friction factor of $f = 0.01589$. The measured exit conditions are: $p_2 = 94$ psia, $p_{t2} = 100$ psia, and $T_t = 540°R$. Find the inlet pressure ratio.

Solution

At $R_2 = 0.94$, $K_{2, *} = 5.3645$ via (6.28) and (6.29). But

$$K_{1, 2} = f \frac{L}{D} = \frac{0.01589 \times 200}{10/12} = 3.8136$$

via (6.34). Thus, according to (6.36) and Figure 6.5

$$K_{1, *} = K_{1, 2} + K_{2, *} = 3.8136 + 5.3645 = 9.1781.$$

Once more applying (6.28), with R_1 the unknown and R_{21} given by (6.29), we obtain for $K_{1, *} = 9.1781$ the result $R_1 = 0.96$.

6.7.3 Combining Loss Coefficients

Whenever the overall piping system consists of two or more piping elements connected so that the gas flows through one element and then through another, we have a series network. We need a method for combining loss coefficients in such cases. In addition, since flow areas can change between inlet and exit and there exists the possibility of choking somewhere in the system, these eventualities also must be considered.

Compressible loss coefficients can be added only when individual loss coefficients of each component are initially adjusted to a common reference area. This entails an evaluation of K according to the usual methods, as already discussed at length, based on the pertinent exit area, and then a reevaluation of K based on a common reference area. Of course, the same flow rate and the same total pressure drop are maintained in this reevaluation. Thus,

$$(K_{0, N})_{ref} = (K_{0, 1})_{ref} + (K_{1, 2})_{ref} + \cdots + (K_{N-1, N})_{ref} \tag{6.37}$$

If changes in area between 1 and 2 are involved, it is important to note that

(6.28) can be used only if R_1 and α_1 are first adjusted to the *exit* area. Thus, to express an overall loss coefficient across any number of loss elements where area changes are involved, (6.28) becomes

$$K_{\text{overall}} = \frac{R_{1R}^2 C_1 - R_{\text{exit, 1}} C_2}{\alpha_{1R}^2} - \left(\frac{\gamma + 1}{\gamma}\right) \ln \left(\frac{R_{1R} C_1}{R_{\text{exit, 1}} C_2}\right) \tag{6.38}$$

where R_{1R} is the inlet pressure ratio *referred* to the exit area, α_{1R} is the inlet flow number *referred* to the exit area, and $R_{\text{exit, 1}}$ is the hybrid exit static to inlet total pressure ratio. C_1 and C_2 are convenient groupings defined by

$$C_1 = \left[1 + \sqrt{1 + E/(R_{1R}/\alpha_{1R})^2}\right]/2 \tag{6.39}$$

$$C_2 = \left[1 + \sqrt{1 + E/(R_{\text{exit, 1}}/\alpha_{1R})^2}\right]/2 \tag{6.40}$$

and

$$E = 2(\gamma - 1)/\alpha \tag{6.41}$$

Similarly, to express an overall loss coefficient across any number of loss elements where area changes are involved, (6.30) becomes

$$K_{\text{overall}} = \frac{1}{\gamma}\left(\frac{1}{\mathbf{M}_{1R}^2} - \frac{1}{\mathbf{M}_{\text{exit}}^2}\right) + \left(\frac{\gamma + 1}{2\gamma}\right) \ln \left[\left(\frac{\mathbf{M}_{1R}^2}{\mathbf{M}_{\text{exit}}^2}\right)\left(\frac{2 + (\gamma - 1)\mathbf{M}_{\text{exit}}^2}{2 + (\gamma - 1)\mathbf{M}_{1R}^2}\right)\right] \tag{6.42}$$

where $\mathbf{M}_{1R}$ is the inlet Mach number *referred* to the exit area.

Whether we are dealing with *overall* loss coefficients, as above, or with summations of *referred* loss coefficients, we apply the same reasoning as follows:

1. $\Gamma_{1R} = \Gamma(A_1/A_R)$ according to (6.15) (where the subscript R signifies a reference area).
2. $R_{1R} = f(\Gamma_{1R})$ according to (4.19).
3. $\mathbf{M}_{1R} = g(R_{1R})$ according to (3.14).
4. $\Gamma_{2R} = \Gamma_{1R} \times \text{TPR}$ according to (6.16).
5. $R_{2R} = f(\Gamma_{2R})$ according to (4.19).
6. $\mathbf{M}_{2R} = g(R_{2R})$ according to (3.14).
7. $K_{\text{referred}} = F(\mathbf{M}_{1R}, \mathbf{M}_{2R})$ according to (6.42).

Note again that the subscript R indicates a quantity based on a specified reference area.

When all loss coefficients are referred to the *same* reference area, they can be added to yield the sum of the referred loss coefficients. When the reference area is taken as the system exit area, the sum of the referred loss coefficients must just equal the overall loss coefficient.

Whenever the possibility of choking (limiting) flow exists, the solution must be executed in a direction backwards to the flow. One starts at the *exit* of the piping system with either the choked condition (as given by R_* of (6.8) or with p_{exit} given. From standard state point relations, all conditions at exit, including R_2, p_{t2}, p_2, and M_2, are determined. One then finds *inlet* conditions to the last loss element by iterating on the given loss coefficient to find in turn R_1, Γ_1, p_t, p_1, M_1, and TPR. If an area change has occurred between the inlet and exit of the given loss element, the above inlet values must be *referred* to the proper inlet area. It should be mentioned that for sudden enlargements, a different (and more complicated) approach is necessary as outlined in [3].

These rather complex ideas and solutions are illustrated by two more examples.

EXAMPLE 6.12

Air flows through a constant area loss element of $K = 13.546$ such that the flow is choked at the exit. Find the inlet pressure ratio and the total pressure loss.

Solution

Because of the choking condition, the problem should be solved in a direction backwards to the flow, that is, from exit to inlet.

By (6.8), $R_2 = R_{exit} = R_* = 0.52828$. By usual means, $M_2 = 1.0$, $\Gamma_2 = 1.0$. For the given K, (6.30) can be solved, iteratively, for M_1 to yield $M_1 = 0.20608$. By usual means, $R_1 = 0.97083$, and $\Gamma_1 = 0.347185$.

To obtain the total pressure ratio across this loss element we observe that TPR $= \Gamma_2/\Gamma_1$ according to (6.10). TPR $= 2.88031$ results.

EXAMPLE 6.13

Air, at a total temperature of 500°F, flows subsonically through two loss elements in series, at a mass flow rate of 2060.163 lbm/hr, to an exit pressure of 14.7 psia. The first loss element is characterized by $(K_{1,2})_2 = 1.0$ with an area of $A_1 = A_2 = 2$ in.^{2}. The second loss element has $(K_{2,3})_3 = 0.1$ with an area of $A_{2'} = A_3 = 1.5$ in.^{2}.

A. Find the overall loss coefficient of this series system and compare it with the sum of the referred loss coefficients.
B. Find the total pressure ratio (TPR) across the combined system.

Solution

The geometry of this example is shown schematically in Figure 6.6.

Working from the exit to inlet, we can obtain the total pressure at exit from (5.8) as $p_{t3} = 22.8954$ psia. Then, $R_3 = p_3/p_{t3} = 0.64205$, $\Gamma_3 = 0.97093$, $M_3 = 0.82146$.

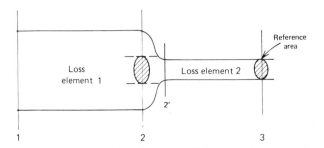

Figure 6.6 Combining two loss elements in series (as in Example 6.13).

Iterating on $\mathbf{M}_{2'}$, the inlet Mach number to the last loss element, via (6.30), given $(K_{2,\,3})_3 = 0.1$, we find $\mathbf{M}_{2'} = 0.73078$, $R_{2'} = 0.70105$, and $\Gamma_{2'} = 0.93135$.

The total pressure ratio across the second loss element is given by (6.10) as 1.04250, the total pressure at 2' is 23.869 psia, and $p_{2'}$ is 16.733 psia.

It is now necessary to express these values in terms of the exit area of the first loss element, that is, at 2. The assumption here is that there is no loss from 2 to 2'. This is reasonable for a reducer. Thus, by (6.15)

$$\Gamma_2 = \left(\frac{A_{2'}}{A_2}\right)\Gamma_{2'} = \left(\frac{1.5}{2.0}\right)0.93135 = 0.69851$$

Accompanying this Γ_2 is $\mathbf{M}_2 = 0.45704$ and $R_2 = 0.86654$.

Since we have assumed that there is no loss in total pressure from 2 to 2', it follows that

$$p_2 = R_2 \times p_{t2} = 0.86654 \times 23.869 = 20.683 \text{ psia}$$

Iterating on $\mathbf{M}_1$, the inlet Mach number to the first loss element, via (6.30), given $(K_{1,\,2})_2 = 1$, we find $\mathbf{M}_1 = 0.39071$, $R_1 = 0.90009$, and $\Gamma_1 = 0.61690$.

The total pressure ratio across the first loss element is given by (6.10) as 1.13229, the total pressure at 1 is 27.0266 psia, and p_1 is 24.326 psia.

The overall loss coefficient, $(K_{1,\,3})_3$, is a function of $\mathbf{M}_{1x}$ in which x signifies that the reference area is the exit area.

$$\mathbf{M}_{1x} = f(\Gamma_{1x}), \text{ via (4.20)}, = 0.57790$$

where

$$\Gamma_{1x} = \Gamma_1\left(\frac{A_1}{A_x}\right) = 0.82253$$

With $\mathbf{M}_{1x}$ and $\mathbf{M}_3$ known, the overall loss coefficient based on the exit area is, by (6.42), $(K_{1,\,3})_3 = 0.530$.

The referred loss coefficients are $(K_{2,\,3})_3 = 0.1$ (given) and $(K_{1,\,2})_3 = 0.430$. The later is based on the use of the referred quantities of R_{1x}, α_{1x}, Γ_{1x}, and $\mathbf{M}_{1x}$

according to items 1, 2, 3 after (6.42), and on the referred quantities of Γ_{2x}, $\text{TPR}_{1,\,2}$, and M_{2x} ($= 0.82146$) according to items 4, 5, 6 after (6.42), all used in (6.42).

It follows that the sum of the *referred* loss coefficients equals 0.530 in agreement with the *overall* loss coefficient.

The overall TPR is obtained from

$$\frac{p_{t2}}{p_{t3}} \times \frac{p_{t1}}{p_{t2}} = 1.04250 \times 1.13229 = 1.18041$$

6.8 GENERALIZED FANNO FLOW MAP

We have seen in Section 4.3 that the envelope of Figure 4.1 has significance in all the flow processes of gas dynamics since it can be interpreted as a dimensionless plot relating the general concepts of continuity and energy.

In Section 6.7, we showed that the Fanno flow could be solved in terms of the empirical loss coefficient K_f of (6.28), where the subscript f stands for friction and signifies a loss coefficient.

In this section we develop a generalized Fanno flow map in terms of the empirical loss coefficient, K_f, and the total pressure ratio, TPR, the innovation being to exploit the interior of Figure 4.1. This is accomplished by introducing on the plot the hybrid pressure ratio, $R_{21} = p_2/p_{t1}$, of (6.28).

K_f has been given by (6.28) and (6.30) and has the coordinates $\Gamma_1 = 0$ when $R_1 = 0$, and Γ_1 reaches a maximum value for a given K_f when $R = (R_{21})^*_{\text{adi}}$ of (6.29).

$\text{TPR}_{\text{FANNO}}$ has been given by (6.33) and has the coordinates $\Gamma_1 = 0$ when $R = (R_{21})_{\text{max}}$ where

$$(R_{21})_{\text{max}} = \frac{1}{\text{TPR}} \tag{6.43}$$

This represents the $\Gamma = 0$ intercept for any TPR value. The minimum R_{21} value for a given TPR is found to be

$$(R_{21})_{\text{min}} = \frac{1}{\text{TPR}} \left(\frac{2}{\gamma + 1} \right)^{\gamma/(\gamma - 1)} \tag{6.44}$$

based on $(\Gamma_1)_{\text{max}} = 1/\text{TPR}$, since then Γ_2 attains its maximum value of $\Gamma_2^* = 1$.

When K_f and TPR are plotted within the generalized envelope of Figure 4.1, we have the desired generalized Fanno flow map. Such a map is given in Figure 6.7 and, in expanded form, in Figure 6.8.

Briefly, one enters the outer envelope, horizontally, with R_1 to obtain, vertically, Γ_1. This vertical Γ line intercepts the chosen K_f parameter to yield at the same intercept the values of R_{21} (on the R scale) and TPR. These, in turn, lead to Γ_2 and the complete Fanno solution.

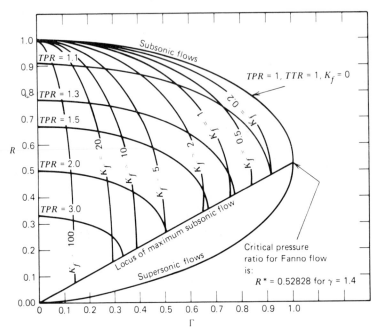

Figure 6.7 Generalized Fanno flow map.

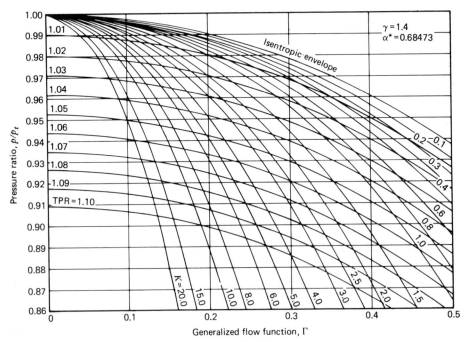

Figure 6.8 Expanded form of generalized Fanno map.

Note that on the outer envelope, the three parameters of interest are found to be TPR = 1, TTR = 1 [where TTR represents the total temperature ratio (T_{t1}/T_{t2})], and $K_f = 0$. In Fanno flow, however, only TTR remains on the outer envelope at 1 since the process is adiabatic. The TPR and K_f parameters are now found inside the envelope of both Figures 6.7 and 6.8.

The Fanno flow map is especially useful for visualizing the flow process in short ducts and piping networks where the flow is essentially adiabatic.

6.9   GENERALIZED FANNO FLOW TABLE

Computer solutions for selected Fanno flow problems are presented in Table 6.1 in terms of the static to total pressure ratio $(R = p/p_t)$, the Mach number (M), the static to total temperature ratio (T/T_t), and the normalized flow function (Γ). For these entries K^* is also given; it represents the maximum loss coefficient from the entry point to the critical point. Finally, iterative solutions for $R_{21} = p_2/p_{t1}$ and TPR = p_{t1}/p_{t2} in terms of various loss coefficients (K) are given. The use of this table is best illustrated by an example.

EXAMPLE 6.14

For the subsonic flow of air in a pipe characterized by $K_f = 2$, find the exit static and total pressures if $T_t = 540°R$, $p_{t1} = 15$ psia, and the flow rate per unit area is 19.974 lbm/ft² − sec (see Figure 6.9).

Solution

By (4.21) or (6.21), $\alpha_1 = 0.27671$.
By (4.25), $\Gamma_1 = 0.40412$, where $\alpha^* = 0.68473$ and by usual means, $R_1 = 0.96$.

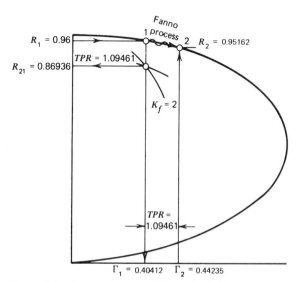

Figure 6.9   Fanno process of Example 6.14.

TABLE 6.1
GENERALIZED FANNO FLOW TABLE ($\gamma = 1.4$)[a]

EXIT STATIC PRESSURE TO INLET TOTAL PRESSURE (p_2/p_{t1}), AND INLET TOTAL PRESSURE TO EXIT TOTAL PRESSURE (p_{t1}/p_{t2}), VERSUS LOSS COEFFICIENT (K or fL/D)

PRESS RATIO p/p_t	MACH NUMBER M	TEMPERATURE RATIO T/T_t	FLOW FACTOR Γ_{isen}	K^*	0.1	0.2	0.4	0.6	1	2	4	6	10	20
0.999	0.038	1.000	0.06528	493.5268	0.99890	0.99880	0.99860	0.99840	0.99800	0.99700	0.99499	0.99297	0.98893	0.97876
					1.00010	1.00020	1.00040	1.00060						
0.99	0.120	0.997	0.20543	45.48177	0.98898	0.98796	0.98592	0.98388	0.97978	0.96944	0.94843	0.92691	0.88225	0.75857
					1.00101	1.00202	1.00405	1.00609	1.01022	1.02077	1.04290	1.06656	1.11923	1.29596
0.98	0.170	0.994	0.28894	21.07852	0.97793	0.97585	0.97169	0.96750	0.95908	0.93765	0.89313	0.84606	0.74204	0.32715
					1.00203	1.00408	1.00821	1.01239	1.02091	1.04324	1.09280	1.15043	1.30127	2.57883
0.97	0.209	0.991	0.35193	13.09545	0.96366	0.96366	0.95728	0.95085	0.93784	0.90439	0.83293	0.75362	0.55333	
					1.00307	1.00618	1.01247	1.01890	1.03213	1.06772	1.15221	1.26216	1.64972	
0.96	0.242	0.988	0.40412	9.17812	0.95570	0.95138	0.94268	0.93388	0.91599	0.86936	0.76589	0.64123		
					1.00413	1.00832	1.01686	1.02564	1.04393	1.09461	1.22532	1.42584		
0.95	0.272	0.985	0.44929	6.87217	0.94452	0.93901	0.92787	0.91656	0.89344	0.83216	0.68841	0.48060		
					1.00521	1.01051	1.02138	1.03263	1.05638	1.12448	1.31988	1.72254		
0.94	0.299	0.982	0.48938	5.36456	0.93330	0.92654	0.91283	0.89886	0.87008	0.79218	0.59227			
					1.00631	1.01274	1.02603	1.03990	1.06958	1.15807	1.45313			
0.93	0.324	0.979	0.52555	4.30904	0.92202	0.91395	0.89753	0.88072	0.84577	0.74853	0.44508			
					1.00742	1.01503	1.03083	1.04746	1.08363	1.19652	1.68330			
0.92	0.347	0.976	0.55858	3.53348	0.91069	0.90124	0.88196	0.86208	0.82034	0.66973				
					1.00856	1.01737	1.03578	1.05537	1.09866	1.24162				
0.91	0.370	0.973	0.58898	2.94285	0.89929	0.88840	0.86606	0.84288	0.79354	0.64307				
					1.00972	1.01976	1.04091	1.06365	1.11485	1.29643				
0.90	0.391	0.970	0.61715	2.48050	0.88783	0.87541	0.84980	0.82301	0.76504	0.57223				
					1.01090	1.02221	1.04622	1.07234	1.13244	1.36726				

0.89	0.411	0.967	0.64338	2.11056	0.87629	1.01210	0.86226	1.02473	0.83313	1.05176	0.80234	1.08153	0.73438	1.15175	0.46172	1.47278
0.88	0.431	0.964	0.66790	1.80929	0.86468	1.01333	0.84893	1.02731	0.81598	1.05752	0.78076	1.09126	0.70081	1.17323		
0.87	0.451	0.961	0.69088	1.56034	0.85298	1.01458	0.83539	1.02997	0.79829	1.06354	0.75804	1.10162	0.66313	1.19757		
0.86	0.469	0.958	0.71249	1.35213	0.84118	1.01586	0.82163	1.03270	0.77996	1.06984	0.73390	1.11275	0.61897	1.22604		
0.85	0.487	0.955	0.73284	1.17618	0.82927	1.01717	0.80761	1.03552	0.76085	1.07648	0.70792	1.12480	0.56273	1.26096		
0.84	0.505	0.951	0.75203	1.02621	0.81725	1.01851	0.79329	1.03843	0.74080	1.08350	0.67948	1.13801	0.46630	1.30964		
0.83	0.523	0.948	0.77016	0.89741	0.80509	1.01988	0.77863	1.04144	0.71957	1.09096	0.64750	1.15273				
0.82	0.540	0.945	0.78729	0.78610	0.79278	1.02128	0.76354	1.04458	0.69683	1.09897	0.60983	1.16961				
0.81	0.557	0.942	0.80348	0.68937	0.78026	1.02274	0.74800	1.04783	0.67205	1.10765	0.56111	1.18981				
0.80	0.574	0.938	0.81880	0.60491	0.76757	1.02423	0.73188	1.05123	0.64437	1.11718	0.46509	1.21742				
0.79	0.590	0.935	0.83330	0.53086	0.75464	1.02576	0.71507	1.05479	0.61199	1.12796						
0.78	0.607	0.931	0.84701	0.46572	0.74145	1.02734	0.69738	10.5853	0.57087	1.14051						

EXIT STATIC PRESSURE TO INLET TOTAL PRESSURE (p_2/p_{t1}), AND INLET TOTAL PRESSURE TO EXIT TOTAL PRESSURE (p_{t1}/p_{t2}), VERSUS LOSS COEFFICIENT (K or fL/D)

PRESS RATIO p/p_t	MACH NUMBER M	TEMPER-ATURE RATIO T/T_t	FLOW FACTOR Γ_{isen}	K^*	0.1	0.2	0.4	0.6	1	2	4	6	10	20
0.77	0.623	0.928	0.85997	0.40825	0.72793	0.67855	0.49854							
					1.02897	1.06251	1.15680							
0.76	0.639	0.925	0.87222	0.35743	0.71403	0.65819								
					1.03066	1.06676								
0.75	0.654	0.921	0.88378	0.31239	0.69965	0.63562								
					1.03242	1.07137								
0.74	0.670	0.918	0.89469	0.27243	0.68468	0.60951								
					1.03425	1.07648								
0.73	0.686	0.914	0.90497	0.23692	0.66896	0.57674								
					1.03617	1.08230								
0.72	0.701	0.910	0.91464	0.20536	0.65222	0.52125								
					1.03820	1.08954								
0.71	0.717	0.907	0.92371	0.17731	0.63409									
					1.04035									
0.70	0.732	0.903	0.93222	0.15237	0.61361									
					1.04275									
0.69	0.748	0.899	0.94016	0.13023	0.58939									
					1.04536									
0.68	0.763	0.896	0.94756	0.11059	0.55581									
					1.04842									

[a]Under loss coefficient is tabulated p_2/p_{t1} as upper figure and p_{t1}/p_{t2} as lower figure. Example: At $p_1/p_{t1} = 0.80$, $M_1 = 0.574$, $T_1/T_t = 0.938$, $\Gamma_1 = 0.81880$, $K^* = 0.60491$, and at $K = 0.4$ $p_2/p_{t1} = 0.64437$ while $p_{t1}/p_{t2} = 1.11718$.

From Table 6.1 at $R_1 = 0.96$ and under $K = 2$ we find $R_{21} = 0.86936$ and TPR $= 1.09461$.

From $\Gamma_2 = \Gamma_1 \times$ TPR $= 0.44235$, we obtain $R_2 = 0.95162$.

It follows that

$$p_{t2} = p_{t1}/\text{TPR} = 15/1.09461 = 13.70 \text{ psia}$$

and

$$p_2 = R_{21} \times p_{t1} = 0.86936 \times 15 = 13.04 \text{ psia}$$

6.10 CONCLUDING REMARKS

Many practical applications in gas dynamics can be approximated by the adiabatic process, including the flow in short pipes and most nozzle flows.

In this chapter, we have applied the generalized gas dynamics equation of (4.18) to the adiabatic process, in the form of (6.1), namely

$$\left(\frac{p_{t1}}{p_{t2}}\right)\left(\frac{A_1}{A_2}\right)\Gamma_1 = \Gamma_2$$

and found it entirely satisfactory.

The entropy change in a general adiabatic process was given by (6.7) as

$$s_2 - s_1 = \frac{\overline{R}}{J} \ln\left(\frac{p_{t1}}{p_{t2}}\right)$$

Constant area adiabatic flow was defined as Fanno flow, and a generalized Fanno flow table (Table 6.1) was given to aid in rapid numerical solutions.

A general adiabatic loss coefficient applying between any two states was defined by (6.28), and an adiabatic critical loss coefficient was given by (6.31), to indicate the maximum length possible for a flow passage from a given inlet state.

The rather complicated problem of combining the loss coefficients of flow devices connected in series was detailed in Section 6.7.3.

Finally, a generalized Fanno flow map was developed, based on plotting K_{adi} and TPR in the interior of the generalized R–Γ envelope, as shown in Figures 6.7 and 6.8.

REFERENCES

1. R. P. Benedict and W. G. Steltz, *Handbook of Generalized Gas Dynamics*, Plenum Press, New York, 1966, p. 6.

2. R. P. Benedict and N. A. Carlucci, *Handbook of Specific Losses in Flow Systems*, Plenum Press, New York, 1966, pp. 3, 4.

3. R. P. Benedict, *Fundamentals of Pipe Flow*, Wiley, New York, 1980, pp. 293–296.
4. Ibid., pp. 311, 312.
5. Ibid., pp. 363–420.
6. D. S. Miller, *Internal Flow Systems*, BHRA Fluid Engineering, 1978, Vol. 5.

NOMENCLATURE

Roman

A	Area
C	Constant
D	Pipe diameter
E	Constant
f	Friction factor
F	Loss term
g_c	Gravitational constant
h	Enthalpy
J	Mechanical equivalent of heat
K, K_f	Loss coefficient
L	Length
$\dot{m}$	Mass flow rate
$\mathbf{M}$	Mach number
p	Pressure
$\mathbf{P}$	Pressure function
R	Static/total pressure ratio
$\overline{R}$	Specific gas constant
s	Specific entropy
T	Absolute temperature
TPR	Total pressure ratio (p_{t1}/p_{t2})
TTR	Total temperature ratio (T_{t1}/T_{t2})
v	Specific volume
V	Volumetric average velocity
x	Length coordinate

Greek

α	Flow number
Δ	Finite difference
γ	Specific heat ratio
Γ	Compressible flow function
ϵ	Error
ρ	Fluid density

Subscripts

1, 2   Axial locations
adi   Adiabatic
t Total
*   Critical

PROBLEMS

6.1   Because of friction air, flowing adiabatically in a constant area pipe, accelerates from a Mach number of 0.2 to 0.6. If the initial pressure and temperature are 20 psia and 70°F, respectively, find the final pressure and the final velocity.

6.2   Air flows along a Fanno line from $M_1 = 0.1$ to $M_2 = 0.5$. Find the pressure and velocity at station 2 if $p_1 = 150,000$ pascals and $T_1 = 50°C$.

6.3   Air flows in a constant area adiabatic process such that the entropy increases by 0.05 Btu/lbm-°R. If the final Mach number is 0.5, find the initial pressure ratio.

6.4   In a Fanno process, the entropy of the flowing air increases by 220 J/kg-K. Find the pressure ratio at the inlet if the exit Mach number is 0.6.

6.5   Air flows adiabatically through a *C–D* nozzle such that the total pressure drops 10 psi and the exit flow is supersonic. For $A_1 = A_2 = 10$ in.^{2}, $p_1 = 20$ psia, $T_1 = 540°R$, and $M_1 = 0.2$, find the exit Mach number and the flow rate.

6.6   The total pressure drops 100,000 pascals across a *C-D* nozzle when air accelerates adiabatically to a supersonic exit flow. If $p_1 = 200,000$ pascals, $T_1 = 50°C$, $M_1 = 0.2$, and $A_1 = A_2 = 0.1$ m^2, find M_2 and $\dot{m}$.

6.7   Find the loss coefficient if air flows adiabatically in a constant area duct from $M_1 = 0.2$ to $M_2 = 0.5$.

6.8   Find the exit Mach number and the total pressure loss when air flows adiabatically from $R_1 = 0.8$ through a constant area loss device described by $K = 0.5$.

6.9   Find the length of 6-in. piping between two points characterized by $R_1 = 0.95$ and $R_2 = 0.8$ if the friction factor is 0.015 and the flow process is adiabatic.

6.10   Air flows adiabatically in a 0.01 m diameter duct having a friction factor of 0.02. Find the length required to accelerate the fluid from $M_1 = 0.209$ to $M_2 = 0.607$.

6.11   For the Fanno flow of air from $R_1 = 0.9$ through a loss device of $K = 1$, find the upstream static and total pressures if the exit pressure is 15 psia.

6.12 Air flows adiabatically through a 1/6 m diameter pipe that is 6 m long and has a friction factor of 0.01667. The pressure and temperature at inlet are 200,000 pascals and 500K, respectively. For an inlet total pressure of 222,222 pascals find p_2, M_2, and V_2.

6.13 Air flows through two loss elements connected in series at a constant total temperature of 1000°R, at a flow rate of 0.5 lbm/sec, and exits the system at 15 psia. If $(K_{1,2})_2 = 2$, $(K_{2,3})_3 = 1$, and $D_1 = D_2 = 2$ in., and $D_{2'} = D_3 = 1.6$ in., find the overall loss coefficient and the overall total pressure ratio across the combined system.

7
DIABATIC FLOW AND THE HEAT TRANSFER COEFFICIENT

7.1 DIABATIC FLOW EQUATION

By diabatic flow we mean that there is significant heat transfer in the process. Thus, neither the total enthalpy nor the total temperature remain constant in the diabatic process.

On an h–S diagram, a general diabatic process for a perfect gas is shown in Figure 7.1. On the generalized R-Γ diagram, the diabatic process plots, as do all processes, as shown in figure 4.2.

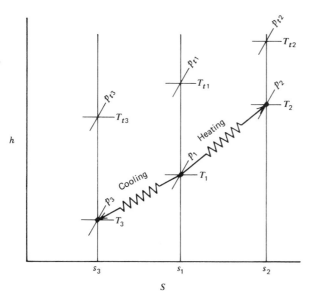

Figure 7.1 General diabatic process.

Because total temperature varies in the diabatic process, the complete generalized gas dynamics equation of (4.18) is required to describe this flow. Thus,

$$\left(\frac{T_{t2}}{T_{t1}}\right)^{1/2} \left(\frac{p_{t1}}{p_{t2}}\right) \left(\frac{A_1}{A_2}\right) \Gamma_1 = \Gamma_2 \tag{7.1}$$

7.2 DIABATIC ENTROPY CHANGE

A general expression for the entropy change that accompanies the general diabatic process (as shown in Figure 7.1) can be obtained as follows. Entropy, via the basic gas dynamics identity of (1.35) and the perfect gas relations of (1.47), can be given as

$$ds = C_p \frac{dT}{T} - \frac{\overline{R}}{J} \frac{dp}{p} \tag{7.2}$$

Upon the integration of (7.2) an expression for the entropy change in a general diabatic process results, namely

$$s_2 - s_1 = C_p \ln\left(\frac{T_2}{T_1}\right) - \frac{\overline{R}}{J} \ln\left(\frac{p_2}{p_1}\right)$$

or

$$s_2 - s_1 = \frac{\overline{R}}{J}\left[\ln\left(\frac{T_2}{T_1}\right)^{\gamma/(\gamma-1)} - \ln\left(\frac{p_2}{p_1}\right)\right] \tag{7.3}$$

where $C_p = (\overline{R}/J) \, (\gamma/(\gamma-1))$.

EXAMPLE 7.1

Find the entropy change when air flows diabatically from a temperature of 800°R and a pressure of 75 psia to 600°R and 100 psia.

(In terms of SI units, these same quantities are: $T_1 = 444.4$ K, $T_2 = 353.3$ K, $p_1 = 517,110$ pascals, and $p_2 = 689,480$ pascals.)

Solution
From

$$\frac{T_2}{T_1} = \frac{600}{800} = \frac{333.3}{444.4} = 0.75$$

and

$$\frac{p_2}{p_1} = \frac{100}{75} = \frac{689,480}{517,110} = 1.333$$

we have by (7.3),

$$(s_2 - s_1)_{US} = \frac{53.35}{778}\left[\ln (0.75)^{1.4/0.4} - \ln (1.333)\right] = -0.088773 \frac{\text{Btu}}{\text{lbm-°R}}$$

and

$$(s_2 - s_1)_{SI} = 287.1 \left[\ln (0.75)^{1.4/0.4} - \ln (1.333)\right] = -371.591 \frac{\text{J}}{\text{kg-K}}$$

where the minus sign signifies that in a cooling process the entropy change will be negative.

As a check on consistency, we can express one result in terms of the other. Thus,

$$-0.088773 \frac{\text{Btu}}{\text{lbm-°R}}\left(\frac{4187\text{J/kg-K}}{\text{Btu/lbm-°R}}\right) = -371.69\frac{\text{J}}{\text{kg-K}}$$

7.3   RAYLEIGH FLOW

A special type of diabatic flow, in the absence of flow losses and at constant flow area, has been called Rayleigh flow. Under the constant area restriction, the general diabatic equation of (7.1) becomes

$$\left(\frac{T_{t2}}{T_{t1}}\right)^{1/2}\left(\frac{p_{t1}}{p_{t2}}\right)\Gamma_1 = \Gamma_2 \tag{7.4}$$

Patterned directly after (6.9), Γ in the Rayleigh process becomes

$$\Gamma_{\text{Rayleigh}} = \left(\frac{T_t}{T_{t*}}\right)^{1/2}\left(\frac{p_{t*}}{p_t}\right) \tag{7.5}$$

premised only on the fact that $\Gamma_{*\text{ Rayleigh}} = 1$. This latter assertion follows from the fact that

$$R_{*,\text{ Rayleigh}} = \left(\frac{2}{\gamma + 1}\right)^{\gamma/(\gamma - 1)} \tag{7.6}$$

in agreement with (4.15), (5.2), and (6.8). Thus, $R_{*,\text{ Ray}} = R_{*,\text{ adi}} = R_{*,\text{ isen}}$.

By algebra alone, we note the useful diabatic identity

$$\left(\frac{T_{t2}}{T_{t1}}\right)\left(\frac{T_{t1}}{T_{t*}}\right) = \left(\frac{T_{t2}}{T_{t*}}\right) \tag{7.7}$$

Equation (7.7) is the diabatic counterpart of (5.4) for isentropic flow and (6.12) for adiabatic flow.

Since Γ of (4.18) is a generalized function that applies equally well to any flow process, it follows from (4.19), (4.20), and (7.5) that

$$\left(\frac{T_t}{T_{t*}}\right)_{\text{Ray}} = \frac{4\left[(\gamma+1)/(\gamma-1)\right](1-R^{(\gamma-1)/\gamma})}{\{R^{(\gamma-1)/\gamma}+[2\gamma/(\gamma-1)](1-R^{(\gamma-1)/\gamma})\}^2} \tag{7.8}$$

and

$$\left(\frac{p_{t*}}{p_t}\right)_{\text{Ray}} = \frac{R^{1/\gamma}\{R^{(\gamma-1)/\gamma}+[2\gamma/(\gamma-1)](1-R^{(\gamma-1)/\gamma})\}}{2\,[2/(\gamma+1)]^{1/(\gamma-1)}} \tag{7.9}$$

In terms of the Mach number, (7.8) and (7.9) can be expressed as

$$\left(\frac{T_t}{T_{t*}}\right)_{\text{Ray}} = \frac{\mathbf{M}^2(\gamma+1)\,(2+(\gamma-1)\mathbf{M}^2)}{(1+\gamma\mathbf{M}^2)^2} \tag{7.10}$$

and

$$\left(\frac{p_{t*}}{p_t}\right)_{\text{Ray}} = \left(\frac{1+\gamma\mathbf{M}^2}{\gamma+1}\right)\left(\frac{\gamma+1}{2+(\gamma-1)\mathbf{M}^2}\right)^{\gamma/(\gamma-1)} \tag{7.11}$$

Of course, when (7.8) and (7.9) are combined according to (7.5), the Γ of (4.19) results, and when (7.10) and (7.11) are combined according to (7.5), the Γ of (4.20) results, showing complete consistency.

Evidently, to solve any Rayleigh flow problem in gas dynamics, which includes diabatic flow in the absence of flow losses in a constant area channel, we need only tabulate the dimensionless quantities R, $\mathbf{M}$, T/T_t, Γ, and $(T_t/T_{t*})_{\text{Ray}}$. It is important to realize that of equation (7.8) through (7.11), the ratio (T_t/T_{t*}) is the most significant since Rayleigh flow is essentially a heat transfer process.

It has been shown [1] that the total pressure ratio of (7.4) is, for Rayleigh flow, an implicit function of the total temperature ratio only. That is,

$$\left(\frac{p_{t1}}{p_{t2}}\right)_{\text{Ray}} = \left(\frac{T_{t1}}{T_{t2}}\right)\left(\frac{R_2}{R_1}\right)^{1/\gamma}\left(\frac{1-R_2^{(\gamma-1)/\gamma}}{1-R_1^{(\gamma-1)/\gamma}}\right)$$
$$\left[\frac{R_1^{(\gamma-1)/\gamma}+[2\gamma/(\gamma-1)](1-R_1^{(\gamma-1)/\gamma})}{R_2^{(\gamma-1)/\gamma}+[2\gamma/(\gamma-1)](1-R_2^{(\gamma-1)/\gamma})}\right] \tag{7.12}$$

A less complex relation for $(p_{t1}/p_{t2})_{\text{Ray}}$ is given later in terms of the Mach number as (7.31).

It is important to note that the change in total pressure in a Rayleigh process does not result from flow losses, but simply occurs because of the change in total temperature that accompanies the heat transfer.

EXAMPLE 7.2

Find the exit Mach number and the total pressure ratio across a constant area combustor when the total temperature rises by a factor of 4, and the air flows reversibly from an inlet Mach number of 0.1.

Solution

This is a Rayleigh flow process. At $M_1 = 0.1$ we have by (7.10), $(T_{t1}T_{t*})_{Ray} = 0.046777$.

By (7.7), $(T_{t2}/T_{t*})_{Ray} = 0.187108$.

If we again apply (7.10), the above results lead by trial and error to $M_2 = 0.20855$, which is the exit Mach number.

Γ_1 and Γ_2 are obtained from M_1 and M_2 via (4.20) or by Table 5.1 as $\Gamma_1 = 0.17177$, $\Gamma_2 = 0.35113$.

Then, by (7.4), we obtain

$$\frac{p_{t1}}{p_{t2}} = \frac{\Gamma_2}{\Gamma_1}\left(\frac{T_{t1}}{T_{t2}}\right)^{1/2} = \frac{0.35113}{0.17177}\left(\frac{1}{2}\right) = 1.02209$$

Note that the total pressure drops in this diabatic reversible process, not because of flow losses, but because of heat transfer.

The solution of Example 7.2 indicates the need for Rayleigh process tables to provide T_t/T_{t*} in terms of R, M, and Γ, in place of the trial and error solution. Such tables will be developed shortly.

It is sometimes useful for visualization, as by graphing, to define the Rayleigh flow line. This is obtained by combining the continuity equation of (2.10) and the energy of (2.28). We have

$$p + \frac{\dot{m}V}{Ag_c} = \text{a constant} \tag{7.13}$$

or in terms of the Mach number

$$p(1 + \gamma M^2) = \text{a constant} \tag{7.14}$$

An impulse function ($=$ thrust function) has been defined by several authors as $pA + \dot{m}V/g_c$, being simply (7.13) or (7.14) multiplied by the area. These Rayleigh flow equations will later be observed to have significance in the normal shock process (see Chapter 9).

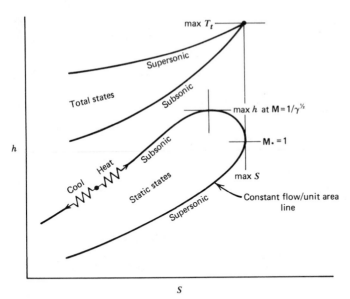

Figure 7.2   Rayleigh flow process.

Equation (7.14) yields the useful static pressure ratio for Rayleigh flow

$$\frac{p_2}{p_1} = \frac{1 + \gamma \mathbf{M}_1^2}{1 + \gamma \mathbf{M}_2^2} \tag{7.15}$$

The analogous static temperature ratio for Rayleigh flow follows directly from (3.18) as

$$\frac{T_2}{T_1} = \left(\frac{p_2 \mathbf{M}_2}{p_1 \mathbf{M}_1}\right)^2 \tag{7.16}$$

A Rayleigh flow line is depicted in Figure 7.2. Since Rayleigh lines are not straight lines on the h–S plot, it follows that if a heating process were to proceed far enough, a point of maximum enthalpy would be reached. This can be shown to occur when the Mach number reaches $1/\gamma^{1/2}$. This result can be obtained by differentiating any temperature expression with respect to any independent variable, such as $\mathbf{M}$. If the heating process were to proceed still further, the change in enthalpy would become negative. In this case, changes of state would occur more rapidly than changes in entropy until a point was reached along the Rayleigh line where there was no further increase in entropy. This, of course, marks the critical state where S_*, $\mathbf{M}_*$, T_{t*}, and Γ_* are all maximized, and where R_* is given by (7.6).

The more general variable area Rayleigh-type process can be treated only when the heat transfer occurs at specified areas. Then, (7.1) is applied directly.

By reasoning similar to that already given in Chapter 6, we note that area changes alone can cause isentropic changes of state, whereas the total temperature changes and the accompanying total pressure changes result in entropy changes.

7.4 DIABATIC HEAT TRANSFER COEFFICIENT

7.4.1 Convective Heat Transfer Coefficient

The steady flow energy equation of (1.27) can be written for Rayleigh flow as

$$\delta q = dh_t \tag{7.17}$$

When (7.17) is combined with the definition of total enthalpy for a perfect gas, (1.47), we have upon integration between any two arbitrary states

$$q_{1.2} = C_p(T_{t2} - T_{t1}) \tag{7.18}$$

The predominant mode of heat transfer between the moving fluid and the bounding walls is forced convection. Newton's law of convective heat transfer is

$$\dot{q} = hA\Delta T \tag{7.19}$$

where h is the convective heat transfer coefficient, usually given by an empirical equation of the form

$$Nu = \frac{hD}{k} = AR_D^B\,Pr^C \tag{7.20}$$

where Nu is the Nusselt number, D is the pipe diameter, k is the thermal conductivity of the fluid, R_D is the pipe Reynolds number, and Pr is the fluid Prandtl number. A, B, and C are the empirical constants of the relation. For convenience, (7.20) can be graphed [2] as given in Figure 7.3. The variable G in this connection represents the mass flow rate per unit area, $(\dot{m}/A)$. A particular reference state is first chosen for a particular fluid to yield h' as a function of G and D. The reference state arbitrarily is based on steam properties at 500 psia and 500°F. This leads to the unique family of straight lines provided in Figure 7.3a. The actual film coefficient (h) is then obtained via correction curves such as those given in Figure 7.3b.

EXAMPLE 7.3

Estimate the convective heat transfer coefficient inside a 1 ft I.D. pipe when air flows at a mass flow rate/unit area of 10 lbm/sec-ft^2 at an air temperature of 500°F.

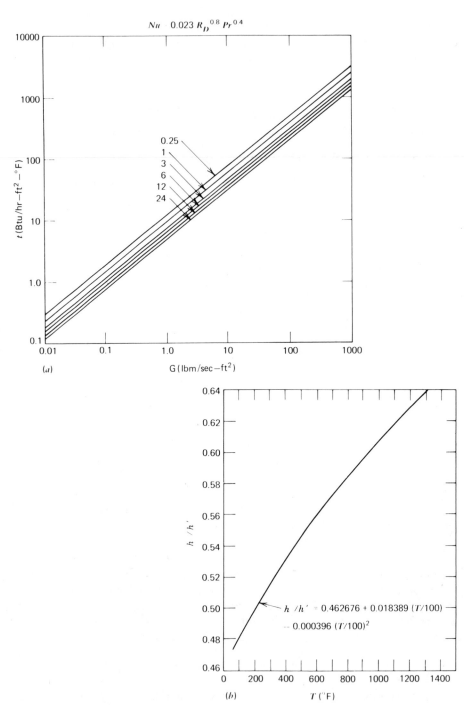

Figure 7.3 Typical heat transfer coefficients. (a) Forced convection film coefficients inside pipes. (b) Correction curve to (a) for air.

Solution

At the intersection of $G = 10$ lbm/sec-ft^2 and $D = 12$ in., on Figure 7.3a, read $h' \approx 35.5$ Btu/hr-ft^2-°F.

By Figure 7.3b, at $T_{air} = 500$°F, $h/h' \approx 0.545$. Therefore, $h = (h/h') \times h' \approx 0.545 \times 35.5 \approx 19.35$ Btu/hr-ft^2-°F. As a check, the standard values of air at 500°F are:

$$\mu = 1.88 \times 10^{-5} \text{ lbm/ft-sec},$$

$$C_p = 0.246 \text{ Btu/lbm-°F},$$

$$k = 0.0244 \text{ Btu/hr-ft-°F}.$$

Thus,

$$R_D = \frac{GD}{\mu} = \frac{10 \times 1}{1.88 \times 10^{-5}} = 5.319 \times 10^5$$

$$P_r = \frac{C_p\mu}{k} = \frac{0.246 \times 1.88 \times 10^{-5}}{0.0244} = 0.682$$

and, by the Nusselt equation given in Figure 7.3a,

$$Nu = \frac{hD}{k} = 0.023 (5.319 \times 10^5)^{0.8} (0.682)^{0.4} = 751.46$$

It follows that

$$h = 751.46 \times 0.0244/1 = 18.34 \text{ Btu/hr-ft}^2\text{-°F}$$

which closely checks the graphical solution.

7.4.2 Dimensionless Heat Transfer Coefficient

In terms of the flow rate ($\dot{m}$), the wall temperature (T_w), and the total temperature (T_t), (7.17) can be given as

$$\dot{m}\delta q = h(\pi Ddx)(T_w - T_t) \tag{7.21}$$

If the Prandtl number ($C_p\mu/k$) of the fluid differs significantly from unity, or if the recovery factor ($\alpha = (T_{adi} - T)/(T_t - T)$) differs significantly from unity, the adiabatic fluid temperature ($T_{adi} = T + \alpha V^2/2Jg_cC_p$) should be used in place of the total temperature [3], but this complication will not be considered any further here.

The total temperature ratio ($T_{t1}/T_{t2} = $ TTR) required for Rayleigh flow [as in (7.4) and (7.7)] can be obtained in terms of the heat transfer as follows.

Equations (7.17), (7.18), and (7.21) are combined to yield an expression that we define as the dimensionless heat transfer coefficient (K_q). Thus,

$$dK_q = \frac{dT_t}{T_w - T_t} = \frac{h\,dx}{900\,GDC_p} \tag{7.22}$$

where h is in Btu/hr-ft²-°F, dx and D are in ft, G is in lbm/sec-ft², C_p is in Btu/lbm-°F, and the subscript q in K_q signifies a heat transfer coefficient, just as the f in K_f of Section 6.8 signifies a frictional loss coefficient.

Equation (7.22) can be integrated directly if the flow element, between axial stations 1 and 2, is of a length such that T_w and h can be considered constants. Two results of this integration are of importance. The first leads, by inspection, to the value of K_q. That is,

$$K_q = \frac{hL}{900\,GDC_p} \tag{7.23}$$

where L is the axial length between stations 1 and 2. The second integration in terms of the general form

$$\int \frac{dx}{ax + b} = \frac{1}{a}\ln(ax + b) \tag{7.24}$$

leads to the total temperature ratio as follows:

$$K_q = \ln\left(\frac{T_{t1} - T_w}{T_{t2} - T_w}\right) \tag{7.25}$$

or , taking antilogarithms and separating variables, we get

$$\frac{1}{\text{TTR}} = \frac{T_w}{T_{t1}}[1 - \exp(-K_q)] + \exp(-K_q) \tag{7.26}$$

where $\exp(A)$ signifies e^A. Thus, TTR (the required total temperature ratio for Rayleigh flow) can be plotted as a simple plane in terms of T_w/T_{t1} and $\exp(K_q)$ as shown in Figure 7.4.

EXAMPLE 7.4

Find the total temperature ratio for Rayleigh flow through the duct of Example 7.3, using the same quantities given there. Assume $T_w = 1055°F$, $T_{t1} = 550°F$, and $L = 80$ ft.

(In SI units, these same quantities are: $D = 0.3048$ m, $G = 48.827$ kg/s-m², $T = 533.2$ K, $h = 107.882$ W/m²-K, $T_w = 841.5$ K, $T_{t1} = 560.9$ K, and $L = 24.348$ m.)

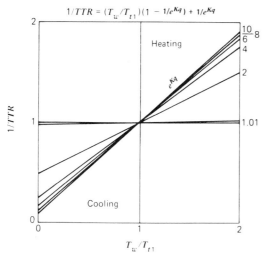

Figure 7.4   Total temperature ratio as a function of wall and fluid temperature and the heat transfer coefficient.

Solution
By (7.23), we obtain K_q as

$$\underset{\text{US}}{K_q} = \frac{hL}{900GDC_p} = \frac{19 \times 80}{900 \times 10 \times 1 \times 0.246} = 0.68654$$

and

$$\underset{\text{SI}}{K_q} = \frac{4hL}{GDC_p} = \frac{4 \times 107.882 \times 24.384}{48.827 \times 0.3048 \times 1030} = 0.68644$$

and $\exp(K_q) = 1.98683$.
    By (7.26),

$$\frac{T_{t2}}{T_{t1}} = 1.248$$

At $T_w/T_{t1} = 1.5$ and $\exp(K_q) = 2$, we confirm this result in Figure 7.4 where we find that $T_{t2}/T_{t1} = 1.25$.

7.5   GENERALIZED RAYLEIGH FLOW MAP
    The envelope of Figure 4.1 has been shown to have significance in all flow processes of gas dynamics. In Chapter 6, a generalized Fanno flow map was presented in terms of the empirical loss coefficient, K_f, and the total pressure

ratio, TPR. In this section, we consider the analogous generalized Rayleigh flow map.

In Section 7.4.2, we saw that Rayleigh flow can be solved in terms of the empirical heat transfer coefficient, K_q, of (7.23). We also learned that given K_q, we could immediately obtain the total temperature ratio, TTR, via (7.24).

The innovation used in defining a generalized Rayleigh flow map is to exploit the interior of the Figure 4.1 generalized envelope by introducing on the plot parameters of the total temperature ratio (TTR) and the total pressure ratio (TPR).

Thus, expressions must be available for the TTR and TPR parameters in terms of the R–Γ coordinates.

We first note that the critical value of R_{21}, the hybrid static to total pressure ratio, has been given [2] in terms of the initial pressure ratio as

$$R_{21}^* = \frac{R_1 + (2\gamma/(\gamma - 1))\,(R_1^{1/\gamma} - R_1)}{\gamma + 1} \tag{7.27}$$

which is the Rayleigh counterpart of the Fanno equation (6.29). This, of course, indicates the locus of maximum subsonic flows possible for Rayleigh flow.

To obtain expressions for TTR and TPR, the following brief derivations are used.

The total temperature ratio, by (3.12), is in general

$$\frac{T_{t2}}{T_{t1}} = \frac{T_2}{T_1}\left[\frac{2 + (\gamma - 1)\mathbf{M}_2^2}{2 + (\gamma - 1)\mathbf{M}_1^2}\right] \tag{7.28}$$

When (7.28) is combined with (7.16) and (7.15), we have for Rayleigh flow

$$\frac{T_{t2}}{T_{t1}} = \left(\frac{1 + \gamma\mathbf{M}_1^2}{1 + \gamma\mathbf{M}_2^2}\right)^2 \left(\frac{\mathbf{M}_2}{\mathbf{M}_1}\right)^2 \left[\frac{2 + (\gamma - 1)\mathbf{M}_2^2}{2 + (\gamma - 1)\mathbf{M}_1^2}\right] \tag{7.29}$$

The total pressure ratio, by (3.13), is in general

$$\frac{p_{t2}}{p_{t1}} = \frac{p_2}{p_1}\left[\frac{2 + (\gamma - 1)\mathbf{M}_2^2}{2 + (\gamma - 1)\mathbf{M}_1^2}\right]^{\gamma/(\gamma - 1)} \tag{7.30}$$

When (7.30) is combined with (7.15), we have for Rayleigh flow

$$\frac{p_{t2}}{p_{t1}} = \left(\frac{1 + \gamma\mathbf{M}_1^2}{1 + \gamma\mathbf{M}_2^2}\right)\left[\frac{2 + (\gamma - 1)\mathbf{M}_2^2}{2 + (\gamma - 1)\mathbf{M}_1^2}\right]^{\gamma/(\gamma - 1)} \tag{7.31}$$

It is interesting to note for consistency that (7.29) yields (7.10) when 2 is taken as the general state, and 1 is taken as the critical state where $\mathbf{M} = 1$. And furthermore, we see that (7.31) reduces to (7.11) under these same conditions.

In terms of the point pressure ratios, R_1 and R_2, (7.29) and (7.31) can be expressed as

$$
TTR = \frac{(1 - R_1^{(\gamma-1)/\gamma})\left\{R_2^{(\gamma-1)/\gamma} + \left(\dfrac{2\gamma}{\gamma-1}\right)(1 - R_2^{(\gamma-1)/\gamma})\right\}^2}{(1 - R_2^{(\gamma-1)/\gamma})\left\{R_1^{(\gamma-1)/\gamma} + \left(\dfrac{2\gamma}{\gamma-1}\right)(1 - R_1^{(\gamma-1)/\gamma})\right\}^2}
\tag{7.32}
$$

and

$$
TPR = \frac{R_2 + \left(\dfrac{2\gamma}{\gamma-1}\right)(R_2^{1/\gamma} - R_2)}{R_1 + \left(\dfrac{2\gamma}{\gamma-1}\right)(R_1^{1/\gamma} - R_1)}
\tag{7.33}
$$

When TTR, of either (7.29) or (7.32), and TPR, of (7.31) or (7.33), are plotted within the generalized envelope of Figure 4.1, we obtain the desired generalized Rayleigh flow map. Such a map is given in Figure 7.5.

Briefly, one enters the outer envelope horizontally with R_1 to obtain vertically Γ_1. This vertical Γ line intercepts the chosen TTR parameter to yield at the same intercept the values of R_{21} (on the R scale) and TPR. These, in turn, lead to Γ_2 and the complete solution.

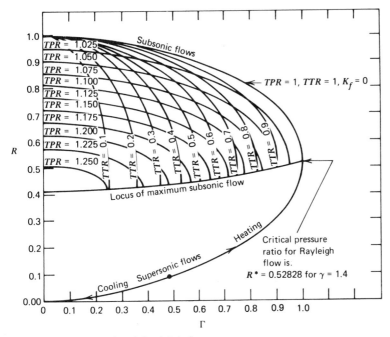

Figure 7.5   Generalized Rayleigh flow map.

Note that on the outer envelope, the three parameters of interest are found to be TPR = 1, and TTR = 1, and K_f = 0. In Rayleigh flow, however, only K_f remains on the outer envelope at 0 since the process is loss-free. The TTR and TPR parameters are now found inside the envelope of Figure 7.5.

Although a Rayleigh flow is difficult to achieve in practice because of the close relationship between frictional effects and heating effects, such solutions are well adapted to flow processes involving large external heat transfer, in which the wall temperature differs greatly from the fluid temperature.

7.6   GENERALIZED RAYLEIGH FLOW TABLE

Computer solutions to selected Rayleigh flow problems are presented in Table 7.1 in terms of static to total pressure ratio ($R = p/p_t$), the Mach number (**M**), the normalized flow function (Γ), and the temperature ratio $(T_t/T_{t*})_{\text{Ray}}$. Also given in Table 7.1 are the iterative solutions for the hybrid pressure ratio ($R_{21} = p_2/p_{t1}$), first as a function of the total pressure ratio (TPR = p_{t1}/p_{t2}), and then as a function of the total temperature ratio (TTR = T_{t1}/T_{t2}) [4]. The use of this table is best illustrated by examples.

EXAMPLE 7.5

If air flows at constant area through a combustor such that T_{t2}/T_{t1} = 2.03038 from an inlet pressure ratio of 0.94, find the exit Mach number and the total pressure ratio across the combustor.

Solution

This is a Rayleigh flow problem. At R_1 = 0.94 we find from Table 7.1, Γ_1 = 0.48938 and $(T_{t1}/T_{t*})_{\text{Ray}}$ = 0.34434.

Thus, according to (7.7),

$$\frac{T_{t2}}{T_{t*}} = \left(\frac{T_{t2}}{T_{t1}}\right)\left(\frac{T_{t1}}{T_{t*}}\right) = 2.03038 \times 0.34434 = 0.69914$$

On the same row in the Table where T_{t2}/T_{t*} = 0.69914, we read

R_2 = 0.84,   **M**$_2$ = 0.50536, Γ_2 = 0.75203

Hence, the exit Mach number is 0.50536. The total pressure ratio is determined via (7.4) as

$$\frac{p_{t1}}{p_{t2}} = \frac{\Gamma_2}{\Gamma_1 \times (1/\text{TTR})^{1/2}} = \frac{0.75203}{0.48938 \times 2.03038^{1/2}} = 1.07845$$

EXAMPLE 7.6

In the subsonic flow of air, heating, with T_{wall} varying linearly with length from 2000 to 3000°R, find all the pertinent conditions for a smooth 1-in. pipe,

TABLE 7.1
GENERALIZED RAYLEIGH FLOW TABLE ($\gamma = 1.4$)[a]

R	M	Γ	$\left(\dfrac{T_t}{T_t*}\right)_{Ray}$	TPR/R_{21} 1.05	1.10	1.15	1.20	1.25	TTR/R_{21} 0.9	0.8	0.7	0.6	0.5
1.00	0.00000	0.00000	0.00000	0.90288	0.81010	0.71896	0.62464	0.51015	1.00000	1.00000	1.00000	1.00000	1.00000
0.99	0.11991	0.20543	0.06651	0.89203	0.79801	0.70490	0.60652	0.47014	0.98771	0.98491	0.98124	0.97632	0.96936
0.98	0.17013	0.28894	0.12907	0.88112	0.78576	0.69041	0.58692		0.97541	0.96962	0.96209	0.95187	0.93722
0.97	0.20905	0.35193	0.18791	0.87015	0.77334	0.67541	0.56519		0.96300	0.95413	0.94247	0.92652	0.90328
0.96	0.24220	0.40412	0.24327	0.85912	0.76071	0.65980	0.54005		0.95050	0.93837	0.92234	0.90010	0.86708
0.95	0.27169	0.44929	0.29535	0.84802	0.74785	0.64342	0.50797		0.93791	0.92236	0.90162	0.87243	0.82792
0.94	0.29863	0.48938	0.34434	0.83684	0.73472	0.62607			0.92521	0.90606	0.88021	0.84318	0.78471
0.93	0.32366	0.52555	0.39044	0.82557	0.72129	0.60743			0.91241	0.88942	0.85800	0.81196	0.73552
0.92	0.34720	0.55858	0.43380	0.81422	0.70750	0.58694			0.89946	0.87239	0.83483	0.77815	0.67626
0.91	0.36954	0.58898	0.47458	0.80276	0.69328	0.56359			0.88639	0.85494	0.81048	0.74075	0.59422
0.90	0.39090	0.61715	0.51294	0.79117	0.67856	0.53495			0.87317	0.83699	0.78467		
0.89	0.41144	0.64338	0.54900	0.77946	0.66320	0.48883			0.85977	0.81844	0.75699		
0.88	0.43127	0.66789	0.58290	0.76761	0.64707				0.84619	0.79919	0.72677		
0.87	0.45051	0.69088	0.61475	0.75559	0.62988				0.83239	0.77910	0.69293		
0.86	0.46922	0.71249	0.64468	0.74338	0.61127				0.81835	0.75797	0.65329		
0.85	0.48749	0.73284	0.67277	0.73095	0.59055				0.80403	0.73552	0.60231		
0.84	0.50536	0.75203	0.69914	0.71826	0.56625				0.78938	0.71133	0.49839		
0.83	0.52287	0.77016	0.72388	0.70527	0.53403				0.77436	0.68472			
0.82	0.54009	0.78729	0.74706	0.69191					0.75888	0.65449			
0.81	0.55702	0.80348	0.76878	0.67810					0.74289	0.61798			
0.80	0.57372	0.81880	0.78911	0.66374					0.72623	0.56646			
0.79	0.59021	0.83330	0.80813	0.64865					0.70874				
0.78	0.60650	0.84701	0.82589	0.63261					0.69018				
0.77	0.62263	0.85997	0.84246	0.61520					0.67017				
0.76	0.63862	0.87222	0.85791	0.59574					0.64807				
0.75	0.65447	0.88378	0.87229	0.57248					0.62270				
0.74	0.67022	0.89469	0.88565	0.53907					0.59102				

[a]Under TPR and TTR is tabulated $R_{21} = p_2/p_{t1}$. Example: At $R_1 = 0.8$ and at TPR $= 1.05$, $R_{21} = 0.66374$; and at TTR $= 0.9$, $R_{21} = 0.72623$.

36 in. long, at $G = 10$ lbm/ft²-sec, $R_1 = 0.931$, and $T_{t1} = 625°R$ (see Figure 7.6).

Solution (in one step)

$$\overline{T}_w = \frac{T_{w1} + T_{w2}}{2} = \frac{2000 + 3000}{2} = 2500°R$$

$$\frac{\overline{T}_w}{T_{t1}} = \frac{2500}{625} = 4, \qquad \frac{T_1}{T_{t1}} = 0.98 \text{ by } (1.56), \qquad \text{and } T_1 = 152°F$$

For an assumed $\overline{T} = 475°F$, we find from Figure 7.3a $h' = f(G, D) \approx 55$ Btu/hr-ft²-°F. From Figure 7.3b we have $h/h' \approx 0.546$. Thus, by (7.21),

$$K_q = \frac{55 \times 0.546 \times 3 \times 12}{900 \times 10 \times 0.24} = 0.5 \qquad \text{and} \qquad \exp(K_q) = 1.65$$

By (7.24),

$$\frac{1}{\text{TTR}} = 4\left(1 - \frac{1}{1.65}\right) + \frac{1}{1.65} = 2.18$$

$$\text{TTR} = 0.4587 \qquad \text{and} \qquad T_{t2} = 1362°R.$$

At $R_1 = 0.931$, $\Gamma_1 = 0.52209$, $(T_{t1}/T_{t*})_{\text{Ray}} = 0.386$. By (7.7), $(T_{t2}/T_{t*})_{\text{Ray}} = (T_{t1}/T_{t*})_{\text{Ray}}/\text{TTR} = 0.842$.

Interpolation of Table 7.1 yields at this 0.842 value $R_2 = 0.76992$, $\Gamma_2 = 0.86007$, and the accompanying $T_2/T_{t2} = 0.928$. Hence, $T_2 = 1264°R = 805°F$. Therefore, $\overline{T} = (152 + 804)/2 \approx 475$, as assumed, and

$$\text{TPR} = \frac{\Gamma_2 (\text{TTR})^{1/2}}{\Gamma_1} = 1.1148$$

and

$$R_{21} = \frac{R_2}{\text{TPR}} = 0.69062$$

which is consistent with the values given in Table 7.1.

Note that for a heating process

$$\frac{T_{t1}}{T_w} < \text{TTR} < 1$$

which, in this example, translates to

$$0.25 < 0.459 < 1$$

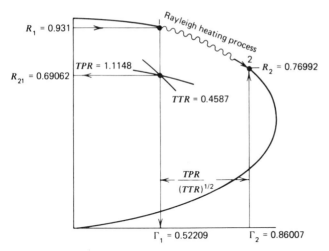

R_1 = 0.931

Rayleigh heating process

2

R_2 = 0.76992

TPR = 1.1148

R_{21} = 0.69062

TTR = 0.4587

$\dfrac{TPR}{(TTR)^{1/2}}$

Γ_1 = 0.52209 Γ_2 = 0.86007

Figure 7.6   Rayleigh heating process of Example 7.6.

Note further that the solution only involved one step. It could have been arrived at in two steps as follows:

Solution (in two steps)

Step 1   (from $X = 0$ to $X = 18$ in.)

$$\overline{T}_w = \frac{2000 + 2500}{2} = 2250°R$$

$$\frac{\overline{T}_w}{T_{t1}} = \frac{2250}{625} = 3.6$$

For an assumed $\overline{T} = 325°F$, $h/h' \approx 0.522$, $K_q = 0.239$, and $\exp(K_q) = 1.27$, TTR = 0.6439, and $T_{t2} = 971°R$, $T_{t2}/T_{t*} = 0.386/0.644 = 0.6$, $\Gamma_2 = 0.68043$.

$$R_2 = 0.875, \ T_2/T_{t2} = 0.962, \ T_2 = 934°R = 474°F$$
$$\overline{T} = (152 + 474)/2 = 313°F$$

TPR = 0.68043 $(0.644)^{1/2}/0.52252 = 1.0449$ and
$$R_{21} = 0.875/1.0449 = 0.837$$

Step 2   (from $X = 18$ to $X = 36$ in.)

$$\overline{T}_w = \frac{2500 + 3000}{2} = 2750°R, \ \overline{T}_w/T_{t1} = 2.83$$

For an assumed $\overline{T} = 640°F$, $h/h' \approx 0.571$, $K_q = 0.262$, $\exp(K_q) = 1.299$, TTR = 0.7032, and $T_{t2} = 1380°R$, $T_{t2}/T_{t*} = 0.6/0.7032 = 0.854$, $\Gamma_1 = 0.68043$, $\Gamma_2 = 0.86878$.

$$R_2 = 0.763, \ T_2/T_{t2} = 0.925, \ T_2 = 1278°R = 818°F$$
$$\overline{T} = (474 + 818)/2 = 646°F$$
$$\text{TPR} = 0.86878 \ (0.7032)^{1/2}/0.68043 = 1.0707 \quad \text{and}$$
$$R_{21} = 0.763/1.0707 = 0.7125$$

Combining these two-step solutions, we get

$$\text{TTR} = \text{TTR}_1 \times \text{TTR}_2 = 0.6439 \times 0.7032 = 0.4528$$

$$\text{TPR} = \text{TPR}_1 \times \text{TPR}_2 = 1.0449 \times 1.0707 = 1.118$$

Figure 7.7 indicates the general effect of the number of steps on the Rayleigh flow solution. In particular, for this example, Figure 7.7 indicates that five steps would be adequate.

For such a complex problem as this, the computer would be very helpful. It also would be in order to consider a stepwise solution to the type of problem given in Example 7.6, such as discussed in Chapter 11.

7.7 CONCLUDING REMARKS

Many applications in gas dynamics that predominantly involve heat transfer can be approximated by the diabatic process, including flow in heat exchangers and combustors.

In this chapter, we have applied the generalized gas dynamics equation of (4.18) to the constant area diabatic process, defined as Rayleigh flow, in the form of (7.4), namely

$$\left(\frac{T_{t2}}{T_{t1}}\right)^{1/2} \left(\frac{p_{t1}}{p_{t2}}\right) \Gamma_1 = \Gamma_2$$

The entropy change in a general diabatic process was given by (7.3) as

$$s_2 - s_1 = \frac{\overline{R}}{J}\left[\ln\left(\frac{T_2}{T_1}\right)^{\gamma/(\gamma-1)} - \ln\left(\frac{p_2}{p_1}\right)\right]$$

A generalized Rayleigh flow table (Table 7.1) was provided to aid in obtaining rapid numerical solutions.

A dimensionless heat transfer coefficient, applying between any two states, was defined by (7.23) and (7.25). This coefficient (K_q) led to the total temperature ratio across the given heat transfer device. The complicated problem of obtaining a solution based on multiple steps taken through a heat transfer device was detailed in Example 7.6.

Finally, a generalized Rayleigh flow map was developed, based on plotting TPR and TTR in the interior of the generalized R–Γ envelope, as shown in Figure 7.5.

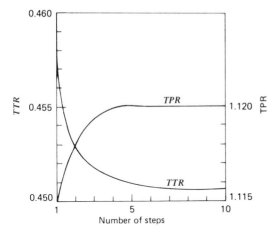

Figure 7.7 Effect of number of steps used in the Rayleigh solution of Example 7.6.

REFERENCES

1. R. P. Benedict and W. G. Steltz, *Handbook of Generalized Gas Dynamics,* Plenum Press, New York, 1966; see also by the same authors, "A Generalized Approach to One-Dimensional Gas Dynamics," *Trans. ASME, J. Engrg. for Power,* June 1962, p. 49.

2. R. P. Benedict, "Some Generalizations in Compressible Flow Characteristics," *Trans. ASME, J. Engrg. for Power,* April 1973, p. 65.

3. R. P. Benedict, *Fundamentals of Temperature, Pressure, and Flow Measurements,* Second Edition, Wiley, New York, 1977, p. 213.

4. R. P. Benedict, *Fundamentals of Pipe Flow,* Wiley, New York, 1980, p. 333.

NOMENCLATURE

Roman

A	Area, constant
B, C	Constants
C_p	Specific heat at constant pressure
D	Pipe diameter
g_c	Gravitational constant
G	Flow rate per unit area
h	Enthalpy, also heat transfer film coefficient
J	Mechanical equivalent of heat
k	Thermal conductivity
K_q	Heat transfer coefficient
L	Length
$\dot{m}$	Mass flow rate

M	Mach number
Nu	Nusselt number
p	Pressure
Pr	Prandtl number
q	Heat transferred per unit mass
$\dot{q}$	Rate of heat transfer
Q	Amount of heat transfer
R	Static/total pressure ratio
$\overline{R}$	Specific gas constant
R_D	Reynolds number
S	Entropy
T	Absolute temperature
TPR	Total pressure ratio (p_{t1}/p_{t2})
TTR	Total temperature ratio (T_{t1}/T_{t2})
v	Specific volume
V	Volumetric average velocity
x	Length coordinate

Greek

α	Recovery factor
Δ	Finite difference
δ	Inexact differential
γ	Specific heat ratio
Γ	Compressible flow function
μ	Fluid viscosity

Subscripts

1, 2	Axial locations
adi	Adiabatic
Ray	Rayleigh
t	Total
*	Critical

PROBLEMS

7.1   In a constant area loss-free duct, air flows from an inlet pressure of 10 psia, an inlet temperature of 80°F, at a flow rate of 10 lbm/sec-ft². If the total temperature ratio across the duct is 0.25, find the inlet Mach number, the exit Mach number, and the exit pressure.

7.2   Air flows in Rayleigh process from p_1 = 70,000 pascals, T_1 = 50°C, at a flow rate of 50 kg/m²-s. For a total temperature ratio across the pipe of 0.5, find M_1, M_2, and p_2.

7.3   Air enters a combustor at $V_1 = 202.8$ ft/sec, $T_1 = 500°$R, $p_1 = 100$ psia, and flows loss-free absorbing 100 Btu/lbm of heat. Find the total temperature and the Mach number at the burner exit.

7.4   Air flows through a combustor in a Rayleigh process. Inlet conditions are $p_1 = 700,000$ pascals, $T_1 = 300$K, and $V_1 = 60$ m/s. Find T_{t2} and $\mathbf{M}_2$ if 250,000 J/kg are absorbed by the air.

7.5   In a heat exchanger the total temperature of air is raised from 400° to 800°R. Find the exit Mach number if $\mathbf{M}_1 = 0.2$.

7.6   How much heat must be transferred in a constant area heat exchanger to yield an exit pressure of 59.95 psia if conditions at the inlet are as follows: $p_1 = 50$ psia, $T_{t1} = 500°$R, $\mathbf{M}_1 = 0.5$.

7.7   Find the heat rejected in a Rayleigh process if $p_1 = 450,000$ pascals, $T_{t1} = 400$K, $\mathbf{M}_1 = 0.4$, and $p_2 = 500,000$ pascals.

7.8   Air flows at 20 lbm/sec through a constant area burner from $\mathbf{M}_1 = 0.3$ and $T_1 = 500°$R. Find the exit Mach number and the total temperature ratio if 227 Btu/lbm are added in the process.

7.9   A Rayleigh flow takes place from $\mathbf{M}_1 = 0.2$ and $T_1 = 400$K at $\dot{m} = 10$ kg/s. If 460,000 J/kg of heat are added in the process, find $\mathbf{M}_2$ and TTR.

7.10   Find the entropy change for air flowing in a Rayleigh process starting at $V_1 = 500$ ft/sec, $p_1 = 10$ psia, and $T_1 = 400°$R when the total temperature ratio across the process is 1.5.

7.11   Air flows in a Rayleigh process from $p_1 = 50,000$ pascals, $T_1 = 200$K, and $V_1 = 150$ m/s. Find the entropy change when the TTR $= 2$.

7.12   Air flows at the inlet conditions: $T_1 = 77.4°$F, $p_1 = 10$ psia, $V_1 = 500$ ft/sec. For a Rayleigh process, find the inlet total temperature, the maximum exit total temperature, and the corresponding exit total pressure.

7.13   Find the total temperature and total pressure ratios for a Rayleigh flow when $G = 20$ lbm/sec-ft^2, $T_1 = 500°$F, $R_1 = 0.95$, $D = 6$ in. $L = 50$ ft, and the wall temperature is 1000°F.

7.14   For a Rayleigh cooling process from $p_1 = 15$ psia and $\mathbf{M}_1 = 0.5$, at a total temperature ratio of 1.25, find the total pressure ratio and the exit conditions: $\mathbf{M}_2, p_2, p_{t2}$.

7.15   For a Rayleigh process starting at $R_1 = 0.92$, the total pressure ratio is 1.10. Find the total temperature ratio across the process.

8
ISOTHERMAL FLOW AND THE LOSS COEFFICIENT

8.1 ISOTHERMAL FLOW EQUATION

By isothermal flow we mean that the static temperature of the fluid remains constant throughout the process.

Since we already have seen that the static temperature drops in a subsonic adiabatic process involving losses, it follows that there must be heat transfer to maintain a constant static fluid temperature in the presence of flow losses. Thus, the isothermal process is a diabatic process involving flow losses, and hence is a step more complex than Rayleigh flow.

On an h–S diagram, a general isothermal process for a perfect gas is depicted in Figure 8.1. On the generalized R-Γ diagram, the isothermal process plots, as do all processes, as shown in Figure 4.2.

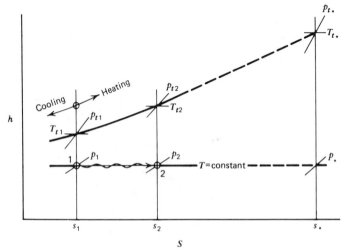

Figure 8.1 Compressible isothermal process.

Because the isothermal process involves heat transfer, the total temperature must change in accordance with (7.18), that is,

$$q_{1,2} = C_p (T_{t2} - T_{t1}) \tag{8.1}$$

and the complete generalized gas dynamics equation of (4.18) and (7.1) is required to describe a general isothermal flow [1]. Thus,

$$\left(\frac{T_{t2}}{T_{t1}}\right)^{1/2} \left(\frac{p_{t1}}{p_{t2}}\right) \left(\frac{A_1}{A_2}\right) \Gamma_1 = \Gamma_2 \tag{8.2}$$

However, no completely general solution is possible for a variable-area iso-thermal flow. As with Rayleigh-type flow, the total pressure ratio is dependent on the definite physical conditions under which the heat transfer and viscous effects occur. Only in the very limited cases when both heat transfer and viscous effects are confined to specified areas can a variable-area isothermal flow be treated.

The constant-area isothermal flow, on the other hand, always can be treated by the more restrictive

$$\left(\frac{T_{t2}}{T_{t1}}\right)^{1/2} \left(\frac{p_{t1}}{p_{t2}}\right) \Gamma_1 = \Gamma_2 \tag{8.3}$$

In fact, the designation "isothermal flow" generally also implies a constant area flow, and we will use it in that context in this chapter.

8.2 ISOTHERMAL ENTROPY CHANGE

A general expression for the entropy change in any diabatic process was given by (7.3). For an isothermal process, this reduces to

$$s_2 - s_1 = \frac{\overline{R}}{J} \ln\left(\frac{p_1}{p_2}\right) \tag{8.4}$$

EXAMPLE 8.1

Find the entropy change when air flows isothermally from a pressure of 75 psia to 100 psia.

Solution

At $p_1/p_2 = 75/100 = 0.75$, we have by (8.4)

$$s_2 - s_1 = \frac{53.35}{778} \ln(0.75) = -0.01973 \frac{\text{Btu}}{\text{lbm-}°\text{R}}$$

where the minus sign signifies that this is a cooling process.

8.3   ISOTHERMAL CRITICAL STATE

Just as we encountered a critical velocity in isentropic, adiabatic, and Rayleigh flows, so must there be a limiting velocity in constant area isothermal flow. Here, we consider this situation for the perfect gas.

In any constant area (pipe) flow, the first condition for flow is that p_{exit} be less than p_{inlet}. Given this, the pressure will decrease uniformly along the pipe because of viscous losses. If the temperature remains constant, as in isothermal flow, then since p/ρ must stay constant, it follows that the density must decrease in step with the pressure. But, by the continuity equation of (2.10), it follows that the velocity must then increase continually in a constant area isothermal flow. If the pipe length is long enough, or if the pressure drop is great enough, a critical velocity will be reached.

It is important to realize that the critical velocity can only be reached at the pipe exit, for if a critical velocity was reached before exit, a pressure drop would still be required to overcome friction in the remaining length of pipe. This would require further acceleration. But we know from the isentropic flow analysis (see Chapter 5) that the flow in a constant area passage cannot become supersonic. Hence, we can claim with assurance that the limiting velocity will be attained, if at all, at the pipe exit.

The general energy equation of (1.27), combined with the first law of (1.21), as given in (6.17), is

$$0 = \delta F + \frac{dp}{\rho} + \frac{V\,dV}{g_c} \tag{8.5}$$

Introducing the friction factor, via the differential Darcy equation of (6.18), namely

$$\delta F = \delta h_{loss} = f\frac{dx}{D}\frac{V^2}{2g_c} \tag{8.6}$$

and multiplying through by g_c/V^2, we obtain

$$\left(\frac{g_c}{\rho V^2}\right)dp + \frac{dV}{V} + \left(\frac{f}{2D}\right)dx = 0 \tag{8.7}$$

The normally inaccessible factor (dV/V) can be replaced by $(-dp/p)$, based on the isothermal perfect gas relation, $p/\rho = $ constant, and the constant area continuity equation, $\rho V = $ constant.

Thus, (8.7) can be rearranged as

$$\left(\frac{g_c p}{\rho V^2}\right)dp - dp + \left(\frac{fp}{2D}\right)dx = 0 \tag{8.8}$$

or, separating variables [2], we obtain

$$\frac{dp}{dx} = \frac{pf/2D}{1 - \frac{g_c p}{\rho V^2}}$$

(8.9)

If the factor $(g_c p/\rho V^2)$ is greater than unity, dp/dx, the pressure gradient along the pipe, is negative which reflects the usual pressure drop with length. But, if this same factor is less than unity, dp/dx would be positive, which is physically impossible. Hence, there is a limiting flow, where the slope (dp/dx) just equals unity, defined by

$$1 = \frac{\gamma \rho V^2}{\gamma g_c p} \quad \text{or} \quad \mathbf{M}^*_{iso} = \frac{1}{\sqrt{\gamma}}$$

(8.10)

in direct contrast to the usual critical condition, $\mathbf{M}^*_{isen, \, Fanno, \, Ray} = 1$.

No longer will the critical pressure ratio (R_*) be given by (4.15), (5.2), (6.8), or (7.6), because for isothermal flow the critical Mach number is no longer unity. By combining (3.14) and (8.10), we then have the following:

$$(R_*)_{iso} = \left(\frac{2\gamma}{3\gamma - 1}\right)^{\gamma/(\gamma - 1)}$$

(8.11)

8.4 CONSTANT AREA ISOTHERMAL FLOW

With the critical state defined by (8.10) and (8.11), it is now possible to arrive at the isothermal forms of the temperature ratio and pressure ratio equations.

Patterned directly after (6.9) and (7.5), Γ in the isothermal process becomes

$$\Gamma_{iso} = \left(\frac{T_t}{T_{t*}}\right)^{1/2} \left(\frac{p_{t*}}{p_t}\right) \gamma^{1/(\gamma - 1)} \left(\frac{\gamma + 1}{3\gamma - 1}\right)^{(\gamma + 1)/2 \, (\gamma - 1)}$$

(8.12)

A useful identity for any diabatic flow is that given by (7.7), which also has direct application in isothermal flow. That is,

$$\left(\frac{T_{t2}}{T_{t1}}\right)\left(\frac{T_{t1}}{T_{t*}}\right) = \left(\frac{T_{t2}}{T_{t*}}\right)$$

(8.13)

Since Γ of (4.18) is a generalized function, it follows from (4.19), (4.20), and

(8.12) that

$$\left(\frac{T_t}{T_{t*}}\right)_{iso} = \left(\frac{2\gamma}{3\gamma - 1}\right) R^{(1-\gamma)/\gamma} \tag{8.14}$$

and

$$\left(\frac{p_{t*}}{p_t}\right)_{iso} = \frac{\left[R^{(\gamma+1)/\gamma}\left(\frac{2\gamma}{\gamma - 1}\right)(1 - R^{(\gamma-1)/\gamma})\right]^{1/2}}{\left(\frac{2\gamma}{3\gamma - 1}\right)^{\gamma/(\gamma-1)}} \tag{8.15}$$

In terms of the Mach number, (8.14) and (8.15) can be expressed as

$$\left(\frac{T_t}{T_{t*}}\right)_{iso} = \left(\frac{\gamma}{3\gamma - 1}\right)(2 + (\gamma - 1)\mathbf{M}^2) \tag{8.16}$$

and

$$\left(\frac{p_{t*}}{p_t}\right)_{iso} = \gamma^{1/2}\,\mathbf{M}\left[\frac{(3\gamma - 1)/\gamma}{2 + (\gamma - 1)\,\mathbf{M}^2}\right]^{(\gamma/(\gamma-1))} \tag{8.17}$$

When (8.14) and (8.15) are combined according to (8.12), the Γ of (4.19) results, and when (8.16) and (8.17) are combined according to (8.12), the Γ of (4.20) follows, showing complete consistency.

In isothermal flow it is not as clear-cut as in Rayleigh flow that the ratio (T_t/T_{t*}) is the more significant of the total ratios. However, it is still true that the total pressure ratio can be given [1] as an implicit function of the total temperature ratio only. That is,

$$\left(\frac{p_{t1}}{p_{t2}}\right)_{iso} = \left(\frac{T_{t1}}{T_{t2}}\right)\left(\frac{R_2}{R_1}\right)^{(3-\gamma)/2\gamma}\left(\frac{1 - R_2^{(\gamma-1)/\gamma}}{1 - R_1^{(\gamma-1)/\gamma}}\right)^{1/2} \tag{8.18}$$

A less complex relation for (p_{t1}/p_{t2}) is given later in terms of the Mach number as (8.40).

EXAMPLE 8.2

Find the exit Mach number and the total pressure across a constant area pipe when air flows irreversibly from an inlet Mach number of 0.2 at constant static temperature, and heat addition raises the total temperature by 10%.

Solution
This is an isothermal flow. At $\mathbf{M}_1 = 0.2$, we find by (8.16)

$$\left(\frac{T_{t1}}{T_{t*}}\right)_{\text{iso}} = \left(\frac{1.4}{3 \times 1.4 - 1}\right)(2 + (1.4 - 1)\,0.2^2) = 0.882$$

Alternatively, by (8.14),

$$\left(\frac{T_{t1}}{T_{t*}}\right)_{\text{iso}} = \left(\frac{2 \times 1.4}{3 \times 1.4 - 1}\right)(0.97250)^{(1 - 1.4)/1.4} = 0.882$$

where R_1 is from Tables 5.1, 6.1, or 7.1.
Similarly, by (8.17) or (8.15),

$$\left(\frac{p_{t*}}{p_{t1}}\right)_{\text{iso}} = 0.36723$$

By (8.12),

$$\Gamma_{1,\,\text{iso}} = (0.882)^{1/2}\,(0.36723)\,(1.4)^{1/0.4}\left(\frac{2.4}{3.2}\right)^{2.4/0.8} = 0.33744$$

as confirmed also by the Tables listed above.
By (8.13),

$$\left(\frac{T_{t2}}{T_{t*}}\right)_{\text{iso}} = 1.1 \times 0.882 = 0.9702$$

An iterative solution of (8.16) leads to $\mathbf{M}_2 = 0.738$, for which any of the tables listed above yields $\Gamma_2 = 0.93516$.
Finally, by (8.3) we obtain the total pressure ratio

$$\text{TPR} = p_{t1}/p_{t2} = \frac{0.93516}{1.1^{1/2} \times 0.33744} = 2.6424$$

Note that this same result is obtained by (8.18), (8.39), and (8.40).

The solution of Example 8.2 indicates the need for isothermal process tables to provide $(T_t/T_{t*})_{\text{iso}}$ in terms of R, $\mathbf{M}$, and Γ, in place of the trial and error solution. Such tables will be developed shortly.

It is useful for visualization to define the isothermal flow line. First of all, compressible isothermal flow lines are straight lines on an h–S plot, so as the combined frictional-heat transfer process proceeds, changes of state occur in step with changes of entropy. Hence, the differential entropy change at the isothermal critical state [see (8.10) and (8.11)] will not be zero as in previous processes.

Instead,

$$ds^*_{iso} = \frac{\delta q}{T_*} = -\frac{\overline{R}dp}{p_*} \tag{8.19}$$

A useful static pressure ratio for isothermal flow (based on $dp/p = -dV/V = -dM/M$) can be given as

$$\frac{p_2}{p_1} = \frac{M_1}{M_2} \tag{8.20}$$

The static temperature ratio for isothermal flow is, trivially, unity.

A useful expression for the exit static pressure in terms of the inlet pressure can be obtained by integrating (8.7), after replacing the factor $(g_c/\rho V^2)$ by its isothermal, constant area equivalent

$$\frac{g_c}{\rho V^2} = g_c \left(\frac{1}{\rho_1 V_1^2}\right)\left(\frac{p}{p_1}\right) \tag{8.21}$$

Thus, we must integrate

$$\left(\frac{g_c}{\rho_1 V_1^2 p_1}\right) \int_2^1 p\, dp + \int_2^1 \frac{dV}{V} + \left(\frac{f}{2D}\right)\int_2^1 dx = 0 \tag{8.22}$$

It should be noted in (8.22) that dV/V is the compressible term since for constant density $dV = 0$ in the constant area case. Upon integration the following results [3]:

$$p_1^2 - p_2^2 = \left(\frac{\rho_1 V_1^2 p_1}{g_c}\right)\left[2\ln\left(\frac{V_2}{V_1}\right) + f\frac{L}{D}\right] \tag{8.23}$$

This is the required isothermal state line equation.

Since $V_2/V_1 = \rho_1/\rho_2$ for constant area flow, and since $\rho_1/\rho_2 = p_1/p_2$ for isothermal flow, it follows that

$$\left(\frac{V_2}{V_1}\right)_{iso} = \frac{p_1}{p_2} \tag{8.24}$$

Upon substitution of (8.24) in (8.23), we have

$$p_1^2 - p_2^2 = \left(\frac{\rho_1 V_1^2 p_1}{g_c}\right)\left[2 \ln\left(\frac{p_1}{p_2}\right) + f\frac{L}{D}\right] \tag{8.25}$$

A method for solving isothermal problems without tables is outlined below, based on (8.25).

1. Make an incompressible estimate for the pressure drop via the Darcy equation of (8.6) as

$$(\Delta p)_{inc} = p_1 - p_2 = \left(f\frac{L}{D}\right)\frac{\rho V_1^2}{2g_c} \tag{8.26}$$

2. Then, $p_2 \simeq p_1 - (\Delta p)_{inc}$ (8.27)
3. Using the incompressible ratio, $(p_1/p_2)_{inc}$, solve (8.25) for a better approximation to p_2.
4. A short iteration will yield a consistent p_2.

EXAMPLE 8.3

Air, at a pressure of 85 psia, a temperature of 68°F, and a velocity of 110 ft/sec, flows isothermally in a 6-in. pipe, 700 ft long. If the friction factor is 0.0152, find the pressure drop.

(In SI units these same quantities are: p_1 = 586,058 pascals, T_1 = 293.3 K, V_1 = 33.528 m/s, D = 0.1524 m, L = 213.36 m.)

Solution

1. An incompressible estimate for the pressure drop is by (8.26):

$$\Delta p_{inc}_{US} = \left(\frac{0.0152 \times 700}{0.5}\right)\left(\frac{0.4345 \times 110^2}{144 \times 2 \times 32.174}\right) = 12 \text{ psia}$$

and

$$\Delta p_{inc}_{SI} = \left(\frac{0.0152 \times 213.36}{0.1524}\right)\left(\frac{6.9598 \times 33.528^2}{2}\right) = 83,244 \text{ pascals}$$

where the densities are from $p/\bar{R}T$.

2. Then,

$$p_2 \simeq 85 - 12 = 73 \text{ psia}$$
$$_{US}$$

and

$$p_2 \underset{\text{SI}}{\approx} 586{,}058 - 83{,}244 = 502{,}814 \text{ pascals}$$

3. By (8.25),

$$p_2^2 \underset{\text{US}}{=} 85^2 - \left(\frac{0.4345 \times 110^2 \times 85}{144 \times 32.174}\right)\left[2\ln\left(\frac{85}{73}\right) + \frac{0.0152 \times 700}{0.5}\right]$$

or

$$p_2^2 \underset{\text{US}}{=} 5142.113 \qquad \text{and} \qquad p_2 \underset{\text{US}}{=} 71.71 \text{ psia}$$

and

$$p_2^2 \underset{\text{SI}}{=} p_1^2 - (\rho_1 V_1^2 p_1)\left(2\ln\frac{p_1}{p_2} + f\frac{L}{D}\right)$$

$$= 586{,}058^2 - (6.9598 \times 33.528^2 \times 586{,}058)(21.586)$$

or

$$p_2^2 \underset{\text{SI}}{=} 2.4449 \times 10^{11} \qquad \text{and} \qquad p_2 \underset{\text{SI}}{=} 494{,}458 \text{ pascals}$$

4. Using this new value of p_2 in (8.25), we obtain a new value for the exit pressure of 71.68 psia, which is very close to our first compressible estimate of 71.71 psia. In SI, the new value for the exit pressure is 494,219 pascals.

   Note how rapidly the solution has closed on the answer when we start by using the incompressible approximation for p_2.

5. The pressure drop is, of course,

$$(p_1 - p_2)_{\text{US}} = 13.32 \text{ psi} \qquad \text{or} \qquad (p_1 - p_2)_{\text{SI}} = 91.839 \text{ pascals}$$

These results are entirely consistent, as seen through the conversion constant, 6894.8 pascals/psi.

Another approach to solving isothermal flow problems is to estimate losses via an isothermal loss coefficient to be discussed next.

8.5   ISOTHERMAL LOSS COEFFICIENT
Beginning with the generalized loss coefficient of (6.20), namely

$$dK = \frac{-2g_c dp}{\rho V^2} - 2\frac{dV}{V} \tag{8.28}$$

we multiply the numerator and denominator of the first term on the right by the perfect gas relation, $\rho = p/\overline{R}T$, to obtain

$$dK = \frac{-2g_c\,p\,dp}{\rho^2 V^2 \overline{R}T} - 2\frac{dV}{V} \tag{8.29}$$

This can be integrated at once, if we note that $\rho^2 V^2 = G^2 = (\dot{m}/A)^2 = $ constant, to obtain

$$K_{1,\,2} = \frac{g_c}{G^2 \overline{R}T}(p_1^2 - p_2^2) + 2\ln\left(\frac{V_1}{V_2}\right) \tag{8.30}$$

But, in the isothermal case,

$$\frac{V_1}{V_2} = \frac{\rho_2}{\rho_1} = \frac{p_2}{p_1} = \frac{R_{21}}{R_1} \tag{8.31}$$

We also introduce the total flow number patterned after (6.21), but based on inlet conditions, as

$$\alpha_1^2 = \left(\frac{\dot{m}}{A}\right)^2\left(\frac{p_{t1}}{\rho_{t1}g_c}\right)\frac{1}{p_{t1}^2} = \frac{G^2 \overline{R}T_{t1}}{p_{t1}^2 g_c} \tag{8.32}$$

When (8.31) and (8.32) are combined with (8.30), we have

$$(K_{\text{iso}})_{1,\,2} = \frac{R_1^{(\gamma+1)/\gamma}}{\alpha_1^2}\left[1 - \left(\frac{R_{21}}{R_1}\right)^2\right] + \ln\left(\frac{R_{21}}{R_1}\right)^2 \tag{8.33}$$

This is the isothermal counterpart of the adiabatic loss coefficient of (6.28) (see [4, 5]).

The term K_{iso} maximizes when the value of R_{21} at the critical state is used. This critical R_{21} is given in terms of the initial pressure ratio by

$$(R_{21})_{\text{iso}}^* = \left\{\left(\frac{2\gamma}{\gamma-1}\right)R_1^{(\gamma+1)/\gamma}\left[1 - R_1^{(\gamma-1)/\gamma}\right]\right\}^{1/2} \tag{8.34}$$

The maximum value of K_{iso} is given by

$$(K_{\text{iso}})_{1,\,*} = \frac{R_1^{(\gamma+1)/\gamma}}{\alpha_1^2}\left\{1 - \left(\frac{2\gamma}{\gamma-1}\right)[R_1^{(1-\gamma)/\gamma} - 1]\right\}$$

$$+ \ln\left\{\left(\frac{2\gamma}{\gamma-1}\right)[R_1^{(1-\gamma)/\gamma} - 1]\right\} \tag{8.35}$$

In terms of the Mach number, the isothermal loss coefficient of (8.33) can be given by

$$(K_{iso})_{1,2} = \frac{1 - (M_1/M_2)^2}{\gamma M_1^2} + \ln\left(\frac{M_1}{M_2}\right)^2 \tag{8.36}$$

which attains the maximum value, according to (8.10), when $M_2 = 1/\sqrt{\gamma}$, of

$$(K_{iso})_{1,*} = \frac{1 - \gamma M_1^2}{\gamma M_1^2} + \ln(\gamma M_1^2) \tag{8.37}$$

EXAMPLE 8.4.

Find $(K_{iso})_{1,2}$ by pressure ratio and Mach number relations for the pressure ratios of Example 6.5, that is, $R_1 = 0.9$ and $R_{21} = 0.76504$.

Solution
By (8.33),

$$(K_{iso})_{1,2} = \frac{0.9^{2.4/1.4}}{\alpha_1^2}\left[1 - \left(\frac{0.76504}{0.9}\right)^2\right] + \ln\left(\frac{0.76504}{0.9}\right)^2$$

$$= \frac{0.834754}{0.178575}(1 - 0.7225756) + \ln(0.7225756)$$

$$= 0.971898$$

where α_1 is determined in this case by (6.22).

By (8.36), with R_2 given by 0.865036 (see Example 8.6), we have from (3.14), $M_2 = 0.459859$, and

$$(K_{iso})_{1,2} = \frac{1 - 0.722577}{1.4 \times 0.390901^2} + \ln(0.722577)$$

$$= 0.971891$$

which closely checks the pressure result.

EXAMPLE 8.5

For the same inlet conditions of Example 8.4, find the maximum isothermal loss coefficient by pressure ratio and Mach number relations.

Solution
By (8.35),

$$(K_{iso})_{1,*} = \frac{0.9^{2.4/1.4}}{\alpha^2}\left[1 - \left(\frac{2.8}{0.4}\right)(0.9^{-0.4/1.4} - 1)\right]$$

$$+ \ln\left[\frac{2.8}{0.4}(0.9^{-0.4/1.4} - 1)\right]$$

$$= 2.132410$$

By (8.37),

$$(K_{iso})_{1,\,*} = \frac{1 - 1.4 \times 0.390901^2}{1.4 \times 0.390901^2} + \ln(1.4 \times 0.390901^2)$$

$$= 2.132405$$

These results check very closely.

EXAMPLE 8.6

For the same conditions given in Example 8.3, show that the general loss coefficient of (6.35) is consistent with the isothermal loss coefficient of (8.36).

Solution

By (3.6) and (3.9),

$$\mathbf{M}_1_{US} = \frac{110}{49.02 \sqrt{528}} = 0.0977$$

and

$$\mathbf{M}_1_{SI} = \frac{33.528}{20.05 \sqrt{293.3}} = 0.0977$$

By (8.20),

$$\mathbf{M}_2_{US} = \mathbf{M}_1\left(\frac{p_1}{p_2}\right)$$

$$\mathbf{M}_2_{US} = 0.0977\left(\frac{85}{71.68}\right) = 0.1158$$

and

$$\mathbf{M}_2_{SI} = 0.0977\left(\frac{586,058}{494,219}\right) = 0.1158$$

By (8.36),

$$K_{iso}_{US\text{-}SI} = \frac{1 - (\mathbf{M}_1/\mathbf{M}_2)^2}{\gamma \mathbf{M}_1^2} + \ln\left(\frac{\mathbf{M}_1}{\mathbf{M}_2}\right)^2 = 21.29$$

Whereas, by (6.35), $K = fL/D = 0.0152 \times 700/0.5 = 21.28$.

The agreement between the two formulations is satisfactory.

8.6 K_{iso} AND THE TOTAL PRESSURE RATIO

The whole purpose of introducing K_{iso} was to aid in estimating the total pressure ratio (TPR). We next develop a relationship between K_{iso} and TPR. The means for determining one of these factors in terms of the other involves an iterative solution.

By the pressure ratio method, we first obtain α_1, the flow number, via (8.32). Then, for any estimate of K_{iso} we can obtain R_{21} iteratively from (8.33). But, in general,

$$\text{TPR}_A = \frac{R_2}{R_{21}} \tag{8.38}$$

and

$$(\text{TPR}_B)_{iso} = \left\{ \left(\frac{R_2}{R_1}\right)^{(\gamma+1)/\gamma} \left[\frac{1 - R_2^{(\gamma-1)/\gamma}}{1 - R_1^{(\gamma-1)/\gamma}}\right] \right\}^{1/2} \tag{8.39}$$

where (8.39) follows directly from (8.15).

When these alternative forms for TPR converge within the required accuracy limits, we have obtained both R_2 and TPR (see Chapter 6 for the similar treatment of adiabatic flow).

By the Mach number method, we obtain $\mathbf{M}_2$, iteratively, from (8.36), for any estimate of K_{iso}, given $\mathbf{M}_1$. The two Mach numbers lead immediately to R_1 and R_2 via (3.14). Then, by applying (8.38) and (8.39), we can obtain R_{21} and TPR.

The Mach number form of (8.39) is

$$\text{TPR}_{iso} = \left(\frac{\mathbf{M}_2}{\mathbf{M}_1}\right)\left(\frac{2 + (\gamma - 1)\,\mathbf{M}_1^2}{2 + (\gamma - 1)\,\mathbf{M}_2^2}\right)^{\gamma/(\gamma-1)} \tag{8.40}$$

where (8.40) follows directly from (8.17).

In isothermal flow, as in adiabatic flow, the same friction factor and the same loss coefficient apply. These already have been given by (1.65) and (6.35).

EXAMPLE 8.7

For the constant area isothermal flow of air from $R_1 = 0.9$ through a loss device characterized by $R_{21} = 0.76504$ (as in Examples 6.5 and 8.4), find the total pressure loss.

Solution

We arbitrarily guess $R_{2,0} = 0.874071$ (where $R_{2,0}$ indicates the initial guess of R_2) and find by (8.38):

$$\text{TPR}_A = \frac{R_2}{R_{21}} = \frac{0.874071}{0.76504} = 1.142517$$

By (8.39), $\text{TPR}_B = 1.10000$.

When TPR_A and TPR_B are compared, we note an error of $e_0 = 0.042517$. A second guess of $R_{2,1}$ is made arbitrarily as 0.866362. This yields $\text{TPR}_A = 1.13244$ and $\text{TPR}_B = 1.126317$, for an error of $e_1 = 0.006123$. This is seen to be closer to zero, but perhaps we require five-place decimal accuracy. The third guess of R_2 need not be arbitrary. Instead, the Newton-Raphson scheme, already given in Example 6.8, can be used. Thus,

$$R_2 = R_{2,1} - e_1 \left(\frac{R_{2,0} - R_{2,1}}{e_0 - e_1} \right) \tag{8.41}$$

$$= 0.866362 - 0.006123 \left(\frac{0.874071 - 0.866362}{0.042517 - 0.006123} \right)$$

$R_2 = 0.865065$ results, which leads to a new error of $e_2 = 0.0001346$. A final calculation, applying (8.41), where e_1 is now called e_0, and where e_2 is now called e_1, yields $R_2 = 0.865036$ and $\text{TPR}_{\text{iso}} = 1.1307067$, at a negligible error. These are the values used in Example 8.4.

8.7 GENERALIZED ISOTHERMAL FLOW MAP

The envelope of Figure 4.1 has significance in all flow processes of gas dynamics since it relates the concepts of continuity and energy. In Chapter 6, a generalized Fanno flow map was presented in terms of K_f and TPR. In Chapter 7, a generalized Rayleigh flow map was given in terms of TTR and TPR. In this section, we consider the analogous generalized isothermal flow map (see [4, 5]).

As in Rayleigh flow, one entry in isothermal flow is the empirical heat transfer coefficient, K_q, of (7.23), for, given K_q, we can immediately obtain the total temperature ratio, TTR, via (7.26). In this connection Figures 7.3 and 7.4 apply in isothermal flow as in Rayleigh flow [6].

Another approach to a solution in isothermal flow is the use of the empirical loss coefficient, K_f, of (8.33) and (8.36). And, of course, the loss in terms of the total pressure ratio, TPR, of (8.39) and (8.40) is also of importance in isothermal flow.

As with Fanno and Rayleigh flow maps, the innovation in defining a generalized isothermal flow map is to exploit the interior of the Figure 4.1 generalized envelope. This we do by introducing on this plot the parameters of TTR,

TPR, and K_f. Thus, expressions must be available for these parameters in terms of the $R-\Gamma$ coordinates.

The critical value of R_{21}, the hybrid static to total pressure ratio, also has significance in the generalized map and has been given in terms of the initial pressure ratio (R_1) by (8.34).

This is the isothermal counterpart of the Fanno equation (6.29) and of the Rayleigh equation (7.27), and indicates the locus of maximum subsonic flows possible for isothermal flow.

The required expression for a total temperature ratio is obtained via the general relation of (3.12) and (7.28) as

$$\frac{T_{t2}}{T_{t1}} = \frac{1}{\text{TTR}} = \left[\frac{2 + (\gamma - 1)\,\mathbf{M}_2^2}{2 + (\gamma - 1)\,\mathbf{M}_1^2} \right] \tag{8.42}$$

Equation (8.42) also follows directly from (8.16).

In terms of the point pressure ratios R_1 and R_2, (8.42) can be given as

$$\frac{T_{t2}}{T_{t1}} = \frac{1}{\text{TTR}} = \left(\frac{R_2}{R_1} \right)^{(1-\gamma)/\gamma} \tag{8.43}$$

The required expressions for TPR already have been given by (8.39) and (8.40), and the required expressions for K_f by (8.33) and (8.36). It should be noted that K_f and K_q cannot both be specified in a given problem unless flow rate is the unknown parameter. Furthermore, although on the Fanno and isothermal maps the location of the K_f parameters is different, the meanings of the loss coefficient (K_f) and of the friction factor (f) are the same in both processes.

When K_f, TTR, and TPR are plotted within the generalized envelope of Figure 4.1, the generalized isothermal map of Figure 8.2 results.

Briefly, one enters the outer envelope of Figure 8.2 with R_1 to obtain Γ_1, which intercepts the chosen K_f parameter. At this intercept R_{21}, TPR, and TTR can also be located which in turn lead to Γ_2 and the complete solution. Note that all three parameters of interest, that is, K_f, TPR, and TTR, are now found inside the envelope, and the circle that began with isentropic flow (with all three parameters on the envelope) is now complete.

An isothermal solution is well adapted to flow in extremely long buried ducts, where there is sufficient area for heat transfer to keep the fluid temperature uniform.

Generalized flow maps, such as those given by Figures 6.6, 7.5, and 8.2, are of value because, in addition to their utility in providing graphical solutions to these specialized flows, they exhibit a certain beauty of symmetry and continuity.

8.8 GENERALIZED ISOTHERMAL FLOW TABLE

In Table 8.1 computer solutions to selected isothermal flow problems are presented in terms of the static to total pressure ratio $(R = p/p_t)$, the Mach

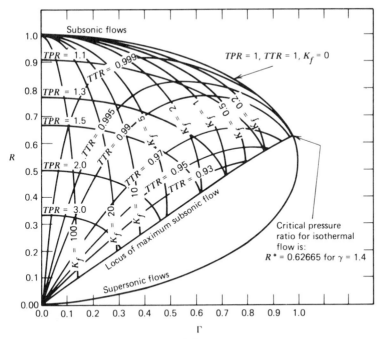

Figure 8.2   Generalized isothermal flow map.

number (**M**), the normalized flow function (Γ), and the temperature ratio (T_t/T_{t*})$_{iso}$. Also given in Table 8.1 are the iterative solutions for the hybrid pressure ratio ($R_{21} = p_2/p_1$), first as a function of the total pressure ratio (TPR $= p_{t1}/p_{t2}$), then as a function of the total temperature ratio (TTR $= T_{t1}/T_{t2}$), and finally as a function of the loss coefficient (K_f). The use of this table is best illustrated by an example.

EXAMPLE 8.8

Air flows through a buried pipe at a constant static temperature from an inlet pressure ratio of 0.98. Its loss is characterized by TPR$=2$, and its heat transfer is characterized by $K_q = 10.89$. If the inlet total temperature is 508°R, find the average earth temperature. (see Figure 8.3).

Solution

By Table 8.1, at $R_1 = 0.98$ we find: $\Gamma_1 = 0.28894$, ($T_{t1}/T_{t*} = 0.88007$, and $R_{21} = 0.45587$.

From (8.38), $R_2 = R_{21} \times$ TPR $= 0.91174$.

By Table 8.1, interpolated, $\Gamma_2 = 0.58386$, and (T_{t2}/T_{t*}) $= 0.898408$. It follows from (8.13) that

$$\text{TTR} = \frac{T_{t1}/T_{t*}}{T_{t2}/T_{t*}} = 0.9796$$

TABLE 8.1
GENERALIZED ISOTHERMAL FLOW TABLE ($\gamma = 1.4$)[a]

R	M	Γ	$\left(\dfrac{T_t}{T_{t*}}\right)_{iso}$	TPR/R_{21}				TTR/R_{21}					K_{iso}/R_{21}		
				1.1	1.3	1.5	2.0	0.999	0.99	0.97	0.95	0.2	1.0	5.0	10.0
1.00	0.00000	0.00000	0.87500	0.90909	0.76923	0.66667	0.50000	0.00000	0.00000	0.00000	0.00000	1.00000	1.00000	1.00000	1.00000
0.99	0.11991	0.20543	0.87752	0.89806	0.75610	0.65140	0.47909	0.85234	0.46546	0.28837	0.22503	0.98796	0.97978	0.93772	0.88219
0.98	0.17013	0.28894	0.88007	0.88696	0.74270	0.63552	0.45587	0.90449	0.59037	0.38818	0.30769	0.97585	0.95906	0.86978	0.74128
0.97	0.20905	0.35193	0.88265	0.87578	0.72897	0.61890	0.42909	0.91840	0.65908	0.45378	0.36470	0.96365	0.93779	0.79370	0.54706
0.96	0.24220	0.40412	0.88527	0.86452	0.71488	0.60135	0.39588	0.92107	0.70177	0.50131	0.40791	0.95137	0.91586	0.70452	
0.95	0.27169	0.44929	0.88792	0.85317	0.70035	0.58262	0.34464	0.91891	0.72981	0.53733	0.44209	0.93897	0.89315	0.58909	
0.94	0.29863	0.48938	0.89061	0.84172	0.68531	0.56231		0.91425	0.74864	0.56531	0.46979	0.92646	0.86953		
0.93	0.32366	0.52555	0.89333	0.83015	0.66964	0.53974		0.90811	0.76129	0.58728	0.49257	0.91383	0.84480		
0.92	0.34720	0.55858	0.89610	0.81845	0.65319	0.51365		0.90104	0.76957	0.60477	0.51145	0.90105	0.81867		
0.91	0.36954	0.58898	0.89890	0.80661	0.63576	0.48097		0.89334	0.77464	0.61865	0.52714	0.88810	0.79076		
0.90	0.39090	0.61715	0.90174	0.79461	0.61703	0.42681		0.88518	0.77729	0.62963	0.54025	0.87497	0.76049		
0.89	0.41144	0.64338	0.90462	0.78241	0.59649			0.87670	0.77804	0.63822	0.55116	0.86162	0.72689		
0.88	0.43127	0.66789	0.90755	0.77000	0.57321			0.86797	0.77731	0.64481	0.56019	0.84802	0.68818		
0.87	0.45051	0.69088	0.91052	0.75734	0.54516			0.85905	0.77537	0.64972	0.56760	0.83413	0.64029		
0.86	0.46922	0.71249	0.91353	0.74437	0.50545			0.84997	0.77245	0.65320	0.57359	0.81990	0.56761		
0.85	0.48749	0.73284	0.91659	0.73105				0.84078	0.76872	0.65545	0.57834	0.80525			
0.84	0.50536	0.75203	0.91969	0.71729				0.83148	0.76431	0.65663	0.58200	0.79009			
0.83	0.52287	0.77016	0.92284	0.70299				0.82210	0.75932	0.65687	0.58468	0.77429			
0.82	0.54009	0.78729	0.92605	0.68800				0.81265	0.75383	0.65629	0.58649	0.75767			
0.81	0.55702	0.80348	0.92930	0.67208				0.80315	0.74792	0.65498	0.58751	0.73997			
0.80	0.57372	0.81880	0.93260	0.65489				0.79360	0.74165	0.65303	0.58783	0.72075			
0.79	0.59021	0.83330	0.93596	0.63580				0.78400	0.73505	0.65050	0.58751	0.69925			
0.78	0.60650	0.87401	0.93937	0.61347				0.77436	0.72818	0.64746	0.58661	0.67384			
0.77	0.62263	0.85997	0.94284	0.58394				0.76470	0.72105	0.64395	0.58518	0.63974			

[a]Under TPR and TTR and K, $R_{21} = p_2/p_{t1}$ is tabulated. Example: At $R_1 = 0.9$ and at TPR $= 1.1$, $R_{21} = 0.79461$; at TTR $= 0.999$, $R_{21} = 0.88518$; and at $K_{iso} = 0.2$, $R_{21} = 0.87497$.

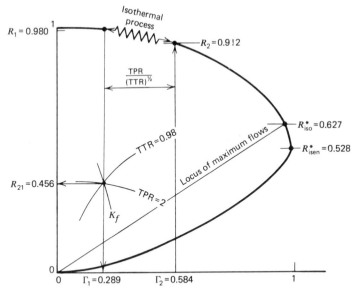

Figure 8.3   Isothermal process of Example 8.8.

This can be checked by (8.3) as

$$\text{TTR} = \left(\frac{\text{TPR} \times \Gamma_1}{\Gamma_2}\right)^2 = 0.9796$$

By (7.26), we have

$$\overline{T}_w = \frac{T_{t1}(1/\text{TTR} - 1/e^{K_q})}{1 - (1/e^{K_q})} = 518.6°R = 58.6°F$$

This average pipe wall temperature must be maintained to achieve isothermal flow under the given conditions.

8.9   CONCLUDING REMARKS

A common application in gas dynamics concerns a long pipe line buried in the ground, such as that encountered in natural gas transport, where there is enough area for heat transfer to ensure essentially uniform gas temperature. Such a situation would be well-approximated by the isothermal process.

In this chapter we have applied the generalized gas dynamics equation of (4.18) once more, this time to constant area isothermal flow, in the form of (8.3), namely

$$\left(\frac{T_{t2}}{T_{t1}}\right)^{1/2}\left(\frac{p_{t1}}{p_{t2}}\right)\Gamma_1 = \Gamma_2$$

The entropy change in the isothermal process was given by (8.4) as

$$s_2 - s_1 = \frac{\overline{R}}{J} \ln\left(\frac{p_1}{p_2}\right)$$

We found that the pattern established in isentropic, Fanno, and Rayleigh flows, namely that the critical Mach number was unity, was broken in isothermal flow, where M_{iso}^* was found to equal $\gamma^{-1/2}$.

We further found that two approaches were available for solving isothermal flow problems. In one, the state line equation of (8.23) is employed, based on the change in static pressure. The other approach is based on the use of the isothermal loss coefficient (K_f) of (8.33).

A generalized isothermal flow table (Table 8.1) was given as an aid in obtaining rapid numerical solutions.

And finally, a generalized isothermal flow map was developed, based on plotting TPR, TTR, and K_f in the interior of the generalized R–Γ envelope, as shown in Figure 8.2.

REFERENCES

1. R. P. Benedict and W. G. Steltz, *Handbook of Generalized Gas Dynamics,* Plenum Press, New York, 1966; see also by the same authors, "A Generalized Approach to One-Dimensional Gas Dynamics," *Trans. ASME, J. Engrg. for Power,* June 1962, p. 49.

2. R. C. Binder, "Limiting Isothermal Flow in Pipes," *Trans. ASME,* April 1944, p. 221.

3. R. C. Binder, *Fluid Mechanics,* 4th ed., Prentice-Hall, Englewood Cliffs, N.J., 1962, p. 275.

4. R. P. Benedict, "Some Generalizations in Compressible Flow Characteristics," *Trans. ASME, J. Engrg. for Power,* April 1973, p. 65.

5. R. P. Benedict, *Fundamentals of Pipe Flow,* Wiley, New York, 1980, p. 327.

6. R. P. Benedict, *Fundamentals of Temperature Pressure, and Flow Measurements,* Second Edition, Wiley, New York, 1977, p. 250.

NOMENCLATURE

Roman

A	Area
C_p	Specific heat at constant pressure
D	Pipe diameter
e	Error
F	Frictional head
g_c	Gravitational constant

G	Flow rate per unit area
h	Heat transfer film coefficient
J	Mechanical equivalent of heat
K_f	Loss coefficient
K_q	Heat transfer coefficient
L	Length
$\dot{m}$	Mass flow rate
M	Mach number
p	Pressure
Q	Amount of heat transfer
R	Static/total pressure ratio
$\bar{R}$	Specific gas constant
s	Specific entropy
T	Absolute temperature
TPR	Total pressure ratio (p_{t1}/p_{t2})
TTR	Total temperature ratio (T_{t2}/T_{t2})
V	Volumetric average velocity
x	Length coordinate

Greek

α	Flow number
Δ	Finite difference
δ	Inexact differential
γ	Specific heat ratio
Γ	Compressible flow function
ρ	Fluid density

Subscripts

0, 1, 2	Axial locations
iso	Isothermal
t	Total
*	Critical

PROBLEMS

8.1 Air flows isothermally at $T = 540°$R. Find the amount of heat required to increase the total temperature by 10% if the inlet Mach number is 0.1.

8.2 For the same conditions as in Problem 8.1, find the exit pressure if the inlet pressure is 30 psia.

8.3 For the same conditions as in Problems 8.1 and 8.2, find the entropy rise across the system.

8.4 In an isothermal process, find the heat required to raise the total temperature by 10% if the inlet Mach number is 0.2 and the air temperature is 50°C.

8.5   For the same conditions as in Problem 8.4, what is the exit pressure for an inlet pressure of 200,000 pascals?

8.6   What is the entropy rise for the process of Problems 8.4 and 8.5?

8.7   Find the exit Mach number and the total pressure ratio across a constant area duct if air flows from an inlet Mach number of 0.4 at constant static temperature and the total temperature increases by 10%.

8.8   If $R_1 = 0.95$ and TTR $= 0.97$, find M_2 and TPR for an isothermal process.

8.9   Air flows at constant temperature in a 12-in. diameter pipe that is 1000 ft long. If $V_1 = 100$ ft/sec, $p_1 = 100$ psia, $\rho_1/g_c = 0.01$ lbf-sec^2/ft^4, and $f = 0.02$, find Δp.

8.10   For the same conditions as in Problem 8.9, if $T = 80°F$, find the heat added.

8.11   Air flows isothermally in a 0.5 m diameter pipe that is 300 m long. If $V_1 = 50$ m/s, $p_1 = 700,000$ pascals, $\rho_1 = 7.5485$ kg/m^3, and $f = 0.015$, find Δp.

8.12   If the temperature in Problem 8.11 is 50°C, find the heat added.

8.13   If $R_1 = 0.96$ and $R_{21} = 0.64123$, find the difference between the isothermal and adiabatic loss coefficients.

9
NORMAL SHOCK

9.1 THE NORMAL SHOCK

Small pressure disturbances were discussed in Chapter 3. Such infinitesimal perturbations, which can be described by a continuous isentropic process, set up acoustic waves that propagate (that is, move) in a perfect gas at a velocity given by (3.6) as

$$a = \sqrt{\gamma g_c \bar{R} T} \tag{9.1}$$

where a is known as the acoustic velocity and represents the local speed of sound in the gas.

When the pressure disturbance is large, however, a standing (that is, stationary) plane wave is set up perpendicular to the flow direction and is known appropriately as a *normal* shock wave. The thermodynamic state of the gas changes abruptly across this plane wave, and this mathematically discontinuous process is called a normal shock process. Such a process is highly irreversible.

Normal shocks occur only when the flow is initially supersonic. That is, whenever a supersonic flow faces a back pressure (that is, a downstream pressure) that is too high to allow its continued progress, a normal shock occurs. In such cases, the flow changes abruptly from supersonic to subsonic flow with attendant large changes in static pressure and temperature, velocity, and so on (see Figures 9.1 and 9.2).

The normal shock occurs over extremely small lengths in the flow direction, nominally from 10^{-5} to 10^{-4} in., so that the normal shock process is rightfully considered to take place at a constant area. Furthermore, changes of state across the shock wave occur very rapidly and the process is assumed to be adiabatic. For the perfect gas, this ensures that the total temperature remains constant. These two conditions ($A = C$, $T_t = C$) are recognized as those for Fanno flow (see Chapter 6).

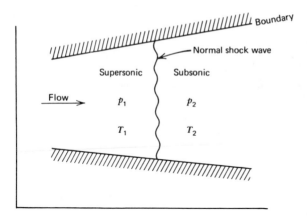

Figure 9.1 The normal shock wave.

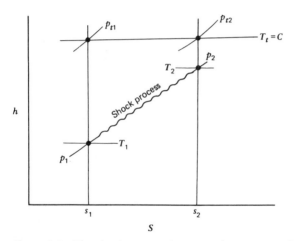

Figure 9.2 The shock process in terms of pressure and temperature.

It is further observed that there is no change in thrust across a normal shock, and frictional effects can be neglected because of the thinness of the shock wave as it contacts the bounding surface. These two conditions, zero thrust change and zero friction, are recognized as those for Rayleigh flow (see Chapter 7).

It follows that the final subsonic state of the gas, after a normal shock, must satisfy both Fanno and Rayleigh flow lines passing through the initially supersonic state (see Figures 9.3 and 9.4). It is important to realize that the normal shock process, being highly discontinuous, follows neither a Fanno nor a Rayleigh process. It simply satisfies both processes at the end points [1–9].

The normal shock process involves flow losses, is thus irreversible, and hence is accompanied by an increase in entropy. Because $s_2 - s_1$ is positive, it

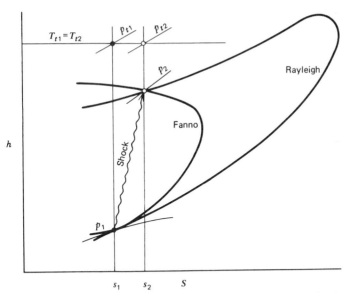

Figure 9.3 The shock process in terms of the Fanno and Rayleigh processes.

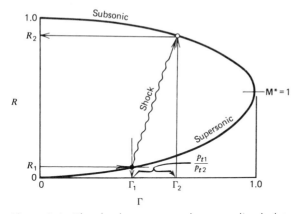

Figure 9.4 The shock process on the generalized plot.

follows from (6.7) that $p_{t2} - p_{t1}$ is negative. Thus, the total pressure always drops across a normal shock, as will be discussed further in Section 9.3.

The basic generalized gas dynamics equation for a normal shock process, according to (4.18), is

$$\left(\frac{p_{t1}}{p_{t2}}\right)\Gamma_1 = \Gamma_2 \tag{9.2}$$

since both A and T_t are constant.

It follows that the key factor in a normal shock process, according to (9.2), is the total pressure ratio.

9.2   NORMAL SHOCK EQUATIONS

The three basic conservation laws of Chapter 2, namely continuity, momentum, and energy, are applied across the normal shock wave so that we may arrive at the normal shock equations. The subscript 1 will signify the supersonic condition just before the shock, while the subscript 2 will represent the subsonic conditions immediately after the shock.

9.2.1   Continuity

From (2.10), we obtain $\rho V = C$, which for the perfect gas can be expressed as

$$\left(\frac{1}{\gamma g_c}\right)\frac{p_1 V_1}{R T_1} = \left(\frac{1}{\gamma g_c}\right)\frac{p_2 V_2}{R T_2}$$

or

$$\frac{p_1 \mathbf{M}_1}{\sqrt{T_1}} = \frac{p_2 \mathbf{M}_2}{\sqrt{T_2}} \tag{9.3}$$

as already given by (3.18).

9.2.2   Momentum

From (2.21), we obtain $p + \rho V^2/g_c = C$ or

$$p_1(1 + \gamma \mathbf{M}_1^2) = p_2(1 + \gamma \mathbf{M}_2^2) \tag{9.4}$$

which is the Rayleigh flow equation of (7.15).

9.2.3   Energy

From (2.28), we obtain $h + V^2/2g_c = C$, which for the perfect gas can be expressed as

$$C_p T_1 + V_1^2/2g_c = C_p T_2 + V_2^2/2g_c$$

or

$$T_1(2 + (\gamma - 1)\mathbf{M}_1^2) = T_2(2 + (\gamma - 1)\mathbf{M}_2^2) \tag{9.5}$$

where C_p has been replaced by its equivalent, $\gamma \overline{R}/(\gamma - 1)$. Equation (9.5) is recognized as the Fanno flow equation of (6.2).

9.2.4 Total Pressure Ratio

Since TPR is the key factor in (9.2), we need a relation between the total pressures and the Mach numbers, in analogous form to (9.3), (9.4), and (9.5). From (3.13), it follows that the required expression is

$$\frac{p_{t2}}{p_{t1}} = \frac{p_2}{p_1}\left[\frac{2 + (\gamma - 1)\,M_2^2}{2 + (\gamma - 1)\,M_1^2}\right]^{\gamma/(\gamma - 1)} \tag{9.6}$$

9.2.5 Shock Equations in Terms of M_1

Equations (9.3) through (9.6) are useful; they remind us that the normal shock process satisfies parts of both Rayleigh flow and Fanno flow. But these equations, as stated so far, do not appear in their most convenient form. That is, we really want the thermodynamic conditions at state 2 to be defined in terms of conditions at state 1 only. These relations we present next.

It is clear that if we first develop an expression for M_2 in terms of M_1, all other relations, in terms of M_1 only, would follow.

Briefly, from (9.3), (9.4), and (9.5) we obtain a quadratic in M_2^2 that has the nontrivial solution

$$M_2^2 = \frac{M_1^2(\gamma - 1) + 2}{2\gamma M_1^2 - (\gamma - 1)} \tag{9.7}$$

This is not a straightforward derivation so the algebraic steps are left to the interested reader. The sharp drop in the Mach number after a shock wave, as given by (9.7), is shown in Figure 9.5.

By combining (9.4) and (9.7), we obtain the static pressure ratio

$$\frac{p_2}{p_1} = \left(\frac{2\gamma}{\gamma + 1}\right)M_1^2 - \left(\frac{\gamma - 1}{\gamma + 1}\right) \tag{9.8}$$

The sharp rise in static pressure across a normal shock, as given by (9.8), also is shown in Figure 9.5. Equation (9.8) is known as the Rankine-Hugoniot relation.

The static temperature ratio can be given in terms of M_1 only by combining (9.5) and (9.7) to obtain

$$\frac{T_2}{T_1} = \frac{[2 + (\gamma - 1)\,M_1^2]\,[2\gamma M_1^2 - (\gamma - 1)]}{(\gamma + 1)^2 M_1^2} \tag{9.9}$$

The rise in static temperature across a normal shock also is shown in Figure 9.5.

Finally, the total pressure ratio can be expressed in terms of M_1 alone by

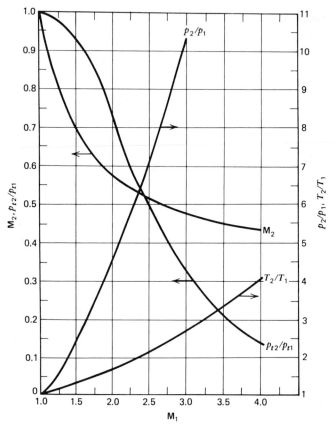

Figure 9.5 Thermodynamic quantities of the normal shock in terms of inlet Mach number.

combining (9.6), (9.7), and (9.8) to obtain

$$\frac{p_{t2}}{p_{t1}} = \left[\frac{(\gamma + 1) M_1^2}{(\gamma - 1) M_1^2 + 2}\right]^{\gamma/(\gamma - 1)} \left[\frac{(\gamma + 1)}{2\gamma M_1^2 - (\gamma - 1)}\right]^{1/(\gamma - 1)} \tag{9.10}$$

The sharp drop in total pressure is also shown in Figure 9.5.

Equation (9.10) has been given [7] in terms of the pressure ratio just before the shock wave as

$$\frac{p_{t2}}{p_{t1}} = \left[\frac{4\gamma(1 - R_1^{(\gamma-1)/\gamma}}{(\gamma + 1)(\gamma - 1) R_1^{(\gamma-1)/\gamma}} - \left(\frac{\gamma - 1}{\gamma + 1}\right)\right]^{1/(1-\gamma)}$$

$$\times \left[\frac{\gamma - 1}{(\gamma + 1)(1 - R_1^{(\gamma-1)/\gamma})}\right]^{\gamma/(1-\gamma)} \tag{9.11}$$

All of these normal shock relations are tabulated in terms of M_1 in Table 9.1, and in terms of R_1 in Table 9.2.

TABLE 9.1

NORMAL SHOCK TABLE IN TERMS OF INITIAL MACH NUMBER ($\gamma = 1.4$)

M_1	R_1	Γ_1	M_2	$\dfrac{p_2}{p_1}$	$\dfrac{T_2}{T_1}$	$\dfrac{p_{t2}}{p_{t1}}$
1.0	0.52828	1.00000	1.00000	1.00000	1.00000	1.00000
1.1	0.46835	0.99214	0.91177	1.24500	1.06494	0.99893
1.2	0.41238	0.97046	0.84217	1.51333	1.12799	0.99280
1.3	0.36091	0.93782	0.78596	1.80500	1.19087	0.97937
1.4	0.31424	0.89692	0.73971	2.12000	1.25469	0.95819
1.5	0.27240	0.85022	0.70109	2.45833	1.32022	0.92979
1.6	0.23527	0.79985	0.66844	2.82000	1.38797	0.89520
1.7	0.20259	0.74760	0.64054	3.20500	1.45833	0.85572
1.8	0.17404	0.69494	0.61650	3.61333	1.53158	0.81268
1.9	0.14924	0.64298	0.59562	4.04500	1.60792	0.76736
2.0	0.12780	0.59259	0.57735	4.50000	1.68750	0.72087
2.1	0.10935	0.54438	0.56128	4.97833	1.77045	0.67420
2.2	0.09352	0.49876	0.54706	5.48000	1.85686	0.62814
2.3	0.07997	0.45597	0.53441	6.00500	1.94680	0.58329
2.4	0.06840	0.41613	0.52312	6.55333	2.04033	0.54014
2.5	0.05853	0.37926	0.51299	7.12500	2.13750	0.49901
2.6	0.05012	0.34531	0.50387	7.72000	2.23834	0.46012
2.7	0.04295	0.31417	0.49563	8.33833	2.34289	0.42359
2.8	0.03685	0.28570	0.48817	8.98000	2.45117	0.38946
2.9	0.03165	0.25976	0.48138	9.64500	2.56321	0.35773
3.0	0.02722	0.23615	0.47519	10.33333	2.67901	0.32834
3.1	0.02345	0.21472	0.46953	11.04500	2.79860	0.30121
3.2	0.02023	0.19528	0.46435	11.78000	2.92199	0.27623
3.3	0.01748	0.17766	0.45959	12.53833	3.04919	0.25328
3.4	0.01512	0.16172	0.45520	13.32000	3.18021	0.23223
3.5	0.01311	0.14728	0.45115	14.12500	3.31505	0.21295
3.6	0.01138	0.13423	0.44741	14.95333	3.45373	0.19531
3.7	0.00990	0.12241	0.44395	15.80500	3.59624	0.17919
3.8	0.00863	0.11172	0.44073	16.68000	3.74260	0.16447
3.9	0.00753	0.10205	0.43774	17.57833	3.89281	0.15103
4.0	0.00659	0.09329	0.43496	18.50000	4.04687	0.13876
5.0	0.00189	0.04000	0.41523	29.00000	5.80000	0.06172
6.0	0.00063	0.01880	0.40416	41.83333	7.94059	0.02965
7.0	0.00024	0.00960	0.39736	57.00000	10.46939	0.01535
8.0	0.00010	0.00526	0.39289	74.50000	13.38672	0.00849
9.0	0.00005	0.00306	0.38980	94.33333	16.69273	0.00496
10.0	0.00002	0.00187	0.38758	116.50000	20.38750	0.00304

TABLE 9.2

NORMAL SHOCK TABLE IN TERMS OF INITIAL PRESSURE RATIO ($\gamma = 1.4$)

R_1	M_1	Γ_1	M_2	$\dfrac{p_2}{p_1}$	$\dfrac{T_2}{T_1}$	$\dfrac{p_{t2}}{p_{t1}}$
0.52828	1.00000	1.00000	1.00000	1.00000	1.00000	1.00000
0.50000	1.04646	0.99825	0.95625	1.11091	1.03054	0.99988
0.49000	1.06318	0.99679	0.94173	1.15208	1.04136	0.99971
0.48000	1.08008	0.99490	0.92765	1.19434	1.05222	0.99943
0.47000	1.09717	0.99256	0.91398	1.23774	1.06314	0.99901
0.46000	1.11446	0.98979	0.90071	1.28235	1.07412	0.99843
0.45000	1.13196	0.98657	0.88780	1.32823	1.08520	0.99767
0.44000	1.14970	0.98291	0.87524	1.37543	1.09639	0.99671
0.43000	1.16767	0.97880	0.86300	1.42404	1.10770	0.99552
0.42000	1.18591	0.97424	0.85107	1.47412	1.11915	0.99408
0.41000	1.20443	0.96923	0.83943	1.52575	1.13077	0.99237
0.40000	1.22324	0.96375	0.82806	1.57904	1.14257	0.99037
0.39000	1.24237	0.95781	0.81695	1.63406	1.15458	0.98806
0.38000	1.26183	0.95139	0.80608	1.69093	1.16681	0.98542
0.37000	1.28166	0.94450	0.79544	1.74975	1.17930	0.98242
0.36000	1.30186	0.93712	0.78501	1.81066	1.19205	0.97905
0.35000	1.32248	0.92925	0.77479	1.87378	1.20511	0.97528
0.34000	1.34353	0.92088	0.76476	1.93926	1.21849	0.97109
0.33000	1.36505	0.91199	0.75490	2.00727	1.23223	0.96646
0.32000	1.38708	0.90258	0.74522	2.07798	1.24636	0.96136
0.31000	1.40964	0.89264	0.73569	2.15158	1.26092	0.95576
0.30000	1.43277	0.88214	0.72630	2.22831	1.27595	0.94964
0.25000	1.55884	0.82091	0.68124	2.66830	1.35978	0.91011
0.20000	1.70854	0.74311	0.63835	3.23895	1.46447	0.85217
0.15000	1.89671	0.64467	0.59626	4.03042	1.60535	0.76887
0.10000	2.15719	0.51795	0.55294	5.26240	1.81944	0.64774
0.05000	2.60149	0.34482	0.50374	7.72902	2.23987	0.45956
0.04000	2.74635	0.30065	0.49208	8.63283	2.39261	0.40747
0.03000	2.93546	0.25113	0.47912	9.88638	2.60383	0.34705
0.02000	3.20771	0.19386	0.46397	11.83762	2.93166	0.27439
0.01000	3.69296	0.12321	0.44418	15.74430	3.58609	0.18028
0.00900	3.76929	0.11489	0.44169	16.40882	3.69725	0.16885
0.00800	3.85551	0.10624	0.43905	17.17576	3.82551	0.15686
0.00700	3.95442	0.09718	0.43620	18.07704	3.97618	0.14421
0.00600	4.07022	0.08764	0.43312	19.16116	4.15737	0.13079
0.00500	4.20951	0.07753	0.42972	20.50659	4.38215	0.11641
0.00400	4.38356	0.06668	0.42588	22.25157	4.67359	0.10083
0.00300	4.61412	0.05485	0.42142	24.67180	5.07767	0.08363
0.00200	4.95168	0.04158	0.41593	28.43904	5.70640	0.06407
0.00100	5.56635	0.02580	0.40826	35.98166	6.96468	0.04036

EXAMPLE 9.1

Air flowing at a Mach number of 1.6, at a pressure of 5 psia, and at a temperature of 1000°R undergoes a normal shock process. Find the static pressure and temperature, the total pressure and temperature, and the velocity after the normal shock wave.

(In SI units, these same quantities are: $p_1 = 34{,}474$ pascals, $T_1 = 555.6$ K.)

Solution

At $M_1 = 1.6$, we find from the tables, $R_1 = 0.23527$, $T_1/T_t = 0.66138$, $M_2 = 0.66844$, $p_2/p_1 = 2.82000$, $T_2/T_1 = 1.38797$, and $p_{t2}/p_{t1} = 0.89520$.

In the US system it follows that

$$p_{t1} = \frac{p_1}{R_1} = \frac{5}{0.23527} = 21.25 \text{ psia}$$

$$p_2 = p_1 \times \frac{p_2}{p_1} = 5 \times 2.82 = 14.1 \text{ psia}$$

and

$$T_t = \frac{T_1}{T_1/T_t} = \frac{1000}{0.66138} = 1512°\text{R}$$

In the SI system we have

$$P_{t1} = \frac{34{,}474}{0.23527} = 146{,}530 \text{ pascals}$$

$$p_2 = 34{,}474 \times 2.82 = 97{,}217 \text{ pascals}$$

and

$$T_t = \frac{555.6}{0.66138} = 840 \text{ K}$$

At $M_2 = 0.66844$, we find from Table 5.1, $R_2 = 0.74113$ and $T_2/T_t = 0.91797$.

In the US system it follows that

$$T_2 = T_t \times \frac{T_2}{T_t} = 1512 \times 0.91797 = 1388°\text{R}$$

and

$$p_{t2} = \frac{p_2}{R_2} = \frac{14.1}{0.74113} = 19 \text{ psia}$$

(As a check, note that $p_{t2}/p_{t1} = 19/21.25 = 0.894$; this is very close to the direct table lookup value.)

In the SI system we have

$$T_2 = 840 \times 0.91797 = 771.1 \text{ K}$$

and

$$p_{t2} = \frac{97,217}{0.74113} = 131,174 \text{ pascals}$$

Finally,

$$V_2 \atop \text{US} = \mathbf{M}_2 \, a_2 = 0.66844 \times 49.02 \, \sqrt{1388} = 1220.76 \text{ ft/sec}$$

and

$$V_2 \atop \text{SI} = 0.66844 \times 20.05 \, \sqrt{771.1} = 372.16 \text{ m/s}$$

All the above results illustrate the consistency between US and SI units. For example, the velocity results show

$$1220.76 \text{ ft/sec} \left(\frac{0.3048 \text{m}}{\text{ft}} \right) = 372.1 \text{ m/s}$$

EXAMPLE 9.2

Show that the generalized gas dynamics equation yields results consistent with those of Example 9.1.

Solution

At $M_1 = 1.6$, $\Gamma_1 = 0.79985$, and $p_{t2}/p_{t1} = 0.89520$.

By (9.2) $\Gamma_2 = \dfrac{0.79985}{0.89520} = 0.893487$.

By interpolation of Table 5.1, this Γ_2 requires a M_2 of 0.66845, which checks favorably with Example 9.1.

9.3   ENTROPY RISE ACROSS A NORMAL SHOCK

In Chapter 6 we arrived at expression (6.7) for the entropy increase in a general adiabatic process, namely

$$s_2 - s_1 = \frac{\overline{R}}{J} \ln \left(\frac{p_{t1}}{p_{t2}} \right) \tag{9.12}$$

Since the normal shock process also is an adiabatic process, (9.12) applies and can be used to determine the entropy rise across the normal shock wave. Of course, the total pressure ratio (p_{t1}/p_{t2}), as required by (9.2) and (9.12), already has been given by (9.6), (9.10), and (9.11).

EXAMPLE 9.3

Find the entropy rise accompanying the normal shock process of Example 9.1.

Solution

By (9.12),

$$s_2 - s_1 = \frac{53.35}{778} \ln\left(\frac{1}{0.89520}\right) = 0.007592 \frac{\text{Btu}}{\text{lbm-}°\text{R}}$$

9.4   NOZZLE FLOW WITH SHOCK WAVES

Isentropic flow through a convergent-divergent nozzle was discussed in Chapter 5. In this section, in keeping with the chapter's subject, we extend the nozzle analysis to include the possibility of shock waves. To simplify the discussion, we divide the convergent-divergent nozzle flow into four regions, as shown in Figure 9.6.

In region 1, the flow is entirely subsonic; the flow rate varies with the back pressure; and the limiting flow in this region occurs when the throat Mach number just reaches unity (that is, the choked condition). The back pressure that first causes this limiting flow is called the first critical pressure.

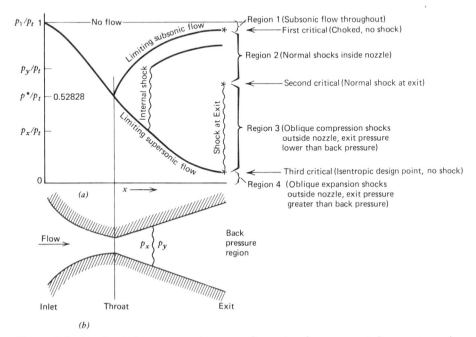

Figure 9.6   Idealized flow pattern in a one-dimensional convergent-divergent nozzle. (a) Pressure versus position. (b) Nozzle geometry.

In region 2, supersonic flow first occurs in the divergent portion of the nozzle. Then, because the back pressure is higher than the local nozzle pressure, a normal shock is established in the nozzle, and the supersonic flow changes abruptly to subsonic flow. As the back pressure is progressively lowered, the shock wave moves progressively downstream until at a given back pressure (the second critical point) the shock wave reaches the nozzle exit. Throughout region 2, the nozzle exit pressure continues to adjust to equal the back pressure, whereas the flow rate remains constant, independent of the back pressure, because the flow is choked at the throat.

In region 3, there is supersonic flow throughout the entire nozzle, and the pressure at the nozzle exit is *lower* than the back pressure. The gas has *over-expanded,* and a compression process is required to balance the pressures. This involves oblique shock waves *outside* the nozzle, and these cannot be treated by the one-dimensional analysis presented here. Of course, in this region, the flow rate continues to be independent of the back pressure.

A unique condition divides region 3 from region 4. Again, the back pressure and the nozzle exit pressure just match (the third critical point), and hence no shock waves are encountered either within or outside the nozzle. This third critical point also is known as the isentropic design point of the nozzle.

In region 4, supersonic flow once more prevails throughout the entire nozzle, but now the pressure at the nozzle exit is *higher* than the back pressure. The gas has *underexpanded,* and an expansion process is required to balance the pressures. This process also involves oblique shock waves *outside* the nozzle, and these are not amenable to one-dimensional analysis. Of course, flow rate continues to be independent of the back pressure since the nozzle is choked.

While one-dimensional theory does not truly represent the actual shock processes encountered in convergent-divergent nozzles, it does serve to indicate gross behavior, and thus provides a useful approximation.

EXAMPLE 9.4

A convergent-divergent nozzle with a 6-in. diameter throat is designed for a pressure ratio of 0.3 and is operating at an inlet total pressure of 100 psia. Find the exit diameter of the nozzle, and the first, second, and third critical pressures.

(In SI units, these same quantities are: $D_2 = 0.1524$ m, $p_{t1} = 689,480$ pascals.)

Solution

See Figure 9.7 for nomenclature.

The *third* critical pressure designates the isentropic design point where the nozzle operates shock-free. Since the pressure ratio for this condition has been

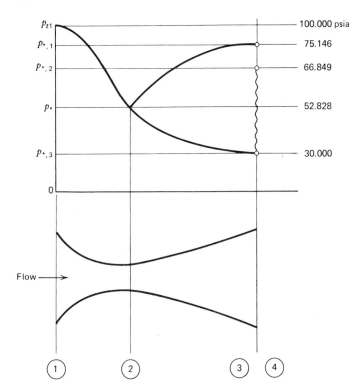

Figure 9.7 Critical pressures and notation for Example 9.4.

given as

$$\frac{p_3}{p_{t1}} = \frac{p_4}{p_{t1}} = 0.3$$

it follows that the third critical pressure is

$$p_{*3 \atop \text{US}} = p_3 = p_4 = 100 \times 0.3 = 30 \, \text{psia}$$

and

$$p_{*3 \atop \text{SI}} = 689,480 \times 0.3 = 206,844 \, \text{pascals}$$

The design Mach number at this point is, by Table 9.2,

$$\mathbf{M}_3 = \mathbf{M}_4 = 1.43277$$

By the isentropic relation (5.1) and since $\Gamma_2 = 1$ at the choked condition, we also find by Table 9.2

$$\frac{A_2}{A_4}(1) = \Gamma_4 = f(R_4) = 0.88214 \tag{9.13}$$

which leads by usual means to the exit diameter

$$D_4 = 6.388 \text{ in.}$$
$$_{\text{US}}$$

$$D_4 = 0.16226 \text{ m}$$
$$_{\text{SI}}$$

The *first* critical pressure designates the back pressure that first causes choked flow in the nozzle. Since the area ratio remains fixed, (9.13) still applies, but now the multivalued nature of Γ must be considered. That is, Γ_4 of 0.88214 also belongs with the subsonic R_4 of 0.75146, according to Table 5.1. Thus, the first critical pressure is

$$P_{*1} = p_3 = p_4 = 100 \times 0.75146 = 75.146 \text{ psia}$$
$$_{\text{US}}$$

and

$$P_{*1} = 689{,}480 \times 0.75146 = 518{,}117 \text{ pascals}$$
$$_{\text{SI}}$$

The *second* critical pressure signifies loss-free flow throughout the nozzle, up to the normal shock positioned just at the nozzle exit. But p_3 and $\mathbf{M}_3$, just before the exit shock, are still the design points of $p_3 = 30$ psia (206,844 pascals) and $\mathbf{M}_3 = 1.43277$ since the same area ratio prevails.

By the normal shock Table 9.1, we find $\mathbf{M}_4 = 0.72631$ and $p_4/p_3 = 2.2283$. These values lead at once to

$$P_{*2} = p_4 = \frac{p_4}{p_3} \times p_3 = 66.8409 \text{ psia}$$
$$_{\text{US}}$$

and

$$P_{*2} = 2.2283 \times 206{,}844 = 460{,}910 \text{ pascals}$$
$$_{\text{SI}}$$

All of these critical pressures are shown in Figure 9.7.

EXAMPLE 9.5

We already have seen for the nozzle of Example 9.4 that any back pressure between the first critical pressure of 75.146 psia and the second critical pressure of 66.849 psia will cause a normal shock to be located somewhere in the diverging section of the convergent-divergent nozzle. If the back pressure is 70 psia, locate the normal shock, using the notation of Figure 9.8.

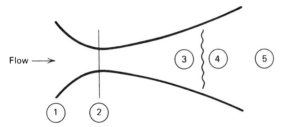

Figure 9.8   Notation for Example 9.5.

Solution

1. Since the same geometry prevails, $A_2/A_5 = 0.88214$.
2. Since the flow is isentropic from 4 to 5, $(A_4/A_5)\Gamma_4 = \Gamma_5$.
3. Since the flow is isentropic from 2 to 3, $(A_2/A_3)(1) = \Gamma_3$.
4. Since the shock takes place at constant area, $A_3 = A_4$.
5. Across the shock, $(p_{t3}/p_{t4})\, \Gamma_3 = \Gamma_4$.
6. From items 2 and 3, $p_{t3} = p_{t1}$ and $p_{t5} = p_{t4}$.

Combining the above items, we have

$$\frac{A_2/A_5}{A_2/A_4} = \frac{0.88214}{\Gamma_3} = \frac{A_4}{A_5} = \frac{\Gamma_5}{\Gamma_4}$$

or

$$0.88214\,(p_{t3}/p_{t4}) = \Gamma_5$$

Introducing $p_{t3} = 100$ psia, $p_{t4} = p_{t5}$, and $\Gamma_5 = f(p_5/p_{t5})$, we obtain

$$\frac{88.214}{p_{t5}} = \Gamma_5 = f\!\left(\frac{70}{p_{t5}}\right)$$

An iterative procedure, based on guessing p_{t5}, via the Newton-Raphson scheme of Examples 6.8 and 8.7, leads to $p_{t5} = 96.805$ psia and $\Gamma_5 = 0.91170$.

Another approach toward these same two quantities (that is, p_{t5} and Γ_5) is the application of (6.2) that in this case becomes

$$p_{t1}A_2 = p_{t5}A_{*5} = p_{t5}A_5\Gamma_5$$

Substituting, we have $p_{t5}\Gamma_5 = p_{t1}A_2/A_5 = 88.214$. An iterative procedure, based on guessing p_{t5}, as above, leads to $p_{t5} = 96.778$ and $\Gamma_5 = 0.91151$. These values closely check those obtained by the first method.

From the normal shock, Table 9.1 we find for $p_{t3}/p_{t5} = 0.968$, $\mathbf{M}_3 \simeq 1.36$, $\Gamma_3 \simeq 0.91411$, $\mathbf{M}_4 \simeq 0.75718$, and $\Gamma_4 \simeq 0.94464$.

By item 3, $A_2/A_3 = \Gamma_3$, which leads to

$$D_4 = D_3 = D_2/\sqrt{0.91411} = 6.275 \text{ in.}$$

If the nozzle diameter is assumed to vary linearly with length (L) from the throat, we have

$$\frac{L}{0.338} = \frac{X}{0.275} \quad \text{or} \quad X = 0.709 L$$

where L is the distance from the throat to the shock.

Finally, as a check on these results, item 2 requires $(A_4/A_5)\Gamma_4 = \Gamma_5$. Thus,

$$\left(\frac{D_4}{D_5}\right)^2 \Gamma_4 = \Gamma_5 = \left(\frac{6.275}{6.388}\right)^2 \times 0.94464 = 0.91152$$

which checks the iterated values closely.

9.5   PITOT TUBE AND THE NORMAL SHOCK

In subsonic flow, the Pitot tube (also called an impact tube, a total pressure tube, or a stagnation tube) directly yields the free stream total pressure. This total pressure, together with the free stream static pressure, as measured by wall taps [10] or static taps on a Pitot-static probe [10], yields the free stream Mach number via (3.13), that is

$$\frac{p_{t1}}{p_1} = \left[1 + \left(\frac{\gamma - 1}{2}\right)\mathbf{M}_1^2\right]^{\gamma/(\gamma-1)} \tag{9.14}$$

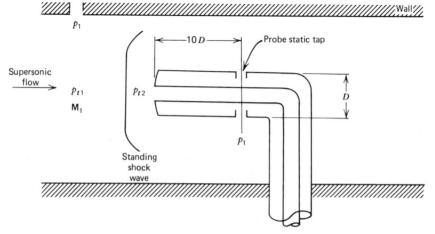

Figure 9.9   Pitot-static probe in supersonic flow.

In supersonic flow, however, the Pitot tube does not directly yield the free stream total pressure, because a normal shock wave is formed and stands just ahead of the Pitot tube (see Figure 9.9). We already have seen via (9.10) that the total pressure indicated by a Pitot tube (p_{t2}), just after the shock, can be given in terms of the Mach number (M_1), just before the shock, provided the total pressure (p_{t1}) before the shock is available.

However, p_{t1} is the very measurement that is not available.

From a slightly different viewpoint, the Mach number (M_1), just before the shock, can be given in terms of the indicated Pitot tube total pressure (p_{t2}) and the static pressure (p_1), just before the shock. Note that

$$\frac{p_{t2}}{p_1} = \frac{p_{t2}}{p_{t1}} \times \frac{p_{t1}}{p_1} \tag{9.15}$$

where p_{t2}/p_{t1} results from (9.10), and p_{t1}/p_1 from (9.14). Thus, the following results:

$$\frac{p_{t2}}{p_1} = \left[\left(\frac{\gamma + 1}{2}\right) M_1^2 \right]^{\gamma/(\gamma-1)} \left[\frac{\gamma + 1}{2\gamma M_1^2 - (\gamma - 1)} \right]^{1/(\gamma-1)} \tag{9.16}$$

which is known as the Rayleigh Pitot tube relation.

By (9.16), we have traded the inaccessible measurement of p_{t1} for the more easily obtainable p_1 in order to determine the Mach number before the shock wave.

The static pressure required of (9.16) can be obtained by wall taps, just as in subsonic flow or, according to [3], by static taps placed on the Pitot tube outer wall, some ten probe diameters back from the impact point of the tube (see Figure 9.9).

Finally, the free stream Mach number also can be determined by the Mach angle, as described in Section 3.3.

EXAMPLE 9.6

A Pitot-static probe is placed in a supersonic air flow, and the indicated total pressure with respect to the static pressure is 10. Find the free stream Mach number.

Solution

By (9.16), we have

$$10 = \left[\left(\frac{2.4}{2}\right) M_1^2 \right]^{1.4/0.4} \left[\frac{2.4}{2.8\, M_1^2 - 0.4} \right]^{1/0.4}$$

Solving for M_1, iteratively, we obtain $M_1 = 2.7198$ (see Examples 6.8, 8.7, and 9.5 for similar Newton-Raphson iterative solutions).

As a check, at $\mathbf{M}_1 = 2.72$ we find by Table 9.1 that $p_{t2}/p_{t1} = 0.41657$ and $R_1 = 0.04166$.

By (9.15), $p_{t2}/p_1 = 0.41657/0.04166 = 9.9993$, which checks the given ratio closely and indicates that the correct $\mathbf{M}_1$ was obtained.

9.6 CONCLUDING REMARKS

In this chapter we have studied large pressure disturbances encountered in supersonic flows and the accompanying normal shock waves.

The basic gas dynamics equation of (4.18) reduced, in the case of a normal shock process, to (9.2) as

$$\left(\frac{p_{t1}}{p_{t2}}\right)\Gamma_1 = \Gamma_2$$

All thermodynamic quantities of interest, just after a normal shock, were expressed in terms of the supersonic Mach number just before the shock wave, as given by equations (9.7) through (9.10). For example,

$$\mathbf{M}_2^2 = \frac{\mathbf{M}_1^2(\gamma - 1) + 2}{2\gamma\,\mathbf{M}_1^2 - (\gamma - 1)}$$

Normal shock tables were given first in terms of $\mathbf{M}_1$, as the independent variable, and then in terms of R_1.

The entropy rise across a normal shock was given by the general adiabatic relation of (9.12) as

$$s_2 - s_1 = \frac{\overline{R}}{J}\ln\left(\frac{p_{t1}}{p_{t2}}\right)$$

We examined in some detail the various regions of flow possible in a convergent-divergent nozzle, ranging from subsonic flow, through isentropic supersonic flow, to the under and overexpanded oblique shock flows. First, second, and third critical pressures were defined and illustrated in Example 9.4.

The use of the Pitot tube to obtain the Mach number existing before a normal shock wave was described.

REFERENCES

1. R. C. Binder, *Fluid Mechanics*, 4th Edition, Prentice-Hall, Englewood Cliffs, N.J., 1962, p. 234.

2. N. A. Hall, *Thermodynamics of Fluid Flow*, Prentice-Hall, Englewood Cliffs, N.J., 1951, p. 128.

3. A. H. Shapiro, *The Dynamics and Thermodynamics of Compressible Fluid Flow*, Ronald Press, New York, Vol. 1, 1953, p. 112.

4. R. M. Rotty, *Introduction to Gas Dynamics,* Wiley, New York, 1962, p. 116.

5. F. Cheers, *Elements of Compressible Flow,* Wiley, New York, 1963, p. 40.

6. R. D. Zucker, *Fundamentals of Gas Dynamics,* Matrix Publishers, Portland, Oregon, 1977, p. 143.

7. R. P. Benedict and W. G. Steltz, *Handbook of Generalized Gas Dynamics,* Plenum Press, New York, 1966; see also by the same authors, "A Generalized Approach to One-Dimensional Gas Dynamics," *Trans. ASME, J. Engrg. for Power,* June 1962, p. 49.

8. R. P. Benedict, "Some Generalizations in Compressible Flow Characteristics," *Trans. ASME, J. Engrg. for Power,* April 1973, p. 65.

9. R. P. Benedict, *Fundamentals of Pipe Flow,* Wiley, New York, April 1980, p. 321.

10. R. P. Benedict, *Fundamentals of Temperature, Pressure, and Flow Measurements,* Second Edition, Wiley, New York, 1977, pp. 343, 360.

NOMENCLATURE

Roman

a	Acoustic velocity
A	Area
C	Constant
C_p	Specific heat at constant pressure
D	Flow diameter
g_c	Gravitational constant
J	Mechanical equivalent of heat
L	Length
$\mathbf{M}$	Mach number
p	Pressure
R	Static/total pressure ratio
$\overline{R}$	Specific gas constant
s	Specific entropy
T	Absolute temperature
TPR	Total pressure ratio (p_{t1}/p_{t2})
V	Volumetric average velocity
x	Length coordinate

Greek

γ	Specific heat ratio
Γ	Compressible flow function
ρ	Fluid density

Subscripts

0, 1, 2   Axial locations
t   Total
*   Critical

PROBLEMS

9.1 A normal shock occurs in the flow of air. If conditions before the shock are: $M_1 = 2$, $p_1 = 10$ psia, $T_1 = 500°R$; find static and total pressures and temperatures after the shock.

9.2 Determine the increase in entropy across the shock wave of Problem 9.1.

9.3 Conditions just before a normal shock are: $M_1 = 2.5$, $p_1 = 100,000$ pascals, $T_1 = 500K$. Find the static and total temperatures and pressures of air just after the shock.

9.4 Find the entropy rise across the shock wave of Problem 9.3.

9.5 A convergent-divergent nozzle having a 10-in. throat is designed for a Mach number of 2 at the exit. If air flows from an inlet total pressure of 50 psia, find the first, second, and third critical pressures, and the exit diameter.

9.6 Locate the normal shock in the nozzle of Problem 9.5, if the back pressure is 40 psia.

9.7 A C–D nozzle has a 1 m diameter throat and is designed for a Mach number of 2.2 at the exit. For air flowing from an inlet total pressure of 350,000 pascals, find the first, second, and third critical pressures, and the exit diameter.

9.8 If the back pressure is 250,000 pascals, find the location of the normal shock in the nozzle of Problem 9.7.

9.9 A Pitot-static tube placed in a supersonic air flow indicates a total pressure of 20 psia and a static pressure of 5 psia. Estimate the free stream Mach number.

10
GENERALIZED GAS DYNAMICS TABLES

10.1 DEVELOPMENT OF A GENERALIZED TABLE

In previous chapters, we have developed and presented specialized tables, separately, for the isentropic, Fanno, Rayleigh, isothermal, and normal shock processes.

But we know there are common bonds between these gas dynamics processes, as evidenced by such equations involving the normalized gas dynamics function (Γ) as

$$\Gamma = \frac{\alpha}{\alpha_*} = \frac{\dot{m}}{\dot{m}_*} = \frac{\mathbf{P}}{\mathbf{P}_*} \tag{10.1}$$

which already was given by (4.25), where α is the flow number of (4.22), $\dot{m}$ is the flow rate of (4.1), and $\mathbf{P}$ is the pressure ratio function of (4.7), and the starred (*) quantities indicate values at the isentropic critical state where $\mathbf{M} = 1$.

Furthermore, this same gas dynamics function (Γ) has been shown to represent the key factors: (A_*/A) of isentropic flow [see (5.3)] and (p_{t*}/p_t) of Fanno flow [see (6.11)], that is

$$\Gamma = \left(\frac{A_*}{A}\right)_{\text{isen}} = \left(\frac{p_{t*}}{p_t}\right)_{\text{Fanno}} \tag{10.2}$$

EXAMPLE 10.1

Show that at any pressure ratio, like $R = 0.9$, (10.2) is confirmed by Tables 5.1 and 6.1.

Solution

By Table 5.1, at $R = 0.9$, $\Gamma_{\text{isen}} = 0.61715$. By Table 6.1, at $R = 0.9$, $\Gamma_{\text{Fanno}} = 0.61715$.

These two results are seen to be identical.

Thus, under many circumstances, a single detailed generalized gas dynamics table would suffice for the solution of gas flow problems [1]. Of course, it almost goes without saying that the specialized Tables 5.1, 6.1, 7.1, 8.1, 9.1, and 9.2 can include more information than any single table.

Since the single generalized table is just a composite of the many individual process tables, all of the equations that serve as the basis of the generalized table already have been developed and presented.

Just as in the normal shock treatment we presented two tables, one with pressure ratio (R) as the independent variables and one with Mach number ($\mathbf{M}$) as the independent variable, so too we will provide two generalized tables here. The reasoning is as follows. For experimental work, it is the pressure ratio that is most easily obtained from measurements of the static and total pressures. Hence, R is the most desirable variable to serve as the table entry in this situation. For desk work, on the other hand, the Mach number is more convenient to specify and thus to serve as the table entry.

To keep the generalized tables a manageable size, only the key factors required for each process will be preserved. These factors include:

$\Gamma = A_*/A$ for isentropic flow.

$\Gamma = p_{t*}/p_t$ for Fanno flow.

$(T_t/T_{t*})_{\text{Ray}}$ for Rayleigh flow.

$(T_t/T_{t*})_{\text{iso}}$ for isothermal flow.

p_{t1}/p_{t2} for the normal shock process.

Factors that apply equally well to all processes include: R, $\mathbf{M}$, T/T_t, and Γ, so naturally these also are included in the generalized table.

The resulting two generalized gas dynamics tables are presented as Tables 10.1 and 10.2.

As general rules for the use of these tables:

1. One enters the table with R_1 (or $\mathbf{M}_1$) to obtain the factors $\mathbf{M}_1$ (or R_1), T_1/T_{t1}, and the key factor for the given process. Thus,

   A. For an isentropic process, Γ is the key factor A_*/A.
   B. For a Fanno process, Γ is the key factor p_{t*}/p_t.
   C. For a Rayleigh process, $(T_{t1}/T_{t*})_{\text{Ray}}$ is the key factor.
   D. For an isothermal process, $(T_{t1}/T_{t*})_{\text{iso}}$ is the key factor.
   E. For a normal shock process, p_{t1}/p_{t2} is the key factor.

2. One then multiplies the key factor of the given process at 1 by the given ratio of conditions to obtain the key factor of the given process at 2. For example, for an isentropic process, the ratio of conditions is given by the area ratio, A_1/A_2. Thus,

$$\frac{A_1}{A_2} \times \frac{A_*}{A_1} = \frac{A_*}{A_2}$$

3. From the same line of the table on which the key factor appears at 2, one then obtains all the other factors of interest at state 2.

TABLE 10.1
GENERALIZED COMPRESSIBLE FLOW TABLE ($\gamma = 1.4$) (in Terms of Pressure Ratio)[a]

$R = p/p_t$	M	T/T_t	Γ	ISOTHERMAL T_t/T_t^*	RAYLEIGH T_t/T_t^*	SHOCK p_{t1}/p_{t2}
1.0000	.00000	1.00000	.00000	.87500	.00000	1.
.9995	.02673	.99986	.04617	.87513	.00342	1.
.9990	.03781	.99971	.06528	.87525	.00684	1.
.9985	.04631	.99957	.07993	.87538	.01024	1.
.9980	.05349	.99943	.09227	.87550	.01363	1.
.9975	.05981	.99929	.10313	.87563	.01701	1.
.9970	.06553	.99914	.11294	.87575	.02038	1.
.9965	.07079	.99900	.12196	.87588	.02374	1.
.9960	.07569	.99886	.13034	.87600	.02709	1.
.9955	.08029	.99871	.13821	.87613	.03043	1.
.9950	.08465	.99857	.14565	.87625	.03376	1.
.9945	.08880	.99843	.15272	.87638	.03708	1.
.9940	.09276	.99828	.15947	.87651	.04039	1.
.9935	.09656	.99814	.16593	.87663	.04369	1.
.9930	.10023	.99799	.17215	.87676	.04698	1.
.9925	.10376	.99785	.17814	.87688	.05026	1.
.9920	.10718	.99771	.18394	.87701	.05353	1.
.9915	.11050	.99756	.18955	.87714	.05679	1.
.9910	.11372	.99742	.19499	.87726	.06004	1.
.9905	.11685	.99728	.20028	.87739	.06328	1.
.9900	.11991	.99713	.20543	.87752	.06651	1.
.9895	.12289	.99699	.21044	.87764	.06973	1.
.9890	.12580	.99684	.21534	.87777	.07294	1.
.9885	.12865	.99670	.22012	.87790	.07614	1.
.9880	.13144	.99656	.22479	.87802	.07933	1.
.9875	.13417	.99641	.22936	.87815	.08251	1.
.9870	.13685	.99627	.23384	.87828	.08568	1.
.9865	.13948	.99612	.23823	.87840	.08884	1.
.9860	.14206	.99598	.24254	.87853	.09199	1.
.9855	.14460	.99584	.24676	.87866	.09513	1.
.9850	.14710	.99569	.25091	.87879	.09827	1.
.9845	.14955	.99555	.25499	.87891	.10139	1.
.9840	.15197	.99540	.25900	.87904	.10450	1.
.9835	.15435	.99526	.26294	.87917	.10761	1.
.9830	.15670	.99511	.26683	.87930	.11070	1.
.9825	.15901	.99497	.27065	.87942	.11378	1.
.9820	.16129	.99482	.27441	.87955	.11686	1.
.9815	.16355	.99468	.27812	.87968	.11992	1.
.9810	.16577	.99453	.28178	.87981	.12298	1.
.9805	.16796	.99439	.28538	.87994	.12603	1.
.9800	.17013	.99424	.28894	.88007	.12907	1.
.9795	.17227	.99410	.29245	.88019	.13209	1.
.9790	.17439	.99395	.29591	.88032	.13511	1.
.9785	.17648	.99381	.29933	.88045	.13812	1.
.9780	.17855	.99366	.30271	.88058	.14112	1.

TABLE 10.1 (Continued)

$R = p/p_t$	M	T/T_t	Γ	ISOTHERMAL T_t/T_t^*	RAYLEIGH T_t/T_t^*	SHOCK p_{t1}/p_{t2}
.9775	.18060	.99352	.30605	.88071	.14412	1.
.9770	.18262	.99337	.30934	.88084	.14710	1.
.9765	.18463	.99323	.31260	.88097	.15007	1.
.9760	.18661	.99308	.31582	.88109	.15304	1.
.9755	.18858	.99294	.31901	.88122	.15599	1.
.9750	.19052	.99279	.32216	.88135	.15894	1.
.9745	.19245	.99265	.32527	.88148	.16188	1.
.9740	.19436	.99250	.32836	.88161	.16480	1.
.9735	.19625	.99236	.33141	.88174	.16772	1.
.9730	.19813	.99221	.33443	.88187	.17063	1.
.9725	.19999	.99206	.33742	.88200	.17353	1.
.9720	.20183	.99192	.34038	.88213	.17643	1.
.9715	.20366	.99177	.34331	.88226	.17931	1.
.9710	.20547	.99163	.34621	.88239	.13219	1.
.9705	.20727	.99148	.34909	.88252	.18505	1.
.9700	.20905	.99134	.35193	.88265	.18791	1.
.9695	.21082	.99119	.35476	.88278	.19076	1.
.9690	.21258	.99104	.35755	.88291	.19360	1.
.9685	.21432	.99090	.36033	.88304	.19643	1.
.9680	.21605	.99075	.36307	.88317	.19925	1.
.9675	.21777	.99060	.36580	.88330	.20207	1.
.9670	.21947	.99046	.36850	.88343	.20487	1.
.9665	.22117	.99031	.37118	.88356	.20767	1.
.9660	.22285	.99017	.37383	.88369	.21046	1.
.9655	.22452	.99002	.37647	.88382	.21324	1.
.9650	.22618	.98987	.37908	.88395	.21601	1.
.9645	.22782	.98973	.38167	.88408	.21878	1.
.9640	.22946	.98958	.38424	.88421	.22153	1.
.9635	.23109	.98943	.38679	.88435	.22428	1.
.9630	.23270	.98929	.38933	.88448	.22701	1.
.9625	.23431	.98914	.39184	.88461	.22974	1.
.9620	.23591	.98899	.39433	.88474	.23247	1.
.9615	.23749	.98885	.39681	.88487	.23518	1.
.9610	.23907	.98870	.39926	.88500	.23788	1.
.9605	.24064	.98855	.40170	.88513	.24058	1.
.9600	.24220	.98840	.40412	.88527	.24327	1.
.9595	.24375	.98826	.40653	.88540	.24595	1.
.9590	.24529	.98811	.40891	.88553	.24862	1.
.9585	.24682	.98796	.41128	.88566	.25128	1.
.9580	.24834	.98782	.41364	.88579	.25394	1.
.9575	.24986	.98767	.41598	.88593	.25659	1.
.9570	.25137	.98752	.41830	.88606	.25923	1.
.9565	.25286	.98737	.42061	.88619	.26186	1.
.9560	.25436	.98723	.42290	.88632	.26448	1.
.9555	.25584	.98708	.42517	.88645	.26710	1.
.9550	.25732	.98693	.42744	.88659	.26971	1.
.9545	.25879	.98678	.42968	.88672	.27231	1.
.9540	.26025	.98664	.43192	.88685	.27490	1.
.9535	.26170	.98649	.43413	.88699	.27748	1.
.9530	.26315	.98634	.43634	.88712	.28006	1.
.9525	.26459	.98619	.43853	.88725	.28263	1.
.9520	.26602	.98604	.44071	.88738	.28519	1.
.9515	.26745	.98590	.44287	.88752	.28774	1.
.9510	.26887	.98575	.44502	.88765	.29028	1.
.9505	.27028	.98560	.44716	.88778	.29282	1.
.950	.27169	.98545	.44929	.88792	.29535	1.
.949	.27449	.98516	.45350	.88818	.30038	1.
.948	.27726	.98486	.45767	.88845	.30539	1.
.947	.28001	.98456	.46178	.88872	.31036	1.
.946	.28273	.98426	.46585	.88899	.31531	1.
.945	.28543	.98397	.46988	.88926	.32022	1.
.944	.28811	.98367	.47386	.88953	.32510	1.
.943	.29077	.98337	.47780	.88980	.32996	1.
.942	.29341	.98307	.48170	.89007	.33478	1.
.941	.29603	.98278	.48556	.89034	.33958	1.

$R = p/p_t$	M	T/T_t	Γ	ISOTHERMAL T_t/T_t^*	RAYLEIGH T_t/T_t^*	SHOCK p_{t1}/p_{t2}
.940	.29863	.98248	.48938	.89061	.34434	1.
.939	.30121	.98218	.49315	.89088	.34908	1.
.938	.30377	.98188	.49690	.89115	.35379	1.
.937	.30632	.98158	.50060	.89142	.35847	1.
.936	.30884	.98128	.50427	.89169	.36312	1.
.935	.31135	.98098	.50790	.89196	.36774	1.
.934	.31385	.98068	.51150	.89224	.37234	1.
.933	.31632	.98038	.51506	.89251	.37691	1.
.932	.31878	.98008	.51859	.89278	.38144	1.
.931	.32123	.97978	.52209	.89306	.38596	1.
.930	.32366	.97948	.52555	.89333	.39044	1.
.929	.32607	.97918	.52899	.89361	.39490	1.
.928	.32847	.97888	.53239	.89388	.39932	1.
.927	.33086	.97858	.53576	.89416	.40373	1.
.926	.33323	.97827	.53911	.89443	.40810	1.
.925	.33559	.97797	.54242	.89471	.41245	1.
.924	.33794	.97767	.54571	.89499	.41677	1.
.923	.34027	.97737	.54897	.89526	.42107	1.
.922	.34259	.97706	.55220	.89554	.42534	1.
.921	.34490	.97676	.55540	.89582	.42958	1.
.920	.34720	.97646	.55858	.89610	.43380	1.
.919	.34948	.97615	.56173	.89637	.43799	1.
.918	.35176	.97585	.56485	.89665	.44216	1.
.917	.35402	.97555	.56795	.89693	.44630	1.
.916	.35627	.97524	.57103	.89721	.45041	1.
.915	.35851	.97494	.57408	.89749	.45450	1.
.914	.36073	.97463	.57711	.89777	.45857	1.
.913	.36295	.97433	.58011	.89805	.46261	1.
.912	.36516	.97402	.58309	.89833	.46663	1.
.911	.36735	.97372	.58605	.89862	.47062	1.
.910	.36954	.97341	.58898	.89890	.47458	1.
.909	.37172	.97311	.59189	.89918	.47853	1.
.908	.37389	.97280	.59478	.89946	.48244	1.
.907	.37604	.97250	.59765	.89975	.48634	1.
.906	.37819	.97219	.60050	.90003	.49021	1.
.905	.38033	.97188	.60332	.90031	.49406	1.
.904	.38246	.97158	.60613	.90060	.49788	1.
.903	.38459	.97127	.60891	.90088	.50168	1.
.902	.38670	.97096	.61168	.90117	.50545	1.
.901	.38880	.97065	.61442	.90145	.50921	1.
.900	.39090	.97035	.61715	.90174	.51294	1.
.899	.39299	.97004	.61985	.90203	.51664	1.
.898	.39507	.96973	.62254	.90231	.52033	1.
.897	.39714	.96942	.62521	.90260	.52399	1.
.896	.39921	.96911	.62786	.90289	.52763	1.
.895	.40126	.96880	.63049	.90318	.53125	1.
.894	.40331	.96849	.63310	.90347	.53484	1.
.893	.40535	.96818	.63570	.90375	.53841	1.
.892	.40739	.96787	.63827	.90404	.54196	1.
.891	.40942	.96756	.64083	.90433	.54549	1.
.890	.41144	.96725	.64338	.90462	.54900	1.
.889	.41345	.96694	.64590	.90491	.55248	1.
.888	.41546	.96663	.64841	.90521	.55595	1.
.887	.41745	.96632	.65090	.90550	.55939	1.
.886	.41945	.96601	.65338	.90579	.56281	1.
.885	.42143	.96570	.65584	.90608	.56621	1.
.884	.42341	.96539	.65828	.90637	.56959	1.
.883	.42539	.96507	.66071	.90667	.57295	1.
.882	.42736	.96476	.66312	.90696	.57629	1.
.881	.42932	.96445	.66551	.90725	.57960	1.
.880	.43127	.96414	.66789	.90755	.58290	1.
.879	.43322	.96382	.67026	.90784	.58617	1.
.878	.43516	.96351	.67261	.90814	.58943	1.
.877	.43710	.96319	.67494	.90844	.59266	1.
.876	.43903	.96288	.67726	.90873	.59588	1.

TABLE 10.1 (Continued)

$R = p/p_t$	M	T/T_t	Γ	ISOTHERMAL T_t/T_t^*	RAYLEIGH T_t/T_t^*	SHOCK p_{t1}/p_{t2}
.875	.44096	.96257	.67957	.90903	.59907	1.
.874	.44288	.96225	.68186	.90932	.60225	1.
.873	.44479	.96194	.68414	.90962	.60540	1.
.872	.44670	.96162	.68640	.90992	.60854	1.
.871	.44861	.96131	.68865	.91022	.61166	1.
.870	.45051	.96099	.69088	.91052	.61475	1.
.869	.45240	.96068	.69310	.91082	.61783	1.
.868	.45429	.96036	.69531	.91112	.62089	1.
.867	.45617	.96004	.69751	.91142	.62393	1.
.866	.45805	.95973	.69969	.91172	.62695	1.
.865	.45993	.95941	.70185	.91202	.62995	1.
.864	.46180	.95909	.70401	.91232	.63293	1.
.863	.46366	.95878	.70615	.91262	.63590	1.
.862	.46552	.95846	.70827	.91292	.63884	1.
.861	.46737	.95814	.71039	.91323	.64177	1.
.860	.46922	.95782	.71249	.91353	.64468	1.
.859	.47107	.95750	.71458	.91383	.64757	1.
.858	.47291	.95719	.71666	.91414	.65044	1.
.857	.47475	.95687	.71872	.91444	.65329	1.
.856	.47658	.95655	.72078	.91475	.65613	1.
.855	.47841	.95623	.72282	.91505	.65895	1.
.854	.48023	.95591	.72485	.91536	.66175	1.
.853	.48205	.95559	.72686	.91567	.66453	1.
.852	.48387	.95527	.72887	.91597	.66730	1.
.851	.48568	.95495	.73086	.91628	.67004	1.
.850	.48749	.95463	.73284	.91659	.67277	1.
.849	.48929	.95431	.73481	.91690	.67549	1.
.848	.49109	.95399	.73677	.91720	.67818	1.
.847	.49289	.95366	.73872	.91751	.68086	1.
.846	.49468	.95334	.74065	.91782	.68352	1.
.845	.49647	.95302	.74258	.91813	.68617	1.
.844	.49825	.95270	.74449	.91844	.68880	1.
.843	.50003	.95237	.74639	.91876	.69141	1.
.842	.50181	.95205	.74828	.91907	.69400	1.
.841	.50359	.95173	.75016	.91938	.69658	1.
.840	.50536	.95141	.75203	.91969	.69914	1.
.839	.50712	.95108	.75389	.92001	.70169	1.
.838	.50889	.95076	.75574	.92032	.70422	1.
.837	.51065	.95043	.75758	.92063	.70673	1.
.836	.51240	.95011	.75941	.92095	.70923	1.
.835	.51416	.94978	.76122	.92126	.71171	1.
.834	.51591	.94946	.76303	.92158	.71417	1.
.833	.51765	.94913	.76483	.92189	.71662	1.
.832	.51940	.94881	.76662	.92221	.71906	1.
.831	.52114	.94848	.76839	.92253	.72148	1.
.830	.52287	.94816	.77016	.92284	.72388	1.
.829	.52461	.94783	.77191	.92316	.72627	1.
.828	.52634	.94750	.77366	.92348	.72864	1.
.827	.52807	.94717	.77540	.92380	.73099	1.
.826	.52979	.94685	.77713	.92412	.73333	1.
.825	.53152	.94652	.77884	.92444	.73566	1.
.824	.53324	.94619	.78055	.92476	.73797	1.
.823	.53495	.94586	.78225	.92508	.74027	1.
.822	.53667	.94554	.78394	.92540	.74255	1.
.821	.53838	.94521	.78562	.92572	.74481	1.
.820	.54009	.94488	.78729	.92605	.74706	1.
.819	.54179	.94455	.78895	.92637	.74930	1.
.818	.54349	.94422	.79060	.92669	.75152	1.
.817	.54519	.94389	.79224	.92702	.75373	1.
.816	.54689	.94356	.79387	.92734	.75592	1.
.815	.54859	.94323	.79550	.92767	.75810	1.
.814	.55028	.94290	.79711	.92799	.76027	1.
.813	.55197	.94257	.79872	.92832	.76242	1.
.812	.55366	.94223	.80032	.92864	.76455	1.
.811	.55534	.94190	.80190	.92897	.76668	1.

$R = p/p_t$	M	T/T_t	Γ	ISOTHERMAL T_t/T_t^*	RAYLEIGH T_t/T_t^*	SHOCK p_{t1}/p_{t2}
.810	.55703	.94157	.80348	.92930	.76878	1.
.809	.55871	.94124	.80505	.92963	.77088	1.
.808	.56038	.94091	.80662	.92996	.77296	1.
.807	.56206	.94057	.80817	.93028	.77503	1.
.806	.56373	.94024	.80971	.93061	.77708	1.
.805	.56540	.93991	.81125	.93094	.77912	1.
.804	.56707	.93957	.81278	.93127	.78114	1.
.803	.56874	.93924	.81430	.93161	.78316	1.
.802	.57040	.93890	.81581	.93194	.78516	1.
.801	.57206	.93857	.81731	.93227	.78714	1.
.800	.57372	.93823	.81880	.93260	.78911	1.
.799	.57538	.93790	.82029	.93294	.79107	1.
.798	.57704	.93756	.82177	.93327	.79302	1.
.797	.57869	.93723	.82324	.93360	.79495	1.
.796	.58034	.93689	.82470	.93394	.79687	1.
.795	.58199	.93656	.82615	.93427	.79878	1.
.794	.58364	.93622	.82760	.93461	.80068	1.
.793	.58528	.93588	.82903	.93495	.80256	1.
.792	.58693	.93554	.83046	.93528	.80443	1.
.791	.58857	.93521	.83188	.93562	.80628	1.
.790	.59021	.93487	.83330	.93596	.80813	1.
.789	.59185	.93453	.83470	.93630	.80996	1.
.788	.59348	.93419	.83610	.93664	.81178	1.
.787	.59512	.93385	.83749	.93698	.81358	1.
.786	.59675	.93351	.83887	.93732	.81538	1.
.785	.59838	.93317	.84025	.93766	.81716	1.
.784	.60001	.93283	.84161	.93800	.81893	1.
.783	.60163	.93249	.84297	.93834	.82069	1.
.782	.60326	.93215	.84433	.93869	.82243	1.
.781	.60488	.93181	.84567	.93903	.82417	1.
.780	.60650	.93147	.84701	.93937	.82589	1.
.779	.60812	.93113	.84834	.93972	.82760	1.
.778	.60974	.93079	.84966	.94006	.82930	1.
.777	.61136	.93045	.85097	.94041	.83098	1.
.776	.61297	.93010	.85228	.94075	.83266	1.
.775	.61459	.92976	.85358	.94110	.83432	1.
.774	.61620	.92942	.85487	.94145	.83597	1.
.773	.61781	.92908	.85616	.94180	.83761	1.
.772	.61942	.92873	.85743	.94214	.83924	1.
.771	.62103	.92839	.85871	.94249	.84086	1.
.770	.62263	.92804	.85997	.94284	.84246	1.
.769	.62424	.92770	.86123	.94319	.84406	1.
.768	.62584	.92736	.86247	.94354	.84564	1.
.767	.62744	.92701	.86372	.94389	.84721	1.
.766	.62904	.92666	.86495	.94425	.84878	1.
.765	.63064	.92632	.86618	.94460	.85033	1.
.764	.63224	.92597	.86740	.94495	.85186	1.
.763	.63384	.92563	.86862	.94531	.85339	1.
.762	.63543	.92528	.86982	.94566	.85491	1.
.761	.63703	.92493	.87102	.94602	.85642	1.
.760	.63862	.92458	.87222	.94637	.85791	1.
.759	.64021	.92424	.87340	.94673	.85940	1.
.758	.64180	.92389	.87459	.94708	.86087	1.
.757	.64339	.92354	.87576	.94744	.86234	1.
.756	.64497	.92319	.87692	.94780	.86379	1.
.755	.64656	.92284	.87808	.94816	.86523	1.
.754	.64815	.92249	.87924	.94852	.86667	1.
.753	.64973	.92214	.88038	.94888	.86809	1.
.752	.65131	.92179	.88152	.94924	.86950	1.
.751	.65289	.92144	.88266	.94960	.87090	1.
.750	.65447	.92109	.88378	.94996	.87229	1.
.749	.65605	.92074	.88490	.95032	.87367	1.
.748	.65763	.92039	.88602	.95068	.87504	1.
.747	.65921	.92004	.88712	.95105	.87641	1.
.746	.66079	.91969	.88823	.95141	.87776	1.

TABLE 10.1 (Continued)

$R = p/p_t$	M	T/T_t	Γ	ISOTHERMAL T_t/T_t^*	RAYLEIGH T_t/T_t^*	SHOCK p_{t1}/p_{t2}
.745	.66236	.91933	.88932	.95178	.87910	1.
.744	.66393	.91898	.89041	.95214	.88043	1.
.743	.66551	.91863	.89149	.95251	.88175	1.
.742	.66708	.91827	.89256	.95287	.88306	1.
.741	.66865	.91792	.89363	.95324	.88436	1.
.740	.67022	.91757	.89469	.95361	.88565	1.
.739	.67179	.91721	.89575	.95398	.88694	1.
.738	.67336	.91686	.89680	.95435	.88821	1.
.737	.67493	.91650	.89784	.95472	.88947	1.
.736	.67649	.91615	.89888	.95509	.89073	1.
.735	.67806	.91579	.89991	.95546	.89197	1.
.734	.67962	.91543	.90093	.95583	.89320	1.
.733	.68119	.91508	.90195	.95620	.89443	1.
.732	.68275	.91472	.90296	.95658	.89565	1.
.731	.68431	.91436	.90397	.95695	.89685	1.
.730	.68587	.91401	.90497	.95732	.89805	1.
.729	.68743	.91365	.90596	.95770	.89924	1.
.728	.68899	.91329	.90695	.95807	.90042	1.
.727	.69055	.91293	.90793	.95845	.90159	1.
.726	.69211	.91257	.90891	.95883	.90275	1.
.725	.69367	.91221	.90988	.95921	.90390	1.
.724	.69522	.91185	.91084	.95958	.90504	1.
.723	.69678	.91149	.91180	.95996	.90618	1.
.722	.69833	.91113	.91275	.96034	.90730	1.
.721	.69989	.91077	.91370	.96072	.90842	1.
.720	.70144	.91041	.91464	.96110	.90953	1.
.719	.70300	.91005	.91557	.96149	.91063	1.
.718	.70455	.90969	.91650	.96187	.91172	1.
.717	.70610	.90933	.91742	.96225	.91280	1.
.716	.70765	.90896	.91834	.96263	.91387	1.
.715	.70920	.90860	.91925	.96302	.91493	1.
.714	.71075	.90824	.92015	.96340	.91599	1.
.713	.71230	.90787	.92105	.96379	.91704	1.
.712	.71385	.90751	.92194	.96418	.91808	1.
.711	.71540	.90715	.92283	.96456	.91911	1.
.710	.71695	.90678	.92371	.96495	.92013	1.
.709	.71849	.90642	.92459	.96534	.92114	1.
.708	.72004	.90605	.92546	.96573	.92215	1.
.707	.72159	.90568	.92632	.96612	.92315	1.
.706	.72313	.90532	.92718	.96651	.92413	1.
.705	.72468	.90495	.92803	.96690	.92512	1.
.704	.72622	.90458	.92888	.96729	.92609	1.
.703	.72777	.90422	.92972	.96769	.92705	1.
.702	.72931	.90385	.93056	.96808	.92801	1.
.701	.73085	.90348	.93139	.96848	.92896	1.
.700	.73240	.90311	.93222	.96887	.92990	1.
.699	.73394	.90274	.93303	.96927	.93083	1.
.698	.73548	.90238	.93385	.96966	.93176	1.
.697	.73702	.90201	.93466	.97006	.93267	1.
.696	.73856	.90164	.93546	.97046	.93358	1.
.695	.74010	.90127	.93626	.97086	.93448	1.
.694	.74164	.90089	.93705	.97126	.93538	1.
.693	.74318	.90052	.93783	.97166	.93626	1.
.692	.74472	.90052	.93862	.97206	.93714	1.
.691	.74626	.89978	.93939	.97246	.93801	1.
.690	.74780	.89941	.94016	.97286	.93888	1.
.689	.74934	.89904	.94093	.97327	.93973	1.
.688	.75088	.89866	.94168	.97367	.94058	1.
.687	.75242	.89829	.94244	.97407	.94142	1.
.686	.75396	.89792	.94319	.97448	.94225	1.
.685	.75550	.89754	.94393	.97489	.94308	1.
.684	.75703	.89717	.94467	.97529	.94390	1.
.683	.75857	.89679	.94540	.97570	.94471	1.
.682	.76011	.89642	.94613	.97611	.94551	1.
.681	.76165	.89604	.94685	.97652	.94631	1.

$R = p/p_t$	M	T/T_t	Γ	ISOTHERMAL T_t/T_t^*	RAYLEIGH T_t/T_t^*	SHOCK p_{t1}/p_{t2}
.680	.76318	.89566	.94756	.97693	.94710	1.
.679	.76472	.89529	.94827	.97734	.94788	1.
.678	.76626	.89491	.94898	.97775	.94866	1.
.677	.76779	.89453	.94968	.97816	.94942	1.
.676	.76933	.89416	.95038	.97858	.95018	1.
.675	.77086	.89378	.95106	.97899	.95094	1.
.674	.77240	.89340	.95175	.97941	.95168	1.
.673	.77394	.89302	.95243	.97982	.95242	1.
.672	.77547	.89264	.95310	.98024	.95316	1.
.671	.77701	.89226	.95377	.98065	.95388	1.
.670	.77854	.89188	.95444	.98107	.95460	1.
.669	.78008	.89150	.95509	.98149	.95531	1.
.668	.78161	.89112	.95575	.98191	.95602	1.
.667	.78315	.89074	.95640	.98233	.95672	1.
.666	.78468	.89036	.95704	.98275	.95741	1.
.665	.78622	.88997	.95768	.98317	.95809	1.
.664	.78775	.88959	.95831	.98360	.95877	1.
.663	.78929	.88921	.95894	.98402	.95944	1.
.662	.79082	.88883	.95956	.98445	.96011	1.
.661	.79236	.88844	.96018	.98487	.96077	1.
.660	.79389	.88806	.96079	.98530	.96142	1.
.659	.79543	.88767	.96140	.98572	.96206	1.
.658	.79696	.88729	.96200	.98615	.96270	1.
.657	.79850	.88690	.96260	.98658	.96334	1.
.656	.80003	.88652	.96319	.98701	.96396	1.
.655	.80157	.88613	.96378	.98744	.96458	1.
.654	.80310	.88574	.96436	.98787	.96519	1.
.653	.80464	.88536	.96494	.98830	.96580	1.
.652	.80617	.88497	.96551	.98874	.96640	1.
.651	.80771	.88458	.96608	.98917	.96700	1.
.650	.80925	.88419	.96664	.98960	.96758	1.
.649	.81078	.88380	.96720	.99004	.96816	1.
.648	.81232	.88341	.96775	.99048	.96874	1.
.647	.81385	.88302	.96830	.99091	.96931	1.
.646	.81539	.88263	.96884	.99135	.96987	1.
.645	.81693	.88224	.96938	.99179	.97043	1.
.644	.81846	.88185	.96991	.99223	.97098	1.
.643	.82000	.88146	.97044	.99267	.97152	1.
.642	.82154	.88107	.97096	.99311	.97206	1.
.641	.82307	.88068	.97148	.99355	.97260	1.
.640	.82461	.88028	.97199	.99400	.97312	1.
.639	.82615	.87989	.97250	.99444	.97364	1.
.638	.82769	.87950	.97300	.99489	.97416	1.
.637	.82923	.87910	.97350	.99533	.97467	1.
.636	.83076	.87871	.97399	.99578	.97517	1.
.635	.83230	.87831	.97448	.99623	.97567	1.
.634	.83384	.87792	.97497	.99668	.97616	1.
.633	.83538	.87752	.97544	.99713	.97664	1.
.632	.83692	.87713	.97592	.99758	.97712	1.
.631	.83846	.87673	.97639	.99803	.97760	1.
.630	.84000	.87633	.97685	.99848	.97807	1.
.629	.84154	.87593	.97731	.99893	.97853	1.
.628	.84308	.87554	.97777	.99939	.97899	1.
.627	.84462	.87514	.97822	.99984	.97944	1.
.626	.84616	.87474	.97866	1.00030	.97988	1.
.625	.84771	.87434	.97910	1.00076	.98032	1.
.624	.84925	.87394	.97954	1.00121	.98076	1.
.623	.85079	.87354	.97997	1.00167	.98119	1.
.622	.85233	.87314	.98040	1.00213	.98161	1.
.621	.85388	.87274	.98082	1.00259	.98203	1.
.620	.85542	.87234	.98123	1.00305	.98244	1.
.619	.85696	.87193	.98165	1.00352	.98285	1.
.618	.85851	.87153	.98205	1.00398	.98325	1.
.617	.86005	.87113	.98246	1.00445	.78365	1.
.616	.85160	.87072	.98285	1.00491	.98404	1.

TABLE 10.1 (Continued)

$R = p/p_t$	M	T/T_t	Γ	ISOTHERMAL T_t/T_t^*	RAYLEIGH T_t/T_t^*	SHOCK p_{t1}/p_{t2}
.615	.86314	.87032	.98325	1.00538	.98442	1.
.614	.86469	.86991	.98364	1.00585	.98480	1.
.613	.86624	.86951	.98402	1.00631	.98518	1.
.612	.86778	.86910	.98440	1.00678	.98555	1.
.611	.86933	.86870	.98477	1.00725	.98591	1.
.610	.87088	.86829	.98514	1.00773	.98627	1.
.609	.87243	.86788	.98551	1.00820	.98663	1.
.608	.87398	.86748	.98587	1.00867	.98698	1.
.607	.87553	.86707	.98622	1.00915	.98732	1.
.606	.87708	.86666	.98658	1.00962	.98766	1.
.605	.87863	.86625	.98692	1.01010	.98799	1.
.604	.88018	.86584	.98726	1.01058	.98832	1.
.603	.88173	.86543	.98760	1.01105	.98864	1.
.602	.88329	.86502	.98793	1.01153	.98896	1.
.601	.88484	.86461	.98826	1.01201	.98928	1.
.600	.88639	.86420	.98858	1.01250	.98959	1.
.599	.88795	.86379	.98890	1.01298	.98989	1.
.598	.88950	.86338	.98922	1.01346	.99019	1.
.597	.89106	.86296	.98953	1.01395	.99048	1.
.596	.89261	.86255	.98983	1.01443	.99077	1.
.595	.89417	.86214	.99013	1.01492	.99105	1.
.594	.89573	.86172	.99043	1.01541	.99133	1.
.593	.89729	.86131	.99072	1.01590	.99161	1.
.592	.89885	.86089	.99101	1.01639	.99188	1.
.591	.90041	.86048	.99129	1.01688	.99214	1.
.590	.90197	.86006	.99157	1.01737	.99240	1.
.589	.90353	.85964	.99184	1.01786	.99266	1.
.588	.93509	.85923	.99211	1.01836	.99291	1.
.587	.90665	.85881	.99237	1.01885	.99315	1.
.586	.90821	.85839	.99263	1.01935	.99339	1.
.585	.90978	.85797	.99288	1.01985	.99363	1.
.584	.91134	.85755	.99313	1.02035	.99386	1.
.583	.91291	.85713	.99938	1.02085	.99409	1.
.582	.91447	.85671	.99362	1.02135	.99431	1.
.581	.91604	.85629	.99386	1.02185	.99453	1.
.580	.91761	.85587	.99409	1.02235	.99474	1.
.579	.91918	.85545	.99432	1.02286	.99495	1.
.578	.92075	.85503	.99454	1.02336	.99515	1.
.577	.92232	.85460	.99476	1.02387	.99535	1.
.576	.92389	.85418	.99497	1.02437	.99555	1.
.575	.92546	.85376	.99518	1.02488	.99574	1.
.574	.92703	.85333	.99539	1.02539	.99593	1.
.573	.92861	.85291	.99559	1.02590	.99611	1.
.572	.93018	.85248	.99578	1.02642	.99629	1.
.571	.93176	.85205	.99597	1.02693	.99646	1.
.570	.93333	.85163	.99616	1.02744	.99663	1.
.569	.93491	.85120	.99634	1.02796	.99679	1.
.568	.93649	.85077	.99652	1.02848	.99695	1.
.567	.93807	.85034	.99669	1.02899	.99711	1.
.566	.93965	.84992	.99686	1.02951	.99726	1.
.565	.94123	.84949	.99703	1.03003	.99741	1.
.564	.94281	.84906	.99719	1.03055	.99755	1.
.563	.94439	.84863	.99734	1.03108	.99769	1.
.562	.94597	.84820	.99750	1.03160	.99782	1.
.561	.94756	.84776	.99764	1.03213	.99795	1.
.560	.94914	.84733	.99778	1.03265	.99808	1.
.559	.95073	.84690	.99792	1.03318	.99820	1.
.558	.95232	.84647	.99806	1.03371	.99832	1.
.557	.95391	.84603	.99818	1.03424	.99843	1.
.556	.95550	.84560	.99831	1.03477	.99854	1.
.555	.95709	.84516	.99843	1.03530	.99865	1.
.554	.95868	.84473	.99854	1.03584	.99875	1.
.553	.96027	.84429	.99866	1.03637	.99884	1.
.552	.96186	.84386	.99876	1.03691	.99894	1.
.551	.96346	.84342	.99886	1.03744	.99903	1.

$R = p/p_t$	M	T/T_t	Γ	ISOTHERMAL T_t/T_t^*	RAYLEIGH T_t/T_t^*	SHOCK p_{t1}/p_{t2}
.550	.96505	.84298	.99896	1.03798	.99911	1.
.549	.96665	.84254	.99906	1.03852	.99919	1.
.548	.96825	.84210	.99915	1.03906	.99927	1.
.547	.96985	.84166	.99923	1.03961	.99934	1.
.546	.97145	.84122	.99931	1.04015	.99941	1.
.545	.97305	.84078	.99939	1.04069	.99948	1.
.544	.97465	.84034	.99946	1.04124	.99954	1.
.543	.97626	.83990	.99952	1.04179	.99960	1.
.542	.97786	.83946	.99959	1.04234	.99965	1.
.541	.97947	.83902	.99964	1.04289	.99970	1.
.540	.98107	.83857	.99970	1.04344	.99974	1.
.539	.98268	.83813	.99975	1.04399	.99979	1.
.538	.98429	.83768	.99979	1.04455	.99983	1.
.537	.98590	.83724	.99983	1.04510	.99986	1.
.536	.98752	.83679	.99987	1.04566	.99989	1.
.535	.98913	.83635	.99990	1.04622	.99992	1.
.534	.99074	.83590	.99993	1.04678	.99994	1.
.533	.99236	.83545	.99995	1.04734	.99996	1.
.532	.99398	.83500	.99997	1.04790	.99997	1.
.531	.99559	.83456	.99998	1.04846	.99999	1.
.530	.99721	.83411	.99999	1.04903	.99999	1.
.529	.99884	.83366	1.00000	1.04959	1.00000	1.
.528	1.00046	.83321	1.00000	1.05016	1.00000	1.00000
.527	1.00208	.83276	1.00000	1.05073	1.00000	1.00000
.526	1.00371	.83230	.99999	1.05130	.99999	1.00000
.525	1.00533	.83185	.99998	1.05187	.99998	1.00000
.524	1.00696	.83140	.99996	1.05244	.99997	1.00000
.523	1.00859	.83094	.99994	1.05302	.99995	1.00000
.522	1.01022	.83049	.99991	1.05359	.99993	1.00000
.521	1.01185	.83004	.99988	1.05417	.99990	1.00000
.520	1.01348	.82958	.99985	1.05475	.99988	1.00000
.519	1.01512	.82912	.99981	1.05533	.99984	1.00000
.518	1.01675	.82867	.99977	1.05591	.99981	1.00001
.517	1.01839	.82821	.99972	1.05650	.99977	1.00001
.516	1.02003	.82775	.99967	1.05708	.99973	1.00001
.515	1.02167	.82729	.99961	1.05767	.99968	1.00001
.514	1.02331	.82683	.99955	1.05825	.99963	1.00002
.513	1.02496	.82637	.99949	1.05884	.99958	1.00002
.512	1.02660	.82591	.99942	1.05943	.99953	1.00002
.511	1.02825	.82545	.99935	1.06003	.99947	1.00003
.510	1.02989	.82499	.99927	1.06062	.99940	1.00003
.509	1.03154	.82453	.99919	1.06121	.99934	1.00004
.508	1.03319	.82406	.99910	1.06181	.99927	1.00004
.507	1.03485	.82360	.99901	1.06241	.99920	1.00005
.506	1.03650	.82314	.99891	1.06301	.99912	1.00006
.505	1.03815	.82267	.99881	1.06361	.99904	1.00007
.504	1.03981	.82220	.99871	1.06421	.99896	1.00008
.503	1.04147	.82174	.99860	1.06482	.99887	1.00009
.502	1.04313	.82127	.99849	1.06542	.99878	1.00010
.501	1.04479	.82080	.99837	1.06603	.99869	1.00011
.500	1.04646	.82034	.99825	1.06664	.99859	1.00012
.499	1.04812	.81987	.99812	1.06725	.99849	1.00013
.498	1.04979	.81940	.99799	1.06786	.99839	1.00015
.497	1.05145	.81893	.99786	1.06847	.99828	1.00016
.496	1.05312	.81845	.99772	1.06909	.99817	1.00018
.495	1.05480	.81798	.99757	1.06970	.99806	1.00019
.494	1.05647	.81751	.99743	1.07032	.99795	1.00021
.493	1.05814	.81704	.99727	1.07094	.99783	1.00023
.492	1.05982	.81656	.99712	1.07156	.99771	1.00025
.491	1.06150	.81609	.99696	1.07219	.99758	1.00027
.490	1.06318	.81561	.99679	1.07281	.99745	1.00029
.489	1.06486	.81514	.99662	1.07344	.99732	1.00031
.488	1.06655	.81466	.99645	1.07407	.99719	1.00034
.487	1.06823	.81418	.99627	1.07470	.99705	1.00036
.486	1.06992	.81371	.99609	1.07533	.99691	1.00039

TABLE 10.1 (Continued)

$R = p/p_t$	M	T/T_t	Γ	ISOTHERMAL T_t/T_t^*	RAYLEIGH T_t/T_t^*	SHOCK p_{t1}/p_{t2}
.485	1.07161	.81323	.99590	1.07596	.99676	1.00041
.484	1.07330	.81275	.99571	1.07659	.99662	1.00044
.483	1.07499	.81227	.99551	1.07723	.99647	1.00047
.482	1.07669	.81179	.99531	1.07787	.99631	1.00050
.481	1.07838	.81131	.99511	1.07851	.99616	1.00054
.480	1.08008	.81082	.99490	1.07915	.99600	1.00057
.479	1.08178	.81034	.99468	1.07979	.99584	1.00061
.478	1.08348	.80986	.99447	1.08044	.99567	1.00064
.477	1.08519	.80937	.99424	1.08109	.99550	1.00068
.476	1.08689	.80889	.99402	1.08173	.99533	1.00072
.475	1.08860	.80840	.99378	1.08238	.99516	1.00076
.474	1.09031	.80791	.99355	1.08304	.99498	1.00080
.473	1.09202	.80743	.99331	1.08369	.99480	1.00085
.472	1.09374	.80694	.99307	1.08435	.99462	1.00089
.471	1.09545	.80645	.99282	1.08500	.99443	1.00094
.470	1.09717	.80596	.99256	1.08566	.99424	1.00099
.469	1.09889	.80547	.99231	1.08632	.99405	1.00104
.468	1.10061	.80498	.99204	1.08698	.99385	1.00109
.467	1.10233	.80449	.99178	1.08765	.99366	1.00115
.466	1.10406	.80399	.99151	1.08832	.99346	1.00120
.465	1.10579	.80350	.99123	1.08898	.99325	1.00126
.464	1.10752	.80301	.99095	1.08965	.99305	1.00132
.463	1.10925	.80251	.99067	1.09033	.99284	1.00138
.462	1.11098	.80202	.99038	1.09100	.99262	1.00144
.461	1.11272	.80152	.99009	1.09168	.99241	1.00150
.460	1.11446	.80102	.98979	1.09235	.99219	1.00157
.459	1.11620	.80053	.98949	1.09303	.99197	1.00164
.458	1.11794	.80003	.98918	1.09371	.99175	1.00171
.457	1.11969	.79953	.98887	1.09440	.99152	1.00178
.456	1.12143	.79903	.98856	1.09508	.99129	1.00185
.455	1.12318	.79853	.98824	1.09577	.99106	1.00193
.454	1.12493	.79802	.98791	1.09646	.99083	1.00200
.453	1.12669	.79752	.98758	1.09715	.99059	1.00208
.452	1.12844	.79702	.98725	1.09784	.99035	1.00216
.451	1.13020	.79651	.98691	1.09854	.99011	1.00225
.450	1.13196	.79601	.98657	1.09923	.98986	1.00233
.449	1.13372	.79550	.98623	1.09993	.98961	1.00242
.448	1.13549	.79500	.98588	1.10063	.98936	1.00251
.447	1.13726	.79449	.98552	1.10134	.98911	1.00260
.446	1.13903	.79398	.98516	1.10204	.98885	1.00269
.445	1.14080	.79347	.98480	1.10275	.98859	1.00279
.444	1.14257	.79296	.98443	1.10346	.98833	1.00289
.443	1.14435	.79245	.98406	1.10417	.98806	1.00299
.442	1.14613	.79194	.98368	1.10488	.98780	1.00309
.441	1.14791	.79143	.98330	1.10560	.98753	1.00320
.440	1.14970	.79091	.98291	1.10631	.98726	1.00330
.439	1.15148	.79040	.98252	1.10703	.98698	1.00341
.438	1.15327	.78989	.98213	1.10776	.98670	1.00352
.437	1.15506	.78937	.98173	1.10848	.98642	1.00364
.436	1.15686	.78885	.98132	1.10921	.98614	1.00375
.435	1.15865	.78834	.98091	1.10993	.98585	1.00387
.434	1.16045	.78782	.98050	1.11066	.98557	1.00399
.433	1.16225	.78730	.98008	1.11140	.98528	1.00412
.432	1.15406	.78678	.97966	1.11213	.98498	1.00424
.431	1.16586	.78626	.97923	1.11287	.98469	1.00437
.430	1.16767	.78574	.97880	1.11361	.98439	1.00450
.429	1.16948	.78521	.97837	1.11435	.98409	1.00464
.428	1.17130	.78469	.97793	1.11509	.98378	1.00477
.427	1.17312	.78417	.97748	1.11584	.98348	1.00491
.426	1.17494	.78364	.97703	1.11658	.98317	1.00505
.425	1.17676	.78311	.97658	1.11733	.98286	1.00520
.424	1.17858	.78259	.97612	1.11809	.98254	1.00535
.423	1.18041	.78206	.97566	1.11884	.98223	1.00549
.422	1.18224	.78153	.97519	1.11960	.98191	1.00565
.421	1.18408	.78100	.97472	1.12036	.98159	1.00580

$R = p/p_t$	M	T/T_t	Γ	ISOTHERMAL T_t/T_t^*	RAYLEIGH T_t/T_t^*	SHOCK p_{t1}/p_{t2}
.420	1.18591	.78047	.97424	1.12112	.98126	1.00596
.419	1.18775	.77994	.97376	1.12188	.98094	1.00612
.418	1.18959	.77941	.97328	1.12265	.98061	1.00628
.417	1.19144	.77887	.97278	1.12342	.98028	1.00645
.416	1.19328	.77834	.97229	1.12419	.97995	1.00662
.415	1.19513	.77781	.97179	1.12496	.97961	1.00679
.414	1.19699	.77727	.97129	1.12574	.97927	1.00696
.413	1.19884	.77673	.97078	1.12651	.97893	1.00714
.412	1.20070	.77619	.97027	1.12729	.97859	1.00732
.411	1.20256	.77566	.96975	1.12808	.97824	1.00751
.410	1.20443	.77512	.96923	1.12886	.97789	1.00769
.409	1.20630	.77458	.96870	1.12965	.97754	1.00788
.408	1.20817	.77403	.96817	1.13044	.97719	1.00807
.407	1.21004	.77349	.96763	1.13123	.97683	1.00827
.406	1.21192	.77295	.96709	1.13203	.97648	1.00847
.405	1.21380	.77240	.96655	1.13283	.97612	1.00867
.404	1.21568	.77186	.96600	1.13363	.97575	1.00887
.403	1.21756	.77131	.96544	1.13443	.97539	1.00908
.402	1.21945	.77076	.96488	1.13524	.97502	1.00929
.401	1.22135	.77022	.96432	1.13604	.97465	1.00951
.400	1.22324	.76967	.96375	1.13686	.97428	1.00973
.399	1.22514	.76912	.96318	1.13767	.97391	1.00995
.398	1.22704	.76857	.96260	1.13848	.97353	1.01017
.397	1.22894	.76801	.96202	1.13930	.97315	1.01040
.396	1.23085	.76746	.96143	1.14012	.97277	1.01063
.395	1.23276	.76691	.96084	1.14095	.97239	1.01086
.394	1.23468	.76635	.96024	1.14178	.97200	1.01110
.393	1.23660	.76579	.95964	1.14260	.97161	1.01134
.392	1.23852	.76524	.95903	1.14344	.97122	1.01159
.391	1.24044	.76468	.95842	1.14427	.97083	1.01184
.390	1.24237	.76412	.95781	1.14511	.97044	1.01209
.389	1.24430	.76356	.95719	1.14595	.97004	1.01234
.388	1.24623	.76300	.95656	1.14679	.96964	1.01260
.387	1.24817	.76244	.95593	1.14764	.96924	1.01286
.386	1.25011	.76187	.95530	1.14849	.96883	1.01313
.385	1.25206	.76131	.95466	1.14934	.96843	1.01340
.384	1.25401	.76074	.95402	1.15019	.96802	1.01367
.383	1.25596	.76018	.95337	1.15105	.96761	1.01395
.382	1.25791	.75961	.95271	1.15191	.96720	1.01423
.381	1.25987	.75904	.95206	1.15277	.96678	1.01451
.380	1.26183	.75847	.95139	1.15364	.96636	1.01480
.379	1.26380	.75790	.95073	1.15451	.96594	1.01509
.378	1.26577	.75733	.95005	1.15538	.96552	1.01539
.377	1.26774	.75675	.94938	1.15625	.96510	1.01569
.376	1.26972	.75618	.94869	1.15713	.96467	1.01599
.375	1.27170	.75560	.94801	1.15801	.96424	1.01630
.374	1.27368	.75503	.94732	1.15890	.96381	1.01661
.373	1.27567	.75445	.94662	1.15978	.96338	1.01692
.372	1.27766	.75387	.94592	1.16067	.96295	1.01724
.371	1.27966	.75329	.94521	1.16157	.96251	1.01757
.370	1.28166	.75271	.94450	1.16246	.96207	1.01789
.369	1.28366	.75213	.94379	1.16336	.96163	1.01823
.368	1.28567	.75155	.94306	1.16426	.96118	1.01856
.367	1.28768	.75096	.94234	1.16517	.96074	1.01890
.366	1.28969	.75038	.94161	1.16608	.96029	1.01925
.365	1.29171	.74979	.94087	1.16699	.95984	1.01959
.364	1.29373	.74920	.94013	1.16791	.95939	1.01995
.363	1.29576	.74862	.93939	1.16882	.95893	1.02030
.362	1.29779	.74803	.93864	1.16975	.95848	1.02066
.361	1.29982	.74744	.93788	1.17067	.95802	1.02103
.360	1.30186	.74684	.93712	1.17160	.95756	1.02140
.359	1.30391	.74625	.93636	1.17253	.95709	1.02177
.358	1.30595	.74566	.93559	1.17346	.95663	1.02215
.357	1.30800	.74506	.93481	1.17440	.95616	1.02253
.356	1.31006	.74446	.93403	1.17534	.95569	1.02292

TABLE 10.1 (Continued)

R = p/p_t	M	T/T_t	Γ	ISOTHERMAL T_t/T_t^*	RAYLEIGH T_t/T_t^*	SHOCK p_{t1}/p_{t2}
.355	1.31212	.74386	.93325	1.17629	.95522	1.02331
.354	1.31418	.74327	.93246	1.17724	.95475	1.02371
.353	1.31625	.74266	.93167	1.17819	.95427	1.02411
.352	1.31832	.74206	.93087	1.17915	.95379	1.02452
.351	1.32040	.74146	.93006	1.18010	.95331	1.02493
.350	1.32248	.74086	.92925	1.18107	.95283	1.02535
.349	1.32456	.74025	.92844	1.18203	.95235	1.02577
.348	1.32665	.73964	.92762	1.18300	.95186	1.02619
.347	1.32875	.73904	.92679	1.18397	.95137	1.02662
.346	1.33085	.73843	.92596	1.18495	.95088	1.02706
.345	1.33295	.73782	.92513	1.18593	.95039	1.02749
.344	1.33506	.73720	.92429	1.18692	.94990	1.02794
.343	1.33717	.73659	.92344	1.18790	.94940	1.02839
.342	1.33929	.73598	.92259	1.18889	.94890	1.02884
.341	1.34141	.73536	.92174	1.18989	.94840	1.02930
.340	1.34353	.73475	.92088	1.19089	.94790	1.02977
.339	1.34566	.73413	.92001	1.19189	.94740	1.03024
.338	1.34780	.73351	.91914	1.19290	.94689	1.03071
.337	1.34994	.73289	.91827	1.19391	.94638	1.03119
.336	1.35208	.73227	.91739	1.19492	.94587	1.03168
.335	1.35423	.73164	.91650	1.19594	.94536	1.03217
.334	1.35639	.73102	.91561	1.19696	.94484	1.03267
.333	1.35855	.73039	.91471	1.19799	.94432	1.03317
.332	1.36071	.72976	.91381	1.19902	.94381	1.03367
.331	1.36288	.72914	.91290	1.20005	.94328	1.03419
.330	1.36505	.72850	.91199	1.20109	.94276	1.03470
.329	1.36723	.72787	.91107	1.20213	.94224	1.03523
.328	1.36942	.72724	.91015	1.20318	.94171	1.03576
.327	1.37161	.72661	.90922	1.20423	.94118	1.03629
.326	1.37380	.72597	.90829	1.20528	.94065	1.03683
.325	1.37600	.72533	.90735	1.20634	.94012	1.03738
.324	1.37820	.72470	.90641	1.20740	.93958	1.03793
.323	1.38041	.72406	.90546	1.20847	.93904	1.03849
.322	1.38263	.72341	.90451	1.20954	.93850	1.03905
.321	1.38485	.72277	.90355	1.21062	.93796	1.03962
.320	1.38708	.72213	.90258	1.21170	.93742	1.04020
.319	1.38931	.72148	.90161	1.21278	.93688	1.04078
.318	1.39154	.72084	.90064	1.21387	.93633	1.04137
.317	1.39379	.72019	.89966	1.21496	.93578	1.04196
.316	1.39603	.71954	.89867	1.21606	.93523	1.04256
.315	1.39829	.71889	.89768	1.21716	.93467	1.04317
.314	1.40054	.71823	.89668	1.21827	.93412	1.04378
.313	1.40281	.71758	.89568	1.21938	.93356	1.04440
.312	1.40508	.71692	.89467	1.22049	.93300	1.04502
.311	1.40735	.71627	.89366	1.22161	.93244	1.04565
.310	1.40964	.71561	.89264	1.22274	.93188	1.04629
.309	1.41192	.71495	.89161	1.22387	.93131	1.04693
.308	1.41422	.71429	.89058	1.22500	.93075	1.04758
.307	1.41651	.71362	.88955	1.22614	.93018	1.04824
.306	1.41882	.71296	.88851	1.22728	.92961	1.04891
.305	1.42113	.71229	.88746	1.22843	.92903	1.04958
.304	1.42345	.71162	.88641	1.22958	.92846	1.05025
.303	1.42577	.71095	.88535	1.23074	.92788	1.05094
.302	1.42810	.71028	.88429	1.23191	.92730	1.05163
.301	1.43043	.70961	.88322	1.23307	.92672	1.05233
.300	1.43277	.70893	.88214	1.23425	.92614	1.05303
.299	1.43512	.70826	.88106	1.23542	.92556	1.05375
.298	1.43747	.70758	.87998	1.23661	.92497	1.05447
.297	1.43983	.70690	.87889	1.23780	.92438	1.05519
.296	1.44220	.70622	.87779	1.23899	.92379	1.05593
.295	1.44457	.70554	.87669	1.24019	.92320	1.05667
.294	1.44695	.70485	.87558	1.24139	.92260	1.05742
.293	1.44934	.70417	.87446	1.24260	.92200	1.05817
.292	1.45173	.70348	.87334	1.24382	.92141	1.05894
.291	1.45413	.70279	.87222	1.24503	.92081	1.05971

R = p/p_t	M	T/T_t	Γ	ISOTHERMAL T_t/T_t*	RAYLEIGH T_t/T_t*	SHOCK p_{t1}/p_{t2}
.290	1.45653	.70210	.87109	1.24626	.92020	1.06049
.289	1.45894	.70141	.86995	1.24749	.91960	1.06127
.288	1.46136	.70071	.86881	1.24873	.91899	1.06207
.287	1.46379	.70002	.86766	1.24997	.91838	1.06287
.286	1.46622	.69932	.86650	1.25122	.91777	1.06368
.285	1.46866	.69862	.86534	1.25247	.91716	1.06450
.284	1.47111	.69792	.86418	1.25373	.91655	1.06532
.283	1.47356	.69722	.86301	1.25499	.91593	1.06616
.282	1.47602	.69651	.86183	1.25626	.91531	1.06700
.281	1.47849	.69580	.86064	1.25754	.91469	1.06785
.280	1.48096	.69510	.85945	1.25882	.91407	1.06871
.279	1.48344	.69439	.85826	1.26011	.91344	1.06958
.278	1.48593	.69367	.85706	1.26140	.91282	1.07045
.277	1.48843	.69296	.85585	1.26270	.91219	1.07134
.276	1.49093	.69224	.85464	1.26400	.91156	1.07223
.275	1.49344	.69153	.85342	1.26532	.91093	1.07313
.274	1.49596	.69081	.85219	1.26663	.91029	1.07404
.273	1.49849	.69009	.85096	1.26796	.90966	1.07496
.272	1.50102	.68936	.84972	1.26929	.90902	1.07589
.271	1.50356	.68864	.84848	1.27062	.90838	1.07683
.270	1.50611	.68791	.84723	1.27197	.90774	1.07778
.269	1.50867	.68718	.84597	1.27332	.90709	1.07873
.268	1.51124	.68645	.84471	1.27467	.90645	1.07970
.267	1.51381	.68572	.84344	1.27603	.90580	1.08067
.266	1.51639	.68498	.84216	1.27740	.90515	1.08166
.265	1.51898	.68425	.84088	1.27878	.90450	1.08265
.264	1.52158	.68351	.83959	1.28016	.90384	1.08365
.263	1.52418	.68277	.83830	1.28155	.90319	1.08467
.262	1.52680	.68203	.83700	1.28294	.90253	1.08569
.261	1.52942	.68128	.83569	1.28435	.90187	1.08672
.260	1.53205	.68053	.83438	1.28576	.90120	1.08777
.259	1.53469	.67978	.83306	1.28717	.90054	1.08882
.258	1.53734	.67903	.83174	1.28860	.89987	1.08988
.257	1.53999	.67828	.83041	1.29003	.89921	1.09096
.256	1.54266	.67753	.82907	1.29146	.89854	1.09204
.255	1.54533	.67677	.82772	1.29291	.89786	1.09314
.254	1.54802	.67601	.82637	1.29436	.89719	1.09424
.253	1.55071	.67525	.82502	1.29582	.89651	1.09536
.252	1.55341	.67448	.82365	1.29729	.89584	1.09649
.251	1.55612	.67372	.82228	1.29876	.89516	1.09762
.250	1.55884	.67295	.82090	1.30025	.89447	1.09877
.249	1.56157	.67218	.81952	1.30173	.89379	1.09993
.248	1.55430	.67141	.81813	1.30323	.89310	1.10111
.247	1.56705	.67063	.81673	1.30474	.89241	1.10229
.246	1.56981	.66986	.81533	1.30625	.89172	1.10348
.245	1.57257	.66908	.81392	1.30777	.89103	1.10469
.244	1.57535	.66830	.81250	1.30930	.89034	1.10591
.243	1.57813	.66751	.81108	1.31084	.88964	1.10714
.242	1.58093	.66673	.80965	1.31238	.88894	1.10838
.241	1.58373	.66594	.80821	1.31394	.88824	1.10964
.240	1.58655	.66515	.80677	1.31550	.88754	1.11091
.239	1.58937	.66435	.80532	1.31707	.88683	1.11218
.238	1.59221	.66356	.80386	1.31865	.88613	1.11348
.237	1.59506	.66276	.80240	1.32024	.88542	1.11478
.236	1.59791	.66196	.80093	1.32183	.88471	1.11610
.235	1.60078	.66116	.79945	1.32344	.88399	1.11743
.234	1.60366	.66035	.79796	1.32505	.88328	1.11877
.233	1.60654	.65955	.79647	1.32667	.88256	1.12013
.232	1.60944	.65874	.79497	1.32830	.88184	1.12150
.231	1.61235	.65792	.79347	1.32994	.88112	1.12289
.230	1.61527	.65711	.79195	1.33159	.88039	1.12428
.229	1.61820	.65629	.79043	1.33325	.87967	1.12570
.228	1.62115	.65547	.78890	1.33492	.87894	1.12712
.227	1.62410	.65465	.78737	1.33660	.87821	1.12856
.226	1.62707	.65382	.78583	1.33828	.87748	1.13002

TABLE 10.1 (Continued)

$R = p/p_t$	M	T/T_t	Γ	ISOTHERMAL T_t/T_t^*	RAYLEIGH T_t/T_t^*	SHOCK p_{t1}/p_{t2}
.225	1.63004	.65299	.78428	1.33998	.87674	1.13149
.224	1.63303	.65216	.78272	1.34169	.87601	1.13297
.223	1.63603	.65133	.78116	1.34340	.87527	1.13447
.222	1.63904	.65049	.77959	1.34513	.87453	1.13598
.221	1.64207	.64966	.77801	1.34687	.87378	1.13751
.220	1.64510	.64881	.77642	1.34861	.87304	1.13906
.219	1.64815	.64797	.77483	1.35037	.87229	1.14062
.218	1.65121	.64712	.77323	1.35214	.87154	1.14219
.217	1.65428	.64627	.77162	1.35391	.87079	1.14378
.216	1.65737	.64542	.77001	1.35570	.87004	1.14539
.215	1.66047	.64457	.76838	1.35750	.86928	1.14702
.214	1.66358	.64371	.76675	1.35931	.86852	1.14866
.213	1.66670	.64285	.76511	1.36113	.86776	1.15031
.212	1.66984	.64198	.76347	1.36296	.86700	1.15199
.211	1.67299	.64112	.76181	1.36480	.86623	1.15368
.210	1.67615	.64025	.76015	1.36666	.86546	1.15539
.209	1.67932	.63938	.75848	1.36852	.86470	1.15711
.208	1.68251	.63850	.75681	1.37040	.86392	1.15886
.207	1.68572	.63762	.75512	1.37229	.86315	1.16062
.206	1.68893	.63674	.75343	1.37419	.86237	1.16240
.205	1.69217	.63586	.75173	1.37610	.86159	1.16420
.204	1.69541	.63497	.75002	1.37802	.86081	1.16602
.203	1.69867	.63408	.74830	1.37996	.86003	1.16785
.202	1.70195	.63318	.74658	1.38191	.85924	1.16971
.201	1.70523	.63229	.74485	1.38387	.85845	1.17158
.200	1.70854	.63139	.74311	1.38584	.85766	1.17348
.199	1.71185	.63048	.74136	1.38783	.85687	1.17539
.198	1.71519	.62957	.73960	1.38983	.85608	1.17733
.197	1.71854	.62866	.73784	1.39184	.85528	1.17928
.196	1.72190	.62775	.73606	1.39386	.85448	1.18126
.195	1.72528	.62683	.73428	1.39590	.85368	1.18326
.194	1.72867	.62591	.73249	1.39796	.85287	1.18527
.193	1.73209	.62499	.73069	1.40002	.85206	1.18731
.192	1.73551	.62406	.72888	1.40210	.85125	1.18938
.191	1.73896	.62313	.72707	1.40419	.85044	1.19146
.190	1.74241	.62220	.72524	1.40630	.84963	1.19357
.189	1.74589	.62126	.72341	1.40842	.84881	1.19569
.188	1.74938	.62032	.72157	1.41056	.84799	1.19785
.187	1.75289	.61938	.71972	1.41271	.84717	1.20002
.186	1.75642	.61843	.71786	1.41488	.84634	1.20222
.185	1.75996	.61748	.71599	1.41706	.84552	1.20445
.184	1.76353	.61652	.71412	1.41925	.84469	1.20669
.183	1.76710	.61556	.71223	1.42147	.84385	1.20897
.182	1.77070	.61460	.71034	1.42369	.84302	1.21126
.181	1.77432	.61363	.70843	1.42594	.84218	1.21359
.180	1.77795	.61266	.70652	1.42819	.84134	1.21593
.179	1.78160	.61169	.70460	1.43047	.84050	1.21831
.178	1.78527	.61071	.70267	1.43276	.83965	1.22071
.177	1.78896	.60973	.70073	1.43507	.83880	1.22314
.176	1.79267	.60874	.69878	1.43739	.83795	1.22560
.175	1.79640	.60775	.69682	1.43974	.83710	1.22808
.174	1.80015	.60676	.69486	1.44210	.83624	1.23059
.173	1.80392	.60576	.69288	1.44447	.83539	1.23313
.172	1.80771	.60476	.69089	1.44687	.83452	1.23570
.171	1.81152	.60375	.68890	1.44928	.83366	1.23830
.170	1.81535	.60274	.68689	1.45171	.83279	1.24093
.169	1.81920	.60172	.68488	1.45416	.83192	1.24359
.168	1.82307	.60070	.68285	1.45663	.83105	1.24628
.167	1.82696	.59968	.68082	1.45911	.83018	1.24900
.166	1.83088	.59865	.67877	1.46162	.82930	1.25176
.165	1.83481	.59762	.67672	1.46414	.82842	1.25454
.164	1.83877	.59658	.67465	1.46669	.82753	1.25736
.163	1.84275	.59554	.67258	1.46926	.82665	1.26022
.162	1.84676	.59449	.67049	1.47184	.82576	1.26310
.161	1.85079	.59344	.66840	1.47445	.82486	1.26602

$R = p/p_t$	M	T/T_t	Γ	ISOTHERMAL T_t/T_t^*	RAYLEIGH T_t/T_t^*	SHOCK p_{t1}/p_{t2}
.160	1.85484	.59239	.66630	1.47707	.82397	1.26898
.159	1.85891	.59133	.66418	1.47972	.82307	1.27197
.158	1.86301	.59026	.66205	1.48239	.82217	1.27500
.157	1.86714	.58919	.65992	1.48508	.82126	1.27806
.156	1.87128	.58812	.65777	1.48780	.82035	1.28117
.155	1.87546	.58704	.65562	1.49053	.81944	1.28431
.154	1.87965	.58595	.65345	1.49329	.81853	1.28749
.153	1.88388	.58486	.65127	1.49607	.81761	1.29071
.152	1.88813	.58377	.64908	1.49888	.81669	1.29396
.151	1.89241	.58267	.64688	1.50171	.81577	1.29726
.150	1.89671	.58156	.64467	1.50456	.81484	1.30061
.149	1.90104	.58045	.64245	1.50744	.81391	1.30399
.148	1.90540	.57934	.64021	1.51034	.81298	1.30742
.147	1.90978	.57822	.63797	1.51327	.81204	1.31089
.146	1.91420	.57709	.63571	1.51623	.81110	1.31440
.145	1.91864	.57596	.63345	1.51921	.81016	1.31796
.144	1.92311	.57482	.63117	1.52221	.80921	1.32157
.143	1.92762	.57368	.62888	1.52525	.80826	1.32522
.142	1.93215	.57253	.62658	1.52831	.80731	1.32892
.141	1.93671	.57137	.62426	1.53140	.80635	1.33267
.140	1.94130	.57021	.62194	1.53452	.80539	1.33647
.139	1.94593	.56905	.61960	1.53766	.80443	1.34032
.138	1.95059	.56787	.61725	1.54084	.80346	1.34423
.137	1.95528	.56669	.61489	1.54404	.80249	1.34818
.136	1.96000	.56551	.61252	1.54728	.80152	1.35219
.135	1.96475	.56432	.61013	1.55054	.80054	1.35625
.134	1.96954	.56312	.60773	1.55384	.79956	1.36037
.133	1.97436	.56192	.60532	1.55717	.79857	1.36455
.132	1.97922	.56071	.60290	1.56053	.79758	1.36878
.131	1.98412	.55949	.60046	1.56393	.79659	1.37308
.130	1.98905	.55827	.59801	1.56735	.79559	1.37743
.129	1.99401	.55704	.59555	1.57082	.79459	1.38184
.128	1.99902	.55580	.59308	1.57431	.79359	1.38632
.127	2.00406	.55455	.59059	1.57784	.79258	1.39086
.126	2.00914	.55330	.58809	1.58141	.79156	1.39547
.125	2.01426	.55204	.58557	1.58502	.79055	1.40015
.124	2.01942	.55078	.58305	1.58866	.78953	1.40489
.123	2.02462	.54951	.58050	1.59234	.78850	1.40970
.122	2.02986	.54823	.57795	1.59606	.78747	1.41459
.121	2.03514	.54694	.57538	1.59981	.78644	1.41954
.120	2.04046	.54564	.57280	1.60361	.78540	1.42458
.119	2.04583	.54434	.57020	1.60745	.78436	1.42968
.118	2.05124	.54303	.56759	1.61133	.78331	1.43487
.117	2.05670	.54171	.56496	1.61525	.78226	1.44013
.116	2.06220	.54038	.56232	1.61922	.78120	1.44548
.115	2.06775	.53903	.55966	1.62323	.78014	1.45091
.114	2.07335	.53771	.55699	1.62729	.77908	1.45643
.113	2.07899	.53635	.55431	1.63139	.77801	1.46203
.112	2.08469	.53499	.55161	1.63554	.77693	1.46772
.111	2.09043	.53362	.54889	1.63973	.77585	1.47350
.110	2.09622	.53225	.54616	1.64398	.77477	1.47938
.109	2.10207	.53086	.54341	1.64827	.77368	1.48535
.108	2.10797	.52946	.54065	1.65262	.77258	1.49142
.107	2.11392	.52806	.53787	1.65702	.77148	1.49759
.106	2.11993	.52664	.53507	1.66147	.77038	1.50387
.105	2.12599	.52522	.53226	1.66597	.76927	1.51025
.104	2.13212	.52378	.52943	1.67054	.76816	1.51674
.103	2.13829	.52234	.52659	1.67515	.76704	1.52334
.102	2.14453	.52089	.52373	1.67983	.76591	1.53005
.101	2.15083	.51942	.52085	1.68456	.76478	1.53688

[a]These tables are excerpted from the *Handbook of Generalized Gas Dynamics*, by R. P. Benedict and W. G. Steltz, with the permission of Plenum Press [1].

Generalized Gas Dynamics Tables

TABLE 10.2
GENERALIZED COMPRESSIBLE FLOW TABLE (γ = 1.4) (in terms of the Mach Number)

M	p/p_t	T/T_t	Γ	ISOTHERMAL T_t/T_t^*	RAYLEIGH T_t/T_t^*	SHOCK p_{t1}/p_{t2}
.000	1.00000	1.00000	.00000	.87500	.00000	1.
.005	.99998	.00000	.00862	.87500	.00012	1.
.010	.99993	.99998	.01727	.87502	.00048	1.
.015	.99984	.99996	.02591	.87504	.00108	1.
.020	.99972	.99992	.03455	.87507	.00192	1.
.025	.99956	.99988	.04318	.87511	.00299	1.
.030	.99937	.99982	.05181	.87516	.00431	1.
.035	.99914	.99976	.06043	.87521	.00586	1.
.040	.99888	.99968	.06905	.87528	.00765	1.
.045	.99858	.99960	.07766	.87535	.00967	1.
.050	.99825	.99950	.08627	.87544	.01192	1.
.055	.99789	.99940	.09487	.87553	.01441	1.
.060	.99748	.99928	.10346	.87563	.01712	1.
.065	.99705	.99916	.11203	.87574	.02006	1.
.070	.99658	.99902	.12060	.87586	.02322	1.
.075	.99607	.99888	.12916	.87598	.02661	1.
.080	.99553	.99872	.13771	.87612	.03021	1.
.085	.99496	.99856	.14624	.87626	.03404	1.
.090	.99435	.99838	.15477	.87642	.03807	1.
.095	.99371	.99820	.16327	.87658	.04232	1.
.100	.99303	.99800	.17177	.87675	.04678	1.
.105	.99232	.99780	.18024	.87693	.05144	1.
.110	.99158	.99759	.18871	.87712	.05630	1.
.115	.99080	.99736	.19715	.87731	.06135	1.
.120	.98999	.99713	.20558	.87752	.06661	1.
.125	.98914	.99688	.21399	.87773	.07205	1.
.130	.98826	.99663	.22238	.87796	.07767	1.
.135	.98735	.99637	.23075	.87819	.08348	1.
.140	.98640	.99610	.23910	.87843	.08947	1.
.145	.98542	.99581	.24743	.87868	.09563	1.
.150	.98441	.99552	.25573	.87894	.10196	1.
.155	.98336	.99522	.26402	.87920	.10846	1.
.160	.98228	.99491	.27228	.87948	.11511	1.
.165	.98117	.99458	.28051	.87976	.12192	1.
.170	.98003	.99425	.28872	.88006	.12888	1.
.175	.97885	.99391	.29691	.88036	.13599	1.
.180	.97765	.99356	.30507	.88067	.14324	1.
.185	.97641	.99320	.31320	.88099	.15062	1.
.190	.97514	.99283	.32131	.88132	.15814	1.
.195	.97383	.99245	.32939	.88165	.16579	1.
.200	.97250	.99206	.33744	.88200	.17355	1.
.205	.97113	.99167	.34546	.88235	.18144	1.
.210	.96973	.99126	.35345	.88272	.18943	1.
.215	.96830	.99084	.36140	.88309	.19754	1.
.220	.96685	.99041	.36933	.88347	.20574	1.
.225	.96536	.98998	.37723	.88386	.21404	1.
.230	.96383	.98953	.38509	.88426	.22244	1.
.235	.96228	.98908	.39292	.88466	.23092	1.
.240	.96070	.98861	.40071	.88508	.23948	1.
.245	.95909	.98814	.40847	.88550	.24812	1.
.250	.95745	.98765	.41620	.88594	.25684	1.
.255	.95578	.98716	.42389	.88638	.26562	1.
.260	.95408	.98666	.43154	.88683	.27446	1.
.265	.95236	.98615	.43915	.88729	.28336	1.
.270	.95060	.98563	.44673	.88776	.29231	1.
.275	.94882	.98510	.45427	.88823	.30131	1.
.280	.94700	.98456	.46178	.88872	.31035	1.
.285	.94516	.98401	.46924	.88921	.31943	1.
.290	.94329	.98346	.47666	.88972	.32855	1.
.295	.94139	.98289	.48404	.89023	.33769	1.
.300	.93947	.98232	.49138	.89075	.34686	1.
.305	.93752	.98173	.49868	.89128	.35605	1.
.310	.93554	.98114	.50594	.89182	.36525	1.

M	p/p_t	T/T_t	Γ	ISOTHERMAL T_t/T_t^*	RAYLEIGH T_t/T_t^*	SHOCK p_{t1}/p_{t2}
.315	.93353	.98054	.51316	.89236	.37447	1.
.320	.93150	.97993	.52033	.89292	.38369	1.
.325	.92945	.97931	.52746	.89348	.39291	1.
.330	.92736	.97868	.53455	.89406	.40214	1.
.335	.92525	.97805	.54159	.89464	.41136	1.
.340	.92312	.97740	.54858	.89523	.42056	1.
.345	.92096	.97675	.55553	.89583	.42976	1.
.350	.91877	.97609	.56244	.89644	.43894	1.
.355	.91656	.97541	.56930	.89705	.44810	1.
.360	.91433	.97473	.57611	.89768	.45723	1.
.365	.91207	.97405	.58288	.89831	.46634	1.
.370	.90979	.97335	.58959	.89896	.47541	1.
.375	.90748	.97264	.59626	.89961	.48445	1.
.380	.90516	.97193	.60288	.90027	.49346	1.
.385	.90280	.97121	.60946	.90094	.50242	1.
.390	.90043	.97048	.61598	.90162	.51134	1.
.395	.89803	.96974	.62245	.90230	.52021	1.
.400	.89561	.96899	.62888	.90300	.52903	1.
.405	.89317	.96824	.63525	.90370	.53780	1.
.410	.89071	.96747	.64157	.90442	.54651	1.
.415	.88823	.96670	.64784	.90514	.55516	1.
.420	.88572	.96592	.65406	.90587	.56376	1.
.425	.88320	.96513	.66023	.90661	.57229	1.
.430	.88065	.96434	.66635	.90736	.58076	1.
.435	.87808	.96354	.67241	.90811	.58915	1.
.440	.87550	.96272	.67842	.90888	.59748	1.
.445	.87289	.96190	.68438	.90965	.60574	1.
.450	.87027	.96108	.69029	.91044	.61393	1.
.455	.86762	.96024	.69614	.91123	.62204	1.
.460	.86496	.95940	.70194	.91203	.63007	1.
.465	.86228	.95855	.70768	.91284	.63802	1.
.470	.85958	.95769	.71337	.91366	.64589	1.
.475	.85686	.95682	.71901	.91448	.65368	1.
.480	.85413	.95595	.72459	.91532	.66139	1.
.485	.85138	.95507	.73011	.91616	.66901	1.
.490	.84861	.95418	.73558	.91702	.67655	1.
.495	.84582	.95328	.74100	.91788	.68400	1.
.500	.84302	.95238	.74636	.91875	.69136	1.
.505	.84020	.95147	.75166	.91963	.69863	1.
.510	.83737	.95055	.75691	.92052	.70581	1.
.515	.83452	.94963	.76210	.92141	.71290	1.
.520	.83165	.94869	.76723	.92232	.71990	1.
.525	.82877	.94776	.77231	.92323	.72680	1.
.530	.82588	.94681	.77733	.92416	.73361	1.
.535	.82297	.94585	.78230	.92509	.74033	1.
.540	.82005	.94489	.78720	.92603	.74695	1.
.545	.81711	.94393	.79205	.92698	.75348	1.
.550	.81417	.94295	.79685	.92794	.75991	1.
.555	.81120	.94197	.80158	.92890	.76625	1.
.560	.80823	.94098	.80626	.92988	.77249	1.
.565	.80524	.93999	.81088	.93086	.77863	1.
.570	.80224	.93898	.81544	.93186	.78468	1.
.575	.79923	.93798	.81995	.93286	.79063	1.
.580	.79621	.93696	.82440	.93387	.79648	1.
.585	.79317	.93594	.82879	.93489	.80223	1.
.590	.79013	.93491	.83312	.93592	.80789	1.
.595	.78707	.93388	.83739	.93695	.81346	1.
.600	.78400	.93284	.84161	.93800	.81892	1.
.605	.78093	.93179	.84577	.93905	.82429	1.
.610	.77784	.93073	.84987	.94012	.82957	1.
.615	.77474	.92967	.85391	.94119	.83474	1.
.620	.77164	.92861	.85789	.94227	.83983	1.

TABLE 10.2 (Continued)

M	p/p_t	T/T_t	Γ	ISOTHERMAL T_t/T_t^*	RAYLEIGH T_t/T_t^*	SHOCK p_{t1}/p_{t2}
.625	.76853	.92754	.86182	.94336	.84481	1.
.630	.76540	.92646	.86569	.94446	.84970	1.
.635	.76227	.92537	.86950	.94556	.85450	1.
.640	.75913	.92428	.87325	.94668	.85920	1.
.645	.75598	.92319	.87694	.94780	.86381	1.
.650	.75283	.92208	.88058	.94894	.86833	1.
.655	.74967	.92098	.88416	.95008	.87275	1.
.660	.74650	.91986	.88768	.95123	.87708	1.
.665	.74332	.91874	.89114	.95239	.88132	1.
.670	.74014	.91762	.89454	.95356	.88547	1.
.675	.73695	.91649	.89789	.95473	.88953	1.
.680	.73376	.91535	.90118	.95592	.89350	1.
.685	.73056	.91421	.90441	.95711	.89738	1.
.690	.72735	.91306	.90759	.95832	.90118	1.
.695	.72414	.91191	.91071	.95953	.90488	1.
.700	.72093	.91075	.91377	.96075	.90850	1.
.705	.71771	.90958	.91677	.96198	.91203	1.
.710	.71448	.90841	.91971	.96322	.91548	1.
.715	.71126	.90724	.92260	.96446	.91884	1.
.720	.70803	.90606	.92544	.96572	.92212	1.
.725	.70479	.90488	.92821	.96698	.92532	1.
.730	.70155	.90369	.93093	.96826	.92843	1.
.735	.69831	.90249	.93360	.96954	.93147	1.
.740	.69507	.90129	.93620	.97083	.93442	1.
.745	.69182	.90009	.93875	.97213	.93730	1.
.750	.68857	.89888	.94125	.97344	.94009	1.
.755	.68532	.89766	.94369	.97475	.94281	1.
.760	.68207	.89644	.94607	.97608	.94546	1.
.765	.67882	.89522	.94840	.97741	.94802	1.
.770	.67556	.89399	.95068	.97876	.95052	1.
.775	.67231	.89276	.95290	.98011	.95293	1.
.780	.66905	.89152	.95506	.98147	.95528	1.
.785	.66579	.89028	.95717	.98284	.95755	1.
.790	.66254	.88903	.95923	.98422	.95975	1.
.795	.65928	.88778	.96123	.98560	.96189	1.
.800	.65602	.88652	.96318	.98700	.96395	1.
.805	.65277	.88527	.96507	.98840	.96594	1.
.810	.64951	.88400	.96691	.98982	.96787	1.
.815	.64625	.88273	.96870	.99124	.96973	1.
.820	.64300	.88146	.97044	.99267	.97152	1.
.825	.63975	.88018	.97212	.99411	.97325	1.
.830	.63650	.87890	.97375	.99556	.97492	1.
.835	.63325	.87762	.97533	.99701	.97652	1.
.840	.63000	.87633	.97685	.99848	.97807	1.
.845	.62675	.87504	.97833	.99995	.97955	1.
.850	.62351	.87374	.97975	1.00144	.98097	1.
.855	.62027	.87244	.98112	1.00293	.98233	1.
.860	.61703	.87114	.98244	1.00443	.98363	1.
.865	.61380	.86983	.98371	1.00594	.98488	1.
.870	.61057	.86852	.98493	1.00746	.98607	1.
.875	.60734	.86721	.98610	1.00898	.98720	1.
.880	.60412	.86589	.98722	1.01052	.98828	1.
.885	.60090	.86457	.98830	1.01206	.98931	1.
.890	.59768	.86324	.98932	1.01362	.99028	1.
.895	.59447	.86192	.99029	1.01518	.99120	1.
.900	.59126	.86059	.99121	1.01675	.99207	1.
.905	.58806	.85925	.99209	1.01833	.99289	1.
.910	.58486	.85791	.99292	1.01992	.99366	1.
.915	.58166	.85657	.99370	1.02151	.99438	1.
.920	.57848	.85523	.99443	1.02312	.99506	1.
.925	.57529	.85388	.99512	1.02473	.99568	1.
.930	.57211	.85253	.99576	1.02636	.99627	1.

M	p/p_t	T/T_t	Γ	ISOTHERMAL T_t/T_t^*	RAYLEIGH T_t/T_t^*	SHOCK p_{t1}/p_{t2}
.935	.56894	.85118	.99635	1.02799	.99680	1.
.940	.56578	.84982	.99690	1.02963	.99729	1.
.945	.56261	.84846	.99740	1.03128	.99774	1.
.950	.55946	.84710	.99786	1.03294	.99814	1.
.955	.55631	.84573	.99827	1.03460	.99851	1.
.960	.55317	.84437	.99864	1.03628	.99883	1.
.965	.55003	.84300	.99896	1.03796	.99911	1.
.970	.54691	.84162	.99924	1.03966	.99935	1.
.975	.54378	.84025	.99947	1.04136	.99955	1.
.980	.54067	.83887	.99966	1.04307	.99971	1.
.985	.53756	.83749	.99981	1.04479	.99984	1.
.990	.53446	.83611	.99992	1.04652	.99993	1.
.995	.53137	.83472	.99998	1.04825	.99998	1.
1.000	.52828	.83333	1.00000	1.05000	1.00000	1.00000
1.005	.52520	.83194	.99998	1.05175	.99998	1.00000
1.010	.52213	.83055	.99992	1.05352	.99993	1.00000
1.015	.51907	.82916	.99981	1.05529	.99985	1.00000
1.020	.51602	.82776	.99967	1.05707	.99973	1.00001
1.025	.51297	.82636	.99949	1.05886	.99958	1.00002
1.030	.50994	.82496	.99926	1.06066	.99940	1.00003
1.035	.50691	.82356	.99900	1.06246	.99919	1.00005
1.040	.50389	.82215	.99870	1.06428	.99895	1.00008
1.045	.50087	.82075	.99836	1.06610	.99868	1.00011
1.050	.49787	.81934	.99798	1.06794	.99838	1.00015
1.055	.49488	.81793	.99756	1.06978	.99805	1.00019
1.060	.49189	.81651	.99710	1.07163	.99769	1.00025
1.065	.48892	.81510	.99661	1.07349	.99731	1.00031
1.070	.48595	.81368	.99608	1.07536	.99690	1.00039
1.075	.48299	.81227	.99551	1.07723	.99647	1.00047
1.080	.48005	.81085	.99491	1.07912	.99601	1.00057
1.085	.47711	.80942	.99427	1.08101	.99552	1.00068
1.090	.47418	.80800	.99359	1.08292	.99501	1.00080
1.095	.47126	.80658	.99288	1.08483	.99448	1.00093
1.100	.46835	.80515	.99214	1.08675	.99392	1.00107
1.105	.46546	.80373	.99136	1.08868	.99335	1.00123
1.110	.46257	.80230	.99054	1.09062	.99275	1.00140
1.115	.45969	.80087	.98970	1.09256	.99212	1.00159
1.120	.45682	.79944	.98881	1.09452	.99148	1.00179
1.125	.45396	.79801	.98790	1.09648	.99082	1.00201
1.130	.45111	.79657	.98695	1.09846	.99013	1.00224
1.135	.44828	.79514	.98597	1.10044	.98943	1.00248
1.140	.44545	.79370	.98496	1.10243	.98871	1.00275
1.145	.44263	.79226	.98392	1.10443	.98797	1.00303
1.150	.43983	.79083	.98285	1.10644	.98721	1.00332
1.155	.43703	.78939	.98174	1.10845	.98643	1.00363
1.160	.43425	.78795	.98060	1.11048	.98564	1.00396
1.165	.43148	.78651	.97944	1.11251	.98483	1.00431
1.170	.42872	.78506	.97824	1.11456	.98400	1.00468
1.175	.42596	.78362	.97702	1.11661	.98316	1.00506
1.180	.42323	.78218	.97576	1.11867	.98230	1.00546
1.185	.42050	.78073	.97448	1.12074	.98143	1.00588
1.190	.41778	.77929	.97317	1.12282	.98054	1.00632
1.195	.41507	.77784	.97183	1.12490	.97963	1.00678
1.200	.41238	.77640	.97046	1.12700	.97872	1.00725
1.205	.40969	.77495	.96906	1.12910	.97779	1.00775
1.210	.40702	.77350	.96764	1.13122	.97684	1.00827
1.215	.40436	.77205	.96619	1.13334	.97589	1.00880
1.220	.40171	.77061	.96472	1.13547	.97492	1.00936
1.225	.39907	.76916	.96322	1.13761	.97394	1.00993
1.230	.39645	.76771	.96169	1.13976	.97294	1.01053
1.235	.39383	.76626	.96014	1.14191	.97194	1.01114
1.240	.39123	.76481	.95856	1.14408	.97092	1.01176
1.245	.38864	.76336	.95696	1.14625	.96990	1.01244

TABLE 10.2 (Continued)

M	p/p_t	T/T_t	Γ	ISOTHERMAL T_t/T_t^*	RAYLEIGH T_t/T_t^*	SHOCK p_{t1}/p_{t2}
1.250	.38606	.76190	.95534	1.14844	.96886	1.01311
1.255	.38349	.76045	.95369	1.15063	.96781	1.01381
1.260	.38093	.75900	.95201	1.15283	.96675	1.01453
1.265	.37839	.75755	.95032	1.15504	.96569	1.01527
1.270	.37586	.75610	.94860	1.15726	.96461	1.01603
1.275	.37334	.75465	.94685	1.15948	.96353	1.01682
1.280	.37083	.75319	.94509	1.16172	.96243	1.01762
1.285	.36833	.75174	.94330	1.16396	.96133	1.01845
1.290	.36585	.75029	.94150	1.16622	.96022	1.01930
1.295	.36337	.74884	.93967	1.16848	.95910	1.02017
1.300	.36091	.74738	.93782	1.17075	.95798	1.02106
1.305	.35847	.74593	.93595	1.17303	.95685	1.02197
1.310	.35603	.74448	.93406	1.17532	.95571	1.02291
1.315	.35360	.74303	.93215	1.17761	.95456	1.02387
1.320	.35119	.74158	.93022	1.17992	.95341	1.02485
1.325	.34879	.74012	.92827	1.18223	.95225	1.02585
1.330	.34640	.73867	.92630	1.18456	.95108	1.02688
1.335	.34403	.73722	.92431	1.18689	.94991	1.02793
1.340	.34166	.73577	.92231	1.18923	.94873	1.02900
1.345	.33931	.73432	.92028	1.19158	.94755	1.03009
1.350	.33697	.73287	.91824	1.19394	.94637	1.03121
1.355	.33464	.73142	.91618	1.19630	.94517	1.03235
1.360	.33233	.72997	.91411	1.19868	.94398	1.03351
1.365	.33002	.72852	.91201	1.20106	.94277	1.03469
1.370	.32773	.72707	.90991	1.20346	.94157	1.03590
1.375	.32545	.72562	.90778	1.20586	.94036	1.03713
1.380	.32319	.72418	.90564	1.20827	.93914	1.03838
1.385	.32093	.72273	.90348	1.21069	.93793	1.03966
1.390	.31869	.72128	.90131	1.21312	.93671	1.04096
1.395	.31646	.71984	.89912	1.21555	.93548	1.04228
1.400	.31424	.71839	.89692	1.21800	.93425	1.04363
1.405	.31203	.71695	.89470	1.22045	.93302	1.04500
1.410	.30984	.71550	.89247	1.22292	.93179	1.04639
1.415	.30766	.71406	.89023	1.22539	.93055	1.04781
1.420	.30549	.71262	.88797	1.22787	.92931	1.04925
1.425	.30333	.71117	.88570	1.23036	.92807	1.05071
1.430	.30119	.70973	.88342	1.23286	.92683	1.05220
1.435	.29905	.70829	.88112	1.23536	.92559	1.05371
1.440	.29693	.70685	.87881	1.23788	.92434	1.05524
1.445	.29482	.70542	.87649	1.24040	.92309	1.05680
1.450	.29272	.70398	.87415	1.24294	.92184	1.05838
1.455	.29064	.70254	.87181	1.24548	.92059	1.05999
1.460	.28856	.70111	.86945	1.24803	.91933	1.06162
1.465	.28650	.69967	.86708	1.25059	.91808	1.06327
1.470	.28445	.69824	.86471	1.25316	.91682	1.06495
1.475	.28241	.69680	.86232	1.25573	.91557	1.06665
1.480	.28039	.69537	.85992	1.25832	.91431	1.06837
1.485	.27837	.69394	.85751	1.26091	.91305	1.07012
1.490	.27637	.69251	.85509	1.26352	.91179	1.07190
1.495	.27438	.69108	.85266	1.26613	.91053	1.07369
1.500	.27240	.68966	.85022	1.26875	.90928	1.07552
1.505	.27044	.68823	.84777	1.27138	.90802	1.07736
1.510	.26848	.68680	.84532	1.27402	.90676	1.07923
1.515	.26654	.68538	.84285	1.27666	.90550	1.08112
1.520	.26461	.68396	.84038	1.27932	.90424	1.08304
1.525	.26269	.68254	.83789	1.28198	.90298	1.08499
1.530	.26078	.68112	.83541	1.28466	.90172	1.08695
1.535	.25888	.67970	.83291	1.28734	.90046	1.08894
1.540	.25700	.67828	.83040	1.29003	.89920	1.09096
1.545	.25512	.67686	.82789	1.29273	.89795	1.09300
1.550	.25326	.67545	.82537	1.29544	.89669	1.09506
1.555	.25141	.67403	.82285	1.29815	.89544	1.09715

M	p/p_t	T/T_t	Γ	ISOTHERMAL T_t/T_t^*	RAYLEIGH T_t/T_t^*	SHOCK p_{t1}/p_{t2}
1.560	.24957	.67262	.82032	1.30088	.89418	1.09927
1.565	.24775	.67121	.81778	1.30361	.89293	1.10141
1.570	.24593	.66980	.81523	1.30636	.89168	1.10357
1.575	.24413	.66839	.81268	1.30911	.89042	1.10576
1.580	.24233	.66699	.81013	1.31187	.88917	1.10797
1.585	.24055	.66558	.80756	1.31464	.88792	1.11021
1.590	.23878	.66418	.80500	1.31742	.88668	1.11247
1.595	.23702	.66278	.80243	1.32020	.88543	1.11476
1.600	.23527	.66138	.79985	1.32300	.88419	1.11707
1.605	.23353	.65998	.79727	1.32580	.88294	1.11941
1.610	.23181	.65858	.79468	1.32862	.88170	1.12177
1.615	.23009	.65718	.79209	1.33144	.88046	1.12415
1.620	.22839	.65579	.78950	1.33427	.87922	1.12657
1.625	.22670	.65440	.78690	1.33711	.87799	1.12900
1.630	.22501	.65301	.78430	1.33996	.87675	1.13147
1.635	.22334	.65162	.78170	1.34281	.87552	1.13395
1.640	.22168	.65023	.77909	1.34568	.87429	1.13647
1.645	.22003	.64884	.77648	1.34855	.87306	1.13900
1.650	.21839	.64746	.77386	1.35144	.87184	1.14157
1.655	.21677	.64608	.77125	1.35433	.87061	1.14416
1.660	.21515	.64470	.76863	1.35723	.86939	1.14677
1.665	.21354	.64332	.76601	1.36014	.86817	1.14941
1.670	.21195	.64194	.76338	1.36306	.86696	1.15208
1.675	.21036	.64056	.76076	1.36598	.86574	1.15477
1.680	.20879	.63919	.75813	1.36892	.86453	1.15748
1.685	.20722	.63782	.75550	1.37186	.86332	1.16022
1.690	.20567	.63645	.75287	1.37482	.86212	1.16299
1.695	.20413	.63508	.75024	1.37778	.86091	1.16579
1.700	.20259	.63371	.74760	1.38075	.85971	1.16860
1.705	.20107	.63235	.74497	1.38373	.85851	1.17145
1.710	.19956	.63099	.74234	1.38672	.85731	1.17432
1.715	.19806	.62963	.73970	1.38971	.85612	1.17722
1.720	.19656	.62827	.73706	1.39272	.85493	1.18014
1.725	.19508	.62691	.73443	1.39573	.85374	1.18309
1.730	.19361	.62556	.73179	1.39876	.85256	1.18607
1.735	.19215	.62420	.72915	1.40179	.85137	1.18907
1.740	.19070	.62285	.72652	1.40483	.85019	1.19209
1.745	.18926	.62150	.72388	1.40788	.84902	1.19515
1.750	.18782	.62016	.72124	1.41094	.84784	1.19823
1.755	.18640	.61881	.71861	1.41400	.84667	1.20133
1.760	.18499	.61747	.71597	1.41708	.84551	1.20447
1.765	.18359	.61613	.71334	1.42016	.84434	1.20763
1.770	.18219	.61479	.71071	1.42326	.84318	1.21081
1.775	.18081	.61345	.70808	1.42636	.84202	1.21403
1.780	.17944	.61212	.70544	1.42947	.84087	1.21727
1.785	.17807	.61078	.70282	1.43259	.83972	1.22053
1.790	.17672	.60945	.70019	1.43572	.83857	1.22382
1.795	.17538	.60812	.69756	1.43885	.83742	1.22714
1.800	.17404	.60680	.69494	1.44200	.83628	1.23049
1.805	.17271	.60547	.69231	1.44515	.83514	1.23386
1.810	.17140	.60415	.68969	1.44832	.83400	1.23726
1.815	.17009	.60283	.68707	1.45149	.83287	1.24069
1.820	.16879	.60151	.68446	1.45467	.83174	1.24415
1.825	.16750	.60020	.68184	1.45786	.83062	1.24763
1.830	.16622	.59888	.67923	1.46106	.82949	1.25114
1.835	.16495	.59757	.67662	1.46426	.82837	1.25468
1.840	.16369	.59626	.67401	1.46748	.82726	1.25824
1.845	.16244	.59495	.67141	1.47070	.82615	1.26183
1.850	.16120	.59365	.66881	1.47394	.82504	1.26545
1.855	.15996	.59235	.66621	1.47718	.82393	1.26910
1.860	.15873	.59104	.66362	1.48043	.82283	1.27277
1.865	.15752	.58975	.66103	1.48369	.82173	1.27647
1.870	.15631	.58845	.65844	1.48696	.82064	1.28020

TABLE 10.2 *(Continued)*

M	p/p_t	T/T_t	Γ	ISOTHERMAL T_t/T_t^*	RAYLEIGH T_t/T_t^*	SHOCK p_{t1}/p_{t2}
1.875	.15511	.58716	.65585	1.49023	.81954	1.28396
1.880	.15392	.58586	.65327	1.49352	.81845	1.28775
1.885	.15274	.58457	.65069	1.49681	.81737	1.29156
1.890	.15156	.58329	.64812	1.50012	.81629	1.29541
1.895	.15040	.58200	.64555	1.50343	.81521	1.29928
1.900	.14924	.58072	.64298	1.50675	.81414	1.30317
1.905	.14809	.57944	.64042	1.51008	.81306	1.30710
1.910	.14695	.57816	.63786	1.51342	.81200	1.31106
1.915	.14582	.57689	.63531	1.51676	.81093	1.31504
1.920	.14470	.57561	.63276	1.52012	.80987	1.31905
1.925	.14358	.57434	.63021	1.52348	.80882	1.32309
1.930	.14247	.57307	.62767	1.52686	.80776	1.32716
1.935	.14137	.57181	.62513	1.53024	.80671	1.33126
1.940	.14028	.57054	.62260	1.53363	.80567	1.33539
1.945	.13920	.56928	.62007	1.53703	.80462	1.33955
1.950	.13813	.56802	.61755	1.54044	.80358	1.34373
1.955	.13706	.56676	.61503	1.54385	.80255	1.34795
1.960	.13600	.56551	.61252	1.54728	.80152	1.35219
1.965	.13495	.56426	.61001	1.55071	.80049	1.35647
1.970	.13390	.56301	.60750	1.55416	.79946	1.36077
1.975	.13287	.56176	.60501	1.55761	.79844	1.36510
1.980	.13184	.56051	.60251	1.56107	.79742	1.36946
1.985	.13082	.55927	.60002	1.56454	.79641	1.37385
1.990	.12981	.55803	.59754	1.56802	.79540	1.37827
1.995	.12880	.55679	.59506	1.57150	.79439	1.38272
2.000	.12780	.55556	.59259	1.57500	.79339	1.38721
2.010	.12583	.55309	.58767	1.58202	.79139	1.39626
2.020	.12389	.55064	.58276	1.58907	.78941	1.40543
2.030	.12197	.54819	.57788	1.59616	.78744	1.41472
2.040	.12009	.54576	.57302	1.60328	.78549	1.42414
2.050	.11823	.54333	.56819	1.61044	.78355	1.43367
2.060	.11640	.54091	.56338	1.61763	.78162	1.44334
2.070	.11460	.53851	.55859	1.62486	.77971	1.45312
2.080	.11282	.53611	.55383	1.63212	.77782	1.46303
2.090	.11107	.53373	.54909	1.63942	.77593	1.47307
2.100	.10935	.53135	.54438	1.64675	.77406	1.48323
2.110	.10766	.52898	.53970	1.65412	.77221	1.49352
2.120	.10599	.52663	.53504	1.66152	.77037	1.50394
2.130	.10434	.52428	.53041	1.66896	.76854	1.51449
2.140	.10273	.52194	.52581	1.67643	.76673	1.52517
2.150	.10113	.51962	.52123	1.68394	.76493	1.53598
2.160	.09956	.51730	.51668	1.69148	.76314	1.54692
2.170	.09802	.51499	.51216	1.69906	.76137	1.55799
2.180	.09650	.51269	.50766	1.70667	.75961	1.56920
2.190	.09500	.51041	.50320	1.71432	.75787	1.58054
2.200	.09352	.50813	.49876	1.72200	.75613	1.59201
2.210	.09207	.50586	.49435	1.72972	.75442	1.60362
2.220	.09064	.50361	.48997	1.73747	.75271	1.61537
2.230	.08923	.50136	.48562	1.74526	.75102	1.62726
2.240	.08785	.49912	.48129	1.75308	.74934	1.63928
2.250	.08648	.49689	.47700	1.76094	.74768	1.65145
2.260	.08514	.49468	.47274	1.76883	.74602	1.66375
2.270	.08382	.49247	.46850	1.77676	.74438	1.67620
2.280	.08252	.49027	.46429	1.78472	.74276	1.68879
2.290	.08123	.48809	.46012	1.79272	.74114	1.70152
2.300	.07997	.48591	.45597	1.80075	.73954	1.71440
2.310	.07873	.48374	.45185	1.80882	.73795	1.72742
2.320	.07751	.48158	.44776	1.81692	.73638	1.74059
2.330	.07631	.47944	.44370	1.82506	.73482	1.75391
2.340	.07512	.47730	.43968	1.83323	.73326	1.76738
2.350	.07396	.47517	.43568	1.84144	.73173	1.78099
2.360	.07281	.47305	.43171	1.84968	.73020	1.79476

M	p/p_t	T/T_t	Γ	ISOTHERMAL T_t/T_t^*	RAYLEIGH T_t/T_t^*	SHOCK p_{t1}/p_{t2}
2.370	.07168	.47095	.42777	1.85796	.72868	1.80868
2.380	.07057	.46885	.42386	1.86627	.72718	1.82275
2.390	.06948	.46676	.41998	1.87462	.72569	1.83698
2.400	.06840	.46468	.41613	1.88300	.72421	1.85136
2.410	.06734	.46262	.41231	1.89142	.72275	1.86589
2.420	.06630	.46056	.40852	1.89987	.72129	1.88059
2.430	.06527	.45851	.40476	1.90836	.71985	1.89544
2.440	.06426	.45647	.40103	1.91688	.71842	1.91045
2.450	.06327	.45444	.39733	1.92544	.71699	1.92563
2.460	.06229	.45242	.39365	1.93403	.71559	1.94096
2.470	.06133	.45041	.39001	1.94266	.71419	1.95646
2.480	.06038	.44841	.38640	1.95132	.71280	1.97212
2.490	.05945	.44642	.38281	1.96002	.71142	1.98795
2.500	.05853	.44444	.37926	1.96875	.71006	2.00395
2.510	.05762	.44247	.37573	1.97752	.70871	2.02011
2.520	.05674	.44051	.37224	1.98632	.70736	2.03644
2.530	.05586	.43856	.36877	1.99516	.70603	2.05294
2.540	.05500	.43662	.36533	2.00403	.70471	2.06962
2.550	.05415	.43469	.36192	2.01294	.70340	2.08646
2.560	.05332	.43277	.35854	2.02188	.70210	2.10348
2.570	.05250	.43085	.35519	2.03086	.70081	2.12068
2.580	.05169	.42895	.35187	2.03987	.69953	2.13805
2.590	.05090	.42705	.34857	2.04892	.69826	2.15560
2.600	.05012	.42517	.34531	2.05800	.69700	2.17333
2.610	.04935	.42329	.34207	2.06712	.69575	2.19124
2.620	.04859	.42143	.33886	2.07627	.69451	2.20933
2.630	.04784	.41957	.33568	2.08546	.69328	2.22761
2.640	.04711	.41773	.33252	2.09468	.69206	2.24607
2.650	.04639	.41589	.32939	2.10394	.69084	2.26471
2.660	.04568	.41406	.32629	2.11323	.68964	2.28354
2.670	.04498	.41224	.32322	2.12256	.68845	2.30256
2.680	.04429	.41043	.32018	2.13192	.68727	2.32177
2.690	.04362	.40863	.31716	2.14132	.68610	2.34118
2.700	.04295	.40683	.31417	2.15075	.68494	2.36077
2.710	.04229	.40505	.31120	2.16022	.68378	2.38056
2.720	.04165	.40328	.30827	2.16972	.68264	2.40054
2.730	.04102	.40151	.30536	2.17926	.68150	2.42072
2.740	.04039	.39976	.30247	2.18883	.68037	2.44110
2.750	.03978	.39801	.29961	2.19844	.67926	2.46168
2.760	.03917	.39627	.29678	2.20808	.67815	2.48246
2.770	.03858	.39454	.29397	2.21776	.67705	2.50345
2.780	.03799	.39282	.29119	2.22747	.67595	2.52464
2.790	.03742	.39111	.28843	2.23722	.67487	2.54603
2.800	.03685	.38941	.28570	2.24700	.67380	2.56763
2.810	.03629	.38771	.28300	2.25682	.67273	2.58944
2.820	.03574	.38603	.28032	2.26667	.67167	2.61146
2.830	.03520	.38435	.27766	2.27656	.67062	2.63369
2.840	.03467	.38268	.27503	2.28648	.66958	2.65614
2.850	.03415	.38103	.27243	2.29644	.66855	2.67880
2.860	.03363	.37937	.26984	2.30643	.66752	2.70167
2.870	.03312	.37773	.26729	2.31646	.66651	2.72477
2.880	.03263	.37610	.26475	2.32652	.66550	2.74808
2.890	.03213	.37447	.26224	2.33662	.66450	2.77162
2.900	.03165	.37286	.25976	2.34675	.66350	2.79538
2.910	.03118	.37125	.25729	2.35692	.66252	2.81936
2.920	.03071	.36965	.25485	2.36712	.66154	2.84357
2.930	.03025	.36806	.25244	2.37736	.66057	2.86801
2.940	.02980	.36647	.25004	2.38763	.65960	2.89267
2.950	.02935	.36490	.24767	2.39794	.65865	2.91757
2.960	.02891	.36333	.24532	2.40828	.65770	2.94270
2.970	.02848	.36177	.24300	2.41866	.65676	2.96807
2.980	.02805	.36022	.24069	2.42907	.65583	2.99367
2.990	.02764	.35868	.23841	2.43952	.65490	3.01951

TABLE 10.2 *(Continued)*

M	p/p_t	T/T_t	Γ	ISOTHERMAL T_t/T_t^*	RAYLEIGH T_t/T_t^*	SHOCK p_{t1}/p_{t2}
3.000	.02722	.35714	.23615	2.45000	.65398	3.04559
3.010	.02682	.35562	.23391	2.46052	.65307	3.07191
3.020	.02642	.35410	.23170	2.47107	.65216	3.09847
3.030	.02603	.35259	.22950	2.48166	.65126	3.12528
3.040	.02564	.35108	.22733	2.49228	.65037	3.15233
3.050	.02526	.34959	.22517	2.50294	.64949	3.17963
3.060	.02489	.34810	.22304	2.51363	.64861	3.20718
3.070	.02452	.34662	.22093	2.52436	.64774	3.23499
3.080	.02416	.34515	.21884	2.53512	.64687	3.26305
3.090	.02380	.34369	.21677	2.54592	.64601	3.29136
3.100	.02345	.34223	.21472	2.55675	.64516	3.31993
3.110	.02310	.34078	.21269	2.56762	.64432	3.34876
3.120	.02276	.33934	.21067	2.57852	.64348	3.37785
3.130	.02243	.33791	.20868	2.58946	.64265	3.40720
3.140	.02210	.33648	.20671	2.60043	.64182	3.43682
3.150	.02177	.33506	.20476	2.61144	.64100	3.46670
3.160	.02146	.33365	.20282	2.62248	.64018	3.49686
3.170	.02114	.33225	.20091	2.63356	.63938	3.52728
3.180	.02083	.33085	.19901	2.64467	.63857	3.55797
3.190	.02053	.32947	.19714	2.65582	.63778	3.58894
3.200	.02023	.32808	.19528	2.66700	.63699	3.62019
3.210	.01993	.32671	.19344	2.67822	.63621	3.65171
3.220	.01964	.32534	.19161	2.68947	.63543	3.68352
3.230	.01936	.32398	.18981	2.70076	.63465	3.71560
3.240	.01908	.32263	.18802	2.71208	.63389	3.74797
3.250	.01880	.32129	.18625	2.72344	.63313	3.78063
3.260	.01853	.31995	.18450	2.73483	.63237	3.81357
3.270	.01826	.31862	.18276	2.74626	.63162	3.84680
3.280	.01799	.31729	.18105	2.75772	.63088	3.88033
3.290	.01773	.31597	.17935	2.76922	.63014	3.91415
3.300	.01748	.31466	.17766	2.78075	.6294C	3.94826
3.310	.01722	.31336	.17600	2.79232	.62868	3.98268
3.320	.01698	.31206	.17434	2.80392	.62795	4.01739
3.330	.01673	.31077	.17271	2.81556	.62724	4.05240
3.340	.01649	.30949	.17109	2.82723	.62652	4.08773
3.350	.01625	.30821	.16949	2.83894	.62582	4.12335
3.360	.01602	.30694	.16790	2.85068	.62512	4.15929
3.370	.01579	.30568	.16633	2.86246	.62442	4.19553
3.380	.01557	.30443	.16478	2.87427	.62373	4.23209
3.390	.01534	.30318	.16324	2.88612	.62304	4.26897
3.400	.01512	.30193	.16172	2.89800	.62236	4.30616
3.410	.01491	.30070	.16021	2.90992	.62168	4.34367
3.420	.01470	.29947	.15871	2.92187	.62101	4.38150
3.430	.01449	.29824	.15723	2.93386	.62034	4.41965
3.440	.01428	.29703	.15577	2.94588	.61968	4.45813
3.450	.01408	.29581	.15432	2.95794	.61902	4.49694
3.460	.01388	.29461	.15288	2.97003	.61837	4.53608
3.470	.01368	.29341	.15146	2.98216	.61772	4.57555
3.480	.01349	.29222	.15006	2.99432	.61708	4.61536
3.490	.01330	.29103	.14866	3.00652	.61644	4.65551
3.500	.01311	.28986	.14728	3.01875	.61580	4.69599
3.510	.01293	.28868	.14592	3.03102	.61517	4.73681
3.520	.01274	.28752	.14457	3.04332	.61455	4.77798
3.530	.01256	.28635	.14323	3.05566	.61393	4.81950
3.540	.01239	.28520	.14190	3.06803	.61331	4.86136
3.550	.01221	.28405	.14059	3.08044	.61270	4.90358
3.560	.01204	.28291	.13929	3.09288	.61209	4.94615
3.570	.01188	.28177	.13801	3.10536	.61149	4.98907
3.580	.01171	.28064	.13673	3.11787	.61089	5.03235
3.590	.01155	.27952	.13547	3.13042	.61029	5.07599
3.600	.01138	.27840	.13423	3.14300	.60970	5.12000
3.610	.01123	.27728	.13299	3.15562	.60911	5.16437
3.620	.01107	.27618	.13177	3.16827	.60853	5.20911
3.630	.01092	.27507	.13056	3.18096	.60795	5.25422
3.640	.01076	.27398	.12936	3.19368	.60738	5.29970

M	p/p_t	T/T_t	Γ	ISOTHERMAL T_t/T_t^*	RAYLEIGH T_t/T_t^*	SHOCK p_{t1}/p_{t2}
3.650	.01062	.27289	.12817	3.20644	.60681	5.34556
3.660	.01047	.27180	.12700	3.21923	.60624	5.39179
3.670	.01032	.27073	.12583	3.23206	.60568	5.43840
3.680	.01018	.26965	.12468	3.24492	.60512	5.48540
3.690	.01004	.26858	.12354	3.25782	.60456	5.53278
3.700	.00990	.26752	.12241	3.27075	.60401	5.58055
3.710	.00977	.26647	.12130	3.28372	.60346	5.62871
3.720	.00963	.26542	.12019	3.29672	.60292	5.67726
3.730	.00950	.26437	.11909	3.30976	.60238	5.72621
3.740	.00937	.26333	.11801	3.32283	.60184	5.77555
3.750	.00924	.26230	.11694	3.33594	.60131	5.82530
3.760	.00912	.26127	.11587	3.34908	.60078	5.87545
3.770	.03899	.26024	.11482	3.36226	.60025	5.92600
3.780	.03887	.25922	.11378	3.37547	.59973	5.97696
3.790	.00875	.25821	.11275	3.38872	.59921	6.02833
3.800	.00863	.25720	.11172	3.40200	.59870	6.08012
3.810	.00851	.25620	.11071	3.41532	.59819	6.13232
3.820	.00840	.25520	.10971	3.42867	.59768	6.18494
3.830	.03828	.25421	.10872	3.44206	.59717	6.23799
3.840	.00817	.25322	.10774	3.45548	.59667	6.29145
3.850	.00806	.25224	.10677	3.46894	.59617	6.34535
3.860	.00795	.25126	.10581	3.48243	.59568	6.39967
3.870	.00784	.25029	.10485	3.49596	.59519	6.45443
3.880	.00774	.24932	.10391	3.50952	.59470	6.50962
3.890	.00763	.24836	.10298	3.52312	.59421	6.56525
3.900	.00753	.24740	.10205	3.53675	.59373	6.62132
3.910	.00743	.24645	.10114	3.55042	.59325	6.67783
3.920	.00733	.24550	.10023	3.56412	.59278	6.73479
3.930	.00723	.24456	.09933	3.57786	.59231	6.79220
3.940	.00714	.24362	.09844	3.59163	.59184	6.85006
3.950	.00704	.24269	.09756	3.60544	.59137	6.90838
3.960	.00695	.24176	.09669	3.61928	.59091	6.96715
3.970	.00686	.24084	.09583	3.63316	.59045	7.02638
3.980	.00676	.23992	.09498	3.64707	.58999	7.08608
3.990	.00667	.23900	.09413	3.66102	.58954	7.14624
4.000	.00659	.23810	.09329	3.67500	.58909	7.20688
4.010	.00650	.23719	.09247	3.68902	.58864	7.26799
4.020	.00641	.23629	.09164	3.70307	.58819	7.32957
4.030	.00633	.23539	.09083	3.71716	.58775	7.39163
4.040	.00624	.23450	.09003	3.73128	.58731	7.45417
4.050	.00616	.23362	.08923	3.74544	.58687	7.51719
4.060	.00608	.23274	.08844	3.75963	.58644	7.58070
4.070	.00600	.23186	.08766	3.77386	.58601	7.64470
4.080	.00592	.23099	.08689	3.78812	.58558	7.70920
4.090	.03585	.23012	.08612	3.80242	.58516	7.77419
4.100	.00577	.22925	.08536	3.81675	.58473	7.83968
4.110	.00569	.22839	.08461	3.83112	.58431	7.90567
4.120	.00562	.22754	.08387	3.84552	.58390	7.97217
4.130	.00555	.22669	.08313	3.85996	.58348	8.03917
4.140	.00547	.22584	.08240	3.87443	.58307	8.10669
4.150	.00540	.22500	.08168	3.88894	.58266	8.17472
4.160	.00533	.22416	.08097	3.90348	.58225	8.24327
4.170	.00526	.22332	.08026	3.91806	.58185	8.31234
4.180	.00520	.22250	.07956	3.93267	.58145	8.38194
4.190	.03513	.22167	.07886	3.94732	.58105	8.45206
4.200	.00506	.22085	.07818	3.96200	.58065	8.52271
4.210	.00500	.22003	.07750	3.97672	.58026	8.59390
4.220	.00493	.21922	.07682	3.99147	.57987	8.66562
4.230	.00487	.21841	.07615	4.00626	.57948	8.73788
4.240	.00481	.21760	.07549	4.02108	.57909	8.81069
4.250	.00474	.21680	.07484	4.03594	.57870	8.88404
4.260	.00468	.21601	.07419	4.05083	.57832	8.95795
4.270	.00462	.21521	.07355	4.06576	.57794	9.03240
4.280	.00457	.21442	.07291	4.08072	.57757	9.10741
4.290	.00451	.21364	.07228	4.09572	.57719	9.18299

TABLE 10.2 (Continued)

M	p/p_t	T/T_t	Γ	ISOTHERMAL T_t/T_t^*	RAYLEIGH T_t/T_t^*	SHOCK p_{t1}/p_{t2}
4.300	.00445	.21286	.07166	4.11075	.57682	9.25912
4.310	.00439	.21208	.07104	4.12582	.57645	9.33583
4.320	.00434	.21131	.07043	4.14092	.57608	9.41310
4.330	.00428	.21054	.06983	4.15606	.57571	9.49094
4.340	.00423	.20977	.06923	4.17123	.57535	9.56937
4.350	.00417	.20901	.06863	4.18644	.57499	9.64837
4.360	.00412	.20825	.06804	4.20168	.57463	9.72796
4.370	.00407	.20750	.06746	4.21696	.57427	9.80813
4.380	.00402	.20674	.06688	4.23227	.57392	9.88889
4.390	.00397	.20600	.06631	4.24762	.57357	9.97025
4.400	.00392	.20525	.06575	4.26300	.57322	10.05220
4.410	.00387	.20451	.06519	4.27842	.57287	10.13476
4.420	.00382	.20378	.06463	4.29387	.57252	10.21792
4.430	.00377	.20305	.06408	4.30936	.57218	10.30168
4.440	.00372	.20232	.06354	4.32488	.57183	10.38606
4.450	.00368	.20159	.06300	4.34044	.57149	10.47106
4.460	.00363	.20087	.06246	4.35603	.57116	10.55667
4.470	.00359	.20015	.06194	4.37166	.57082	10.64290
4.480	.00354	.19944	.06141	4.38732	.57049	10.72976
4.490	.00350	.19873	.06089	4.40302	.57015	10.81725
4.500	.00346	.19802	.06038	4.41875	.56982	10.90537
4.510	.00341	.19732	.05987	4.43452	.56950	10.99413
4.520	.00337	.19662	.05937	4.45032	.56917	11.08353
4.530	.00333	.19592	.05887	4.46616	.56885	11.17357
4.540	.00329	.19522	.05837	4.48203	.56852	11.26426
4.550	.00325	.19453	.05788	4.49794	.56820	11.35560
4.560	.00321	.19385	.05740	4.51388	.56789	11.44760
4.570	.00317	.19316	.05692	4.52986	.56757	11.54026
4.580	.00313	.19248	.05644	4.54587	.56726	11.63357
4.590	.00309	.19181	.05597	4.56192	.56694	11.72756
4.600	.00305	.19113	.05550	4.57800	.56663	11.82221
4.610	.00302	.19046	.05504	4.59412	.56632	11.91754
4.620	.00298	.18979	.05458	4.61027	.56602	12.01355
4.630	.00294	.18913	.05413	4.62646	.56571	12.11023
4.640	.00291	.18847	.05368	4.64268	.56541	12.20761
4.650	.00287	.18781	.05323	4.65894	.56510	12.30567
4.660	.00284	.18716	.05279	4.67523	.56480	12.40442
4.670	.00280	.18651	.05235	4.69156	.56451	12.50387
4.680	.00277	.18586	.05192	4.70792	.56421	12.60403
4.690	.00273	.18521	.05149	4.72432	.56391	12.70488
4.700	.00270	.18457	.05107	4.74075	.56362	12.80645
4.710	.00267	.18393	.05064	4.75722	.56333	12.90873
4.720	.00264	.18330	.05023	4.77372	.56304	13.01172
4.730	.00260	.18266	.04981	4.79026	.56275	13.11544
4.740	.00257	.18203	.04940	4.80683	.56246	13.21988
4.750	.00254	.18141	.04900	4.82344	.56218	13.32505
4.760	.00251	.18078	.04860	4.84008	.56190	13.43095
4.770	.00248	.18016	.04820	4.85676	.56161	13.53759
4.780	.00245	.17954	.04781	4.87347	.56133	13.64497
4.790	.00242	.17893	.04742	4.89022	.56106	13.75309
4.800	.00239	.17832	.04703	4.90700	.56078	13.86197
4.810	.00237	.17771	.04665	4.92382	.56050	13.97159
4.820	.00234	.17710	.04627	4.94067	.56023	14.08198
4.830	.00231	.17650	.04589	4.95756	.55996	14.19312
4.840	.03228	.17590	.04552	4.97448	.55969	14.30503
4.850	.00226	.17530	.04515	4.99144	.55942	14.41771
4.860	.00223	.17471	.04478	5.00843	.55915	14.53116
4.870	.00220	.17411	.04442	5.02546	.55888	14.64540
4.880	.00218	.17352	.04406	5.04252	.55862	14.76041
4.890	.00215	.17294	.04370	5.05962	.55836	14.87621
4.900	.00213	.17235	.04335	5.07675	.55809	14.99280
4.910	.00210	.17177	.04300	5.09392	.55783	15.11019
4.920	.00208	.17120	.04266	5.11112	.55758	15.22837

M	p/p_t	T/T_t	Γ	ISOTHERMAL T_t/T_t^*	RAYLEIGH T_t/T_t^*	SHOCK p_{t1}/p_{t2}
4.930	.00205	.17062	.04231	5.12836	.55732	15.34736
4.940	.00203	.17005	.04197	5.14563	.55706	15.46716
4.950	.00200	.16948	.04164	5.16294	.55681	15.58777
4.960	.00198	.16891	.04130	5.18028	.55655	15.70920
4.970	.00196	.16835	.04097	5.19766	.55630	15.83144
4.980	.00193	.16778	.04065	5.21507	.55605	15.95451
4.990	.00191	.16722	.04032	5.23252	.55580	16.07842

10.2   APPLICATIONS OF THE GENERALIZED TABLES

To illustrate the use of the generalized table and the general rules just given, a number of simplified examples are given next [2].

EXAMPLE 10.2

In an isentropic process involving air, if $M_1 = 0.25$ and $A_1/A_2 = 1.8$, find M_2.

Solution

At $M_1 = 0.25$, Table 10.2 yields $\Gamma_1 = A_*/A_1 = 0.41217$. The significant ratio of conditions in this process is A_1/A_2. Hence, we obtain the key factor at 2 via

$$\Gamma_2 = \frac{A_*}{A_2} = \frac{A_1}{A_2} \times \frac{A_*}{A_1}$$

or $\Gamma_2 = 1.8 \times 0.41217 = 0.74191$.

On the same line as Γ_2, we find $M_2 = 0.5$.

EXAMPLE 10.3

In a Fanno process with $\gamma = 1.4$, if $R_1 = 0.95$ and $p_{t1}/p_{t2} = 1.63111$, find R_2.

Solution

At $R_1 = 0.95$, Table 10.1 yields $\Gamma_1 = p_{t*}/p_{t1} = 0.44929$. The significant ratio of conditions in this process is p_{t1}/p_{t2}. Hence, we obtain the key factor at 2 via

$$\Gamma_2 = \frac{p_{t*}}{p_{t2}} = \frac{p_{t1}}{p_{t2}} \times \frac{p_{t*}}{p_{t1}}$$

or $\Gamma_2 = 1.63111 \times 0.44929 = 0.73284$.

On the same line as Γ_2, we find $R_2 = 0.85$.

EXAMPLE 10.4

In a Rayleigh process in air, if $M_1 = 0.5$ and $T_{t2}/T_{t1} = 1.1845$, find M_2.

Solution

At $M_1 = 0.5$, Table 10.2 yields $(T_{t1}/T_{t*})_{Ray} = 0.69136$. The significant ratio of conditions in this process is T_{t2}/T_{t1}. Hence, we obtain the key factor at 2 via

$$\frac{T_{t2}}{T_{t*}} = \frac{T_{t2}}{T_{t1}} \times \frac{T_{t1}}{T_{t*}}$$

$$= 1.1845 \times 0.69136 = 0.81892$$

On the same line as T_{t2}/T_{t*}, we find $M_2 = 0.6$.

EXAMPLE 10.5

In an isothermal process with $\gamma = 1.4$, if $R_1 = 0.8$ and $T_{t2}/T_{t1} = 0.98283$, find R_2.

Solution

At $R_1 = 0.8$, Table 10.1 yields $(T_{t1}/T_{t*})_{iso} = 0.93260$. The significant ratio of conditions in this process is T_{t2}/T_{t1}. Hence, we obtain the key factor at 2 via

$$\frac{T_{t2}}{T_{t*}} = \frac{T_{t2}}{T_{t1}} \times \frac{T_{t1}}{T_{t*}}$$

$$= 0.98283 \times 0.93260 = 0.91659$$

On the same line as T_{t2}/T_{t*}, we find $R_2 = 0.85$.

EXAMPLE 10.6

In a normal shock process in air, if $M_1 = 2$, find M_2.

Solution

At $M_1 = 2$, Table 10.2 yields $\Gamma_1 = 0.59259$ and the key factor, $(p_{t2}/p_{t1})_{shock} = 0.72087$. We obtain the normalized gas dynamics function (Γ) at 2 via

$$\Gamma_2 = \frac{\Gamma_1}{p_{t2}/p_{t1}}$$

$$= \frac{0.59259}{0.72087} = 0.82205$$

On the same line as Γ_2, we find by interpolation $M_2 = 0.57736$ (note Table 9.1 gives $M_2 = 0.57735$ directly for a close check).

Of course, most of the more complex problems of gas dynamics also can be solved with the aid of the generalized gas dynamics Tables 10.1 and 10.2.

REFERENCES

1. R. P. Benedict and W. G. Steltz, *Handbook of Generalized Gas Dynamics*, Plenum Press, New York, 1966, pp. 17–18.

2. R. P. Benedict, *Fundamentals of Pipe Flow*, Wiley, New York, 1980, pp. 315–318.

NOMENCLATURE

Roman

A	Area
$\dot{m}$	Mass flow rate
$\mathbf{M}$	Mach number
p	Pressure
$\mathbf{P}$	Pressure ratio function
R	Static/total pressure ratio
T	Absolute temperature

Greek

α	Flow number
γ	Specific heat ratio
Γ	Normalized gas dynamics function

Subscripts

t	Total
$*$	At the critical state

PROBLEMS

10.1 In an isentropic process involving air, if $\mathbf{M}_1 = 0.5$ and $A_1/A_2 = 1.2$, find $\mathbf{M}_2$.

10.2 In a Fanno process, with $\gamma = 1.4$, if $R_1 = 0.9$ and TPR $= 1.5$, find R_2.

10.3 In a Rayleigh process in air, if $\mathbf{M}_1 = 0.4$ and TTR $= 0.9$, find $\mathbf{M}_2$.

10.4 In an isothermal process, with $\gamma = 1.4$, if $R_1 = 0.85$ and TTR $= 0.95$, find R_2.

10.5 In a normal shock process in air, if $\mathbf{M}_1 = 3$, find $\mathbf{M}_2$.

11
STEPWISE SOLUTIONS

11.1 GENERAL REMARKS

It will be noticed that although a generalized gas dynamics equation was developed in Chapter 4, said to apply to all flow processes, in practice (4.18) applied only to various specialized processes.

For examples: in Chapter 5, we dealt only with isentropic flows; in Chapter 6, we dealt only with adiabatic flows; in Chapter 7, we dealt only with diabatic-reversible flows; in Chapter 8, we dealt only with isothermal flows; and in Chapter 9, we dealt only with the normal shock process. In Chapter 10, generalized gas dynamics tables were developed, said to be useful in all flow processes. However, in practice, Tables 10.1 and 10.2 were applied just in various specialized processes. Why is this so?

The general gas dynamics process, including arbitrary heat transfer, arbitrary area change, and arbitrary flow losses, has resisted solution for several reasons. First, the location of the heat transfer must be specified (at what axial position? at what area? and so on). Second, we have been using closed-form solutions that do not always admit to all applications.

Evidently, we are in need of another method by which we can solve an arbitrary gas dynamics problem including the combined flow loss-heat transfer problems that have resisted our efforts until now. A method of solution that is easily understood and that will provide us with more generalization than the various tables, graphs, and closed-form equations that have been presented thus far is based on a stepwise numerical approach.[1] By its very nature, the stepwise solution is dependent in any practical case on the use of a computer or a programmable hand-held calculator.

In this final chapter, differential equations are developed that can be solved

---

[1]"The complexity of the phenomena makes it desirable to be able to integrate the equation of motion at least step by step by the method of 'small increments'. That is, as is well known, always possible". Aurel Stodola, 1945.

numerically, in a stepwise fashion, for any arbitrary combination of heat transfer and flow loss, that is, for the truly generalized gas dynamics process.

Although making these advances, we will avoid the variable area case, in the interest of simplicity of presentation, noting here that the constant area solution could be further generalized to handle the more complex variable area situation.

11.2 THE STEPWISE DIFFERENTIAL EQUATIONS

The three basic conservation equations of Chapter 2 are employed toward a general solution [1-5]. These include the conservation of mass, momentum, and energy. In all cases, a differential flow element is considered as shown in Figure 11.1.

11.2.1 Continuity

By (2.10), we have

$$\dot{m} = \rho A_F V \tag{11.1}$$

and, by (7.22),

$$G = \frac{\dot{m}}{A_F} = \rho V \tag{11.2}$$

11.2.2 Momentum

Applying $\Sigma F_X = \dot{m}\, dV/g_c$ of (2.21) to the fluid element of Figure 11.1, we obtain

$$pA_F - (p + dp)A_F - \tau_w A_s = \frac{\dot{m}}{g_c}[(V + dV) - V] \tag{11.3}$$

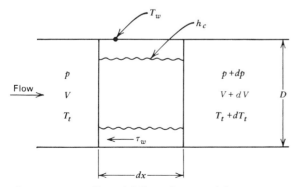

Figure 11.1   Differential flow element of the stepwise solution.

where

A_F = the flow area, $\pi D^2/4$.

A_S = the surface area, $\pi D\,dx$.

τ_w = the wall shear stress, $\dfrac{f}{4}\left(\dfrac{\rho V^2}{2g_c}\right)$.

f = the Darcy friction factor, $f(R_D, \epsilon/D)$.

Making appropriate substitutions, we get the following results from (11.3):

$$dp + \frac{f\rho V^2\,dx}{2g_c\,D} + \frac{\rho V\,dV}{g_c} = 0 \tag{11.4}$$

This same equation, given also by [1], can be integrated to yield

$$p_2 - p_1 + \frac{fG}{2g_cD}(\overline{V}\Delta X) + \frac{G}{g_c}(V_2 - V_1) = 0 \tag{11.5}$$

When the steps (Δx) in the solution are small enough so that

$$\overline{V} \simeq \frac{V_1 + V_2}{2} \tag{11.6}$$

the following results from (11.5):

$$V_2 = \frac{(p_1 - p_2) - \dfrac{V_1 G}{g_c}\left(\dfrac{f\Delta x}{4D} - 1\right)}{\dfrac{G}{g_c}\left(\dfrac{f\Delta x}{4D} + 1\right)} \tag{11.7}$$

Of course, (6.19) and (6.35), namely

$$K_f = \frac{f\Delta x}{D} \tag{11.8}$$

could be introduced into (11.7) to involve the loss coefficient, K_f.

11.2.3 Energy

The necessary equation involving heat transfer already has been provided by (7.22) as

$$dK_q = \frac{dT_t}{T_w - T_t} = \frac{h_c dx}{900GDC_p} \tag{11.9}$$

One integrated form of (11.9) already has been given by (7.23) as

$$K_q = \frac{h_c \Delta x}{900 G D C_p} \tag{11.10}$$

Another integrated form of (11.9) has been provided by (7.25) in the alternative forms

$$T_{t2} = \overline{T}_w + (T_{t1} - \overline{T}_w) \exp(-K_q) \tag{11.11}$$

and

$$\overline{T}_w = \frac{T_{t1}\left(\dfrac{T_{t2}}{T_{t1}} - \exp(-K_q)\right)}{1 - \exp(-K_q)} \tag{11.12}$$

depending on which variable (T_{t2} or $\overline{T}_w$) is the unknown.

11.3   STEPWISE SOLUTION METHOD

Suppose that total conditions at the inlet are given and that exit conditions are required. To be specific, say we have p_{t1}, T_{t1}, $\overline{T}_w$, $\dot{m}$, L, and D, and we require p_2, p_{t2}, T_2, and T_{t2} for arbitrary heat addition and smooth pipe viscous loss.

Solution steps are as follows:

1. Iteratively, find $R_1 = p_1/p_{t1}$ and hence p_1 via the total flow number of (4.21) and (4.22). That is, find R_1 by comparing the alternative forms

$$\left(\frac{\alpha_1}{2\gamma/(\gamma - 1)}\right) = \left(\frac{\dot{m}}{Ap_{t1}}\right)^2 \left(\frac{\overline{R}T_{t1}}{g_c}\right)\left(\frac{\gamma - 1}{2\gamma}\right) \tag{11.13}$$

and

$$\left(\frac{\alpha_1}{2\gamma/(\gamma - 1)}\right) = (R_1^{2/\gamma} - R_1^{(\gamma + 1)/\gamma}) \tag{11.14}$$

2. However, R_1 leads to T_1 via the isentropic relation of (1.56) as

$$T_1 = T_{t1} \times R_1^{(\gamma - 1)/\gamma} \tag{11.15}$$

and hence to V_1 via (11.1) as

$$V_1 = \frac{\dot{m}\,\overline{R}T_1}{A_F\,p_1} \tag{11.16}$$

3. The Reynolds number can be formed via (1.62) as

$$R_D = \frac{48\,\dot{m}}{\pi D \mu} \tag{11.17}$$

where $\dot{m}$ is expressed in lbm/sec, D in inches, and μ in lbm/ft-sec. R_D leads to the friction factor. For example, for smooth pipes, by (1.63) we have

$$\frac{1}{\sqrt{f_s}} = 2 \log (R_D \sqrt{f_s}) - 0.8 \tag{11.18}$$

4. With the number of flow elements (N) chosen, the loss coefficient per element can be formed via (11.8) in which $\Delta x = L/N$.

5. A calculated exit velocity (V_2) of the first element is then obtained by (11.7) in terms of an assumed p_2.

6. Once again, a short iterative procedure is employed to close on V_2 and p_2 by comparing

$$G_{\text{calculated}} = \frac{V_{2c}p_2}{RT_2} \tag{11.19}$$

with the given G of (11.2).

7. The convective heat transfer coefficient, h_c, of (7.20) is obtained by an equation of the form

$$h_c = \left(\frac{k}{D}\right) A R_D^B \, Pr^C \tag{11.20}$$

8. The dimensionless heat transfer coefficient, K_q, of (11.10) and the total temperature at the exit of the element, T_{t2}, of (11.11) are next formed.

9. Finally, the element exit total pressure, p_{t2}, is obtained by the isentropic relation of (1.56) as

$$p_{t2} = p_2 \left(\frac{T_{t2}}{T_2}\right)^{\gamma/(\gamma-1)} \tag{11.21}$$

With all quantities now specified for element 1, the exit conditions of element 1 are considered the inlet conditions of element 2, and the process is repeated until all N elements have been dealt with. At this point, the problem has been solved by a stepwise solution.

If a special situation is to be noted as zero loss, zero heat transfer, or constant temperature, the solution is modified slightly by program inputs. Such special cases will become apparent when we apply the stepwise method to certain selected examples.

11.4 STEPWISE FORTRAN PROGRAM OUTLINE

Most programs in the United States, as set up by engineers, are written in the FORTRAN language. The word FORTRAN is a contraction of the words *FOR*mula *TRAN*slator. Only the most basic FORTRAN methods are considered here, in the belief that nothing will substitute for hands-on practice. All input-output FORMAT statements will be omitted, for simplicity, and only the bare logic of a program for the stepwise solution of the general gas dynamics problem will be given.

1. The subscripted variables, meaning those variables that apply to the individual flow elements, are first listed in a DIMENSION statement such as:

   DIMENSION   TW(50), X(50).

2. READ statements are used next to input initial values for the specific problem into the computer such as:

   READ   PT1, TT1, TW(1), FLϕ, D, and so on.

3. The constants in the problem and the simple calculations of items that remain fixed throughout the problem are next formed such as:

   RBAR = 53.35
   GC   = 32.174
   G   = 1.4
   DELX = XL/NL
   RD   = 48.*FLϕ/(3.14159*D**2)*144., and so on.

4. The inlet conditions of the first element are computed via such statements as:

   Z = FLϕ/(AREA*PT1)*SQRT(RBAR*TT1*(G − 1.)/ (GC*2.*G))

   CALL ITER (Z, R)
   R1 = R
   P1 = R1*PT1
   T1 = TT1*R1**((G − 1.)/G)
   V1 = GF*RBAR*T1/(P1*144.), and so on.

5. The exit conditions of the first and all later elements are computed via such statements as:

   DO 10 I = 1,N
   TT2   = TW(I) + (TT1 − TW(I))/EXP(XKQ)
   P   = 0.98*P1
   V2   = ((P1 − P)*144. − V1*GF/GC*(XKF/4. − 1.))
              / (GF/GC*(XKF/4. + 1.))
   T2   = TT2 − V2**2/(50062.744*CP)
   GFC   = V2*P/(RBAR*T2)*144.
   IF (ABS ((GF − GFC)/GF) < .00001)GO TO 20

Here, a Newton-Raphson iteration scheme is employed to close on V_2 and p_2. After convergence, we have

```
P2  = P
PT2 = P2*(TT2/T2)**(G/(G − 1.))
```

6. WRITE all outputs of interest.
7. Update all exit conditions of the current element to be inlet conditions of the next element such as:

```
P1  = P2
PT1 = PT2
TT1 = TT2, and so on.
```

8. Now go, via a DO loop, to the next element, and continue until all N elements have been considered.

11.5   CONFIRMATIONS OF THE STEPWISE SOLUTION METHOD

Certain selected examples, already solved in the text by closed-form equations, will be re-solved by the stepwise method. Of course, one of the key variables in the stepwise solution is the number of steps into which the overall length of the flow path is divided. This is because of the definite assumption in the stepwise equations that the steps are small enough so the (11.6) is satisfied. That is, the effective velocity in the flow element must be well-approximated by the simple straight line average value, $(V_1 + V_2)/2$.

EXAMPLE 11.1

The Fanno flow problem given in Example 6.14 had the inlet values: $T_t = 540°R$, $p_{t1} = 15$ psia, a flow rate per unit area of $G = 19.974$ lbm/ft²-sec, and an overall loss coefficient of $K_f = 2$. The static and total pressures at exit were found to be $p_2 = 13.04$ psia and $p_{t2} = 13.70$ psia. This same example will now be solved by the stepwise method using 5, 10, 20, and 40 steps to compare results.

Solution

Although not required in the closed-form solution of Example 6.14, the values for diameter, length, flow rate, viscosity, conductivity, and specific heat consistent with the given information are required in the stepwise method. Such values are:

$D = 6$ in.

$L = 1000$ in.

$\dot{m} = 3.92189$ lbm/sec.

$\mu = 1.242 \times 10^{-5}$ lbm/ft-sec.

$k = 0.0153$ Btu/hr-ft-°F.

$C_p = 0.24$ Btu/lbm-°F.

These values lead to:

$Pr = 0.700.$

$R_D = 8.04 \times 10^5.$

$h_c = 0.$

$K_q = 0.$

$f = 0.0121.$

Now, by a stepwise computer solution, we obtain:

For 5 steps, $K_f = 0.4034.$
For 10 steps, $K_f = 0.2017.$
For 20 steps, $K_f = 0.1009.$
For 40 steps, $K_f = 0.0504.$

In each case, with the proper step multiplier, $K_{f, \text{overall}} \simeq 2.$
The results, namely p_2 and p_{t2}, are given below.

NUMBER OF STEPS	p_2(psia)	p_{t2}(psia)
5	12.73	13.41
10	12.88	13.55
20	12.96	13.62
40	12.99	13.66
Closed-form	13.04	13.70

It is clear that the results of the stepwise solution converge on the closed-form solution as the number of steps used increases.

EXAMPLE 11.2

The Rayleigh flow problem given in Example 7.4 had the inlet values: $T_{t1} = 550°F$, $T_{w2} = 1055°F$, $L = 80$ ft, $D = 1$ ft, and $G = 10$ lbm/ft²-sec. The total temperature ratio across the pipe was found to be $T_{t2}/T_{t1} = 1.250.$ This same example will now be solved by the stepwise method using 5, 10, 20 and 40 steps to compare results.

Solution

Although not required in the closed-form solution of Example 7.4, the flow rate consistent with the given information is

$\dot{m} = 7.85398$ lbm/sec

Input values lead to:

$Pr = 0.637.$

$R_D = 5.173 \times 10^5.$

$h_c = 18.7$ Btu/hr-ft²-°F.

$f = 0.$

$K_f = 0.$

Now, by a stepwise computer solution, we obtain:

For 5 steps, K_q = 0.1388.
For 10 steps, K_q = 0.0694.
For 20 steps, K_q = 0.0347.
For 40 steps, K_q = 0.0174.

In each case, with the proper step multiplier K_q overall $\simeq 0.694$.
The results, namely T_{t2}/T_{t1}, are given below.

NUMBER OF STEPS	T_{t2}/T_{t1}
5	1.283
10	1.267
20	1.259
40	1.254
Closed-form	1.250

Again, it is clear that the results of the stepwise solution converge on the closed-form solution as the number of steps used increases.

EXAMPLE 11.3

The isothermal flow problem given in Example 8.8 had the inlet values: T_{t1} = 508°R, p_{t1} = 50 psia, R_1 = 0.98; and a total pressure ratio across the device of TPR = 2, and a dimensionless heat transfer coefficient of K_q = 10.89. The average wall temperature was found to be $\overline{T}_w$ = 518.6°R. This same example will now be solved by the stepwise method using 10, 20, and 40 steps to compare results.

Solution

Although not required in the closed-form solution of Example 8.8 the values for diameter, length, flow rate, viscosity, conductivity, and specific heat consistent with the given information are required in the stepwise method.
Such values are:

D = 4 in.

L = 6475 in.

$\dot{m}$ = 4.283 lbm/sec.

$\mu = 1.178 \times 10^{-5}$ lbm/ft-sec.

k = 0.0145 Btu/hr-ft-°F.

C_p = 0.24 Btu/lbm-°F.

These values lead to:

Pr = 0.701.

$R_D = 1.389 \times 10^6$.

h_c = 71.3 Btu/hr-ft²-°F.

f = 0.011.

Now, by a stepwise computer solution, we obtain:

For 10 steps, $K_q = 1.0885$, and $K_f = 1.7846$.
For 20 steps, $K_q = 0.5443$, and $K_f = 0.8923$.
For 40 steps, $K_q = 0.2721$, and $K_f = 0.4461$.

In each case, with the proper step multipliers, $K_{q,\text{ overall}} \simeq 10.89$ and $K_{f,\text{ overall}} \simeq 17.84$.

The results, namely R_{21}, TPR, TTR, and $\bar{T}_w$, are given below.

NUMBER OF STEPS	R_{21}	TPR	TTR	$\bar{T}_w$
10	0.328	2.55	0.9564	515
20	0.402	2.21	0.9723	513
40	0.429	2.10	0.9763	512
Closed-form	0.456	2.00	0.9796	518

Again, it is clear that the results of the stepwise solution converge on the closed-form solution as the number of steps used increases.

11.6 APPLICATIONS OF THE STEPWISE SOLUTION METHOD

The whole purpose of introducing the stepwise solution method was to be able to solve the general gas dynamics process, with arbitrary heat transfer and arbitrary flow loss.

In this final section, several examples of a more general nature than can be handled by the simplified closed-form solutions presented will be solved numerically with the aid of a computer.

Although the results cannot be checked precisely by any of the simplified process tables or equations, we can see the convergence trend, and we have developed a certain confidence in the stepwise solution method with the examples of Section 11.5.

Then, of course, the generalized gas dynamics equation of (4.18) can confirm that indeed a solution has been reached. Furthermore, when either flow loss or heat transfer effects predominate, the stepwise solution can be checked, roughly, by one of the simplified process solutions.

We illustrate these ideas by the following examples.

EXAMPLE 11.4

Consider a constant area flow of air involving both heat transfer and flow loss. Inlet conditions are given by $p_{t1} = 50$ psia, $T_{t1} = 600°R$, and $T_w = 610°R$, a constant. The pipe is of $D = 6$ in., $L = 1160$ in., and the flow rate is $\dot{m} = 20$ lbm/sec. The fluid properties can be taken as $\mu = 1.35 \times 10^{-5}$ lbm/ft-sec, $k = 0.0168$ Btu/hr-ft-°F, and $C_p = 0.24$ Btu/lbm-°F. The exit conditions are required.

Solution

The given values lead to the constants:

$Pr = 0.694$.

$R_D = 3.77 \times 10^6$.

$h_c = 121.9$ Btu/hr-ft²-°F.

$f = 0.0094$.

$p_1 = 44.33$ psia.

The problem was solved for 20 steps, 40 steps, and 99 steps. In each case, $K_{q,\,overall} \approx 1.07$, and $K_{f,\,overall} \approx 1.81$.

The results, namely the exit conditions, are given below.

NUMBER OF STEPS	p_2	p_{t2}	T_2	T_{t2}	M_2
20	21.59	33.72	534.19	606.75	0.82
40	23.19	34.42	541.93	606.66	0.77
99	23.96	34.80	545.22	606.61	0.75

Although there is no closed-form solution against which to check these results, we can see the convergence tendency as the number of steps used increases. We would therefore accept the 99-step solution as the best approximation available for the exit conditions for this example.

As a check on the consistency of the stepwise solution, we can apply the generalized gas dynamics equation of (4.18) to the results of the 99-step solution to obtain

$$\left(\frac{606.61}{600}\right)^{1/2}\left(\frac{50}{34.8}\right)0.6519 = 0.94178$$

This Γ_2 value of 0.94178 leads, by the interpolation of Tables 10.1 or 10.2, to $M_2 = 0.751$, which closely checks the stepwise solution.

Because the heat transfer effects (as seen by the small change in T_t) are minimal in this example, a Fanno flow closed-form solution should result in a fair approximation to the stepwise solution.

Fanno Approximation to Example 11.4. Overlooking heat transfer effects, we have for the given inlet pressure ratio $R_1 = 0.8866$, the isentropic values $M_1 = 0.41825$ and $\Gamma_1 = 0.65190$, and the Fanno value $K_{1,\,*} = 2.00141$.

But, by (6.35) and (11.8), $K_{1,\,2} = fL/D = 0.0094 \times 1160/6 = 1.8173$. By (6.36), we have

$$K_{2,\,*} = K_{1,\,*} - K_{1,\,2} = 0.18411$$

Corresponding to this $K_{2,*}$ is the Fanno value

M$_2$ = 0.7125

This result should not be expected to agree precisely with the given example result of **M**$_2$ = 0.75 because of complicating heat transfer effects, but the Fanno result is seen to be a fair approximation in this case.

EXAMPLE 11.5

Consider a constant area flow of air involving both heat transfer and flow loss. Inlet conditions are given by: p_{t1} = 100 psia, T_{t1} = 960°R, and T_w varies linearly with length from 535 to 735°R. The pipe is of D = 4 in, L = 1000 in., and the flow rate is $\dot{m}$ = 4 lbm/sec. The fluid properties can be taken as: μ = 1.868 × 10^{-5}, lbm/ft-sec, k = 0.0251 Btu/hr-ft-°F, and C_p = 0.24 Btu/lbm-°F. The exit conditions are required.

Solution

The given values lead to the constants:

$$Pr = 0.644.$$
$$R_D = 8.18 \times 10^5.$$
$$h_c = 77.9 \text{ Btu/hr-ft}^2\text{-°F.}$$
$$f = 0.0121.$$
$$p_1 = 99.19 \text{ psia}$$

The problem was solved for 10 steps, 20 steps, and 40 steps. In each case, $K_{q,\text{ overall}} \simeq 1.968$. and $K_{f,\text{ overall}} \simeq 3.016$.
   The results, namely the exit conditions, are given below.

NUMBER OF STEPS	p_2	p_{t2}	T_2	T_{t2}	**M**$_2$
10	97.47	98.07	703.43	704.67	0.0943
20	97.55	98.16	704.37	705.63	0.0942
40	97.59	98.20	704.99	706.24	0.0942

Again, there is no closed-form solution available for checking purposes, but we can observe the convergence tendency as the number of steps used increases. We would therefore accept the 40-step solution as the best approximation available for the exit conditions for this example.
   As a check on the consistency of the stepwise solution, we can apply the generalized gas dynamics equation of (4.18) to the results of the 40-step solution to obtain

$$\left(\frac{706.24}{960}\right)^{1/2}\left(\frac{100}{98.2}\right)0.18506 = 0.16164$$

This Γ_2 value of 0.16164 leads, by the interpolation of Tables 10.1 or 10.2, to $M_2 = 0.0940$, which closely checks the stepwise solution.

Because the flow loss effects (as seen by the small change in p_t) are minimal in this example, a Rayleigh flow closed-form solution should result in a fair approximation to the stepwise solution.

Rayleigh Approximation to Example 11.5. Overlooking loss effects, we have for the given inlet pressure ratio $R_1 = 0.9919$, the isentropic values $M_1 = 0.10784$ and $\Gamma_1 = 0.18506$, and the Rayleigh value $T_{t1}/T_{t*} = 0.05418$.

But, by (7.23) and (11.10),

$$K_{q,\text{ overall}} = \frac{77.9 \times 1000}{900 \times 45.837 \times 4 \times 0.24} = 1.967$$

By (7.26),

$$\frac{T_{t2}}{T_{t1}} = \left(\frac{635}{960}\right)\left(1 - \frac{1}{e^{1.967}}\right) + \frac{1}{e^{1.967}} = 0.709$$

It follows from (7.7) that

$$\frac{T_{t2}}{T_{t*}} = (0.709)(0.05418) = 0.03841$$

Corresponding to this T_{t2}/T_{t*} is the Rayleigh value $M_2 = 0.0904$.

This result should not be expected to agree precisely with the given example result of $M_2 = 0.0942$ because of complicating flow loss effects, but the Rayleigh result is seen to be a fair approximation in this case.

11.7 CONCLUDING REMARKS

In this chapter we recognized that the specialized closed-form solutions addressed in the bulk of our study do not apply to the general gas dynamics problem that involves arbitrary flow losses and heat transfer.

For the truly generalized gas dynamics process we require a stepwise numerical solution based on applying to a differential flow element the conservation equations of mass, momentum, and energy.

The equations to be satisfied are:

$$V_2 = \frac{(p_1 - p_2) - \dfrac{V_1 G}{g_c}\left(\dfrac{f\Delta x}{4D} - 1\right)}{\dfrac{G}{g_c}\left(\dfrac{f\Delta x}{4D} + 1\right)}$$

of (11.7) and

$$K_q = \frac{h_c \Delta x}{900 G D C_p}$$

of (11.10).

A FORTRAN program was outlined for formalizing the iterative stepwise solution.

Two types of examples were given to illustrate the stepwise solution. The first type dealt with examples already solved by the closed-form equations to give us confidence in the stepwise method. The second type of example considered the truly general gas dynamics process, in which the number of steps for the solution was shown to be the main variable.

The means for approximating general solutions by closed-form solutions also were discussed.

REFERENCES

1. R. C. Binder, *Fluid Mechanics,* Fourth Edition, Prentice-Hall, Englewood Cliffs, N.J., 1962, pp. 264–279.

2. R. M. Rotty, *Introduction to Gas Dynamics,* Wiley, New York, 1962, pp. 142–143.

3. N. A. Hall, *Thermodynamics of Fluid Flow,* Prentice-Hall, Englewood Cliffs, N.J., 1951, pp. 175–179.

4. A. H. Shapiro, *The Dynamics and Thermodynamics of Compressible Fluid Flow,* Vol. 1, Ronald Press, New York, 1953, pp. 190–213.

5. M. F. Valerino and R. B. Boyle, *"Method for Determining Pressure Drop of Monatomic Gases Flowing in Turbulent Motion Through Constant-Area Passages with Simultaneous Friction and Heat Addition,"* NACA TN 2328, April 1951.

NOMENCLATURE

Roman

A	Area
A, B, C	Constants
C_p	Specific heat at constant pressure
D	Diameter
f	Friction factor
g_c	Gravitational constant
G	Flow rate per unit area
h_c	Heat transfer coefficient
k	Thermal conductivity

K_f	Dimensionless loss coefficient
K_q	Dimensionless heat transfer coefficient
L	Length
$\dot{m}$	Flow rate
$\mathbf{M}$	Mach number
N	Number of flow elements
p	Pressure
Pr	Prandtl number
R	Static to total pressure ratio
$\overline{R}$	Specific gas constant
R_D	Reynolds number
T	Absolute temperature
V	Directed fluid velocity
x	axial coordinate

Greek

α	flow number
γ	Specific heat ratio
Γ	Normalized gas dynamics function
Δ	Finite difference
ϵ	Roughness
μ	Fluid viscosity
ρ	Fluid density
τ	Shear stress

Subscripts

1, 2	Inlet and exit stations
F	Flow
S	Surface, smooth
t	Total
w	wall
$*$	Critical state

PROBLEMS

11.1 Air flows adiabatically at $\dot{m} = 10$ lbm/sec in a constant area pipe of $D = 6$ in. and $L = 1000$ in. Inlet conditions are $T_{t1} = T_w = 100°F$ and $p_{t1} = 30$ psia. Find the exit static and total pressures by a 50-step numerical solution.

11.2 Air flows with negligible loss at $\dot{m} = 10$ lbm/sec through a pipe of $D = 6$ in. and $L = 500$ in. Inlet conditions are $T_{t1} = 500°F$, $p_{t1} = 50$ psia, and $T_w = 1000°F$. Find the total temperature ratio across the pipe by a 50-step numerical solution.

11.3 Air flows isothermally at $\dot{m} = 5$ lbm/sec through a 6-in. diameter pipe of $L = 5000$ in. Inlet conditions are $T_{w1} = T_{t1} = 80°F$ and $p_{t1} = 25$ psia. Find the total pressure ratio and the total temperature ratio across the pipe.

11.4 Air flows with both loss and heat transfer at $\dot{m} = 5$ lbm/sec in a 8-in. diameter pipe of $L = 1000$ in. Inlet conditions are $T_{t1} = 100°F$, $p_{t1} = 20$ psia, and $T_w = 200°F$. Find the exit conditions by a 50-step numerical solution.

11.5 Air flows with both loss and heat transfer at $\dot{m} = 10$ lbm/sec in a 6-in. diameter pipe of $L = 1000$ in. Inlet conditions are $T_{t1} = 400°F$, $p_{t1} = 50$ psia, and T_w varies linearly from 75 to 325°F. Find the exit conditions by a 50-step numerical solution.

ANSWERS
TO
PROBLEMS

CHAPTER ONE
1.1 $Q_{ADD} = 1135$ Btu.
1.2 $Q_{ADD} = 23.1$ mega joules.
1.3 $T_2 = 69.2°$R.
1.4 $T_2 = -45.9°$C
1.5 **A.** KE $= 5$ Btu. **B. W** $= 3885$ ft-lbf.
1.6 **A.** KE $= 125$ kilo joules. **B. W** $= 125$ kJ.
1.7 $V = 339.6$ ft/sec.
1.8 $V = 399.2$ m/s.
1.9 **A.** 3.966×10^{-7} slugs/ft-sec, 1.899×10^{-5} kg/m-s.
　　　B. 1.416×10^{-5} lbm/ft-sec, 4.401×10^{-7} slugs/ft-sec.
1.10 **A.** $R_{D.\,AIR} = 2.96 \times 10^6$. **B.** $R_{D.\,STEAM} = 4.04 \times 10^6$.
1.11 $R_{D.\,AIR} = 3.185 \times 10^6$.
1.12 **A.** $f_s = 0.02589$. **B.** $f_R = 0.01198$. **C.** $f_T = 0.03907$.
1.14 $\Delta h = 164$ Btu/lbm.

CHAPTER TWO
2.1 $V_2 = 1366$ ft/sec.
2.2 $V_2 = 600.3$ m/s.
2.3 **A.** $T_{t1} = 596.9°$R. **B.** $p_2 = 70$ psia. **C.** $q_{ADD} = 20.5$ Btu/lbm.
2.4 **A.** $T_{t1} = 346$ K. **B.** $p_2 = 300,000$ pascals. **C.** $q_{ADD} = 120,000$ J/kg.
2.5 $q_{ADD} = 1.348$ Btu/lbm.
2.6 $q_{ADD} = 3750$ J/kg.
2.7 $\mathbf{W}_{By} = 679$ horsepower.

CHAPTER THREE
3.1 $V = 2320$ ft/sec, $\theta = 30°$.
3.2 $V = 901$ m/s, $\theta = 23.6°$.

3.3 $V_{\text{max}} = \sqrt{\left(\dfrac{2\gamma}{\gamma + 1}\right) g_c \overline{R} T_t}$

3.4 $V_{\text{max}} = \sqrt{\left(\dfrac{2\gamma}{\gamma + 1}\right) \overline{R} T_t}$

3.5 $M = 0.684$, $V = 745$ ft/sec, $p_t = 13.68$ psia.
3.6 $M = 0.631$, $V = 219$ m/s, $p_t = 65,360$ pascals.
3.7 $T_2 = 357.3°R = -102.7°F$.
3.8 $T_2 = 324.8$ K $= 51.8°C$.
3.9 $V_1 = 728.6$ ft/sec, $V_2 = 1099.5$ ft/sec.
3.10 $V_1 = 215.2$ m/s, $V_2 = 415.5$ m/s.

CHAPTER FOUR
4.1 $M_2 = 0.45051$.
4.2 $(T_{t2}/T_{t1}) = 3.131$.
4.3 $(T_{t2}/T_{t1}) = 7.540$.
4.4 Given.
4.5 $V = 873$ ft/sec.
4.6 $V = 228.8$ m/s.
4.7 $R_2 = 0.928$.
4.8 $R_2 = 0.663$.
4.9 $p_2 = 19.7$ psia.
4.10 $p_{t2} = 73.33$ psia.

CHAPTER FIVE
5.1 $T_2 = 713°R$, $V_2 = 751$ ft/sec, $M_2 = 0.57372$, $\dot{m} = 7.8968$ lbm/sec.
5.2 $T_2 = 391$ K, $V_2 = 253$ m/s, $M_2 = 0.63862$, $\dot{m} = 1.371$ kg/s.
5.3 $M_2 = 0.14582$, $p_2 = 23.4$ psia, $T_2 = 125.5°F$.
5.4 $M_2 = 0.18576$, $p_2 = 163,500$ pascals, $T_2 = 331$ K.
5.5 $\dot{m} = 25.706$ lbm/sec, $A_* = 11.852$ in.^{2}.
5.6 $\dot{m} = 6.34$ kg/s, $A_* = 0.0085$ m^2.
5.7 $(V_1)_{\text{max}} = 228.5$ ft/sec.
5.8 $(V_1)_{\text{max}} = 42.4$ m/s.
5.9 $M_2 = 0.06931$.
5.10 $A_2 = 2.174$ in.^{2}.
5.11 $\dot{m} = 49.4$ lbm/sec, $A_2 = 0.844$ ft^2.
5.12 $M_2 = 1.5$, $T_2 = -73.8°F$, $p_2 = 13.62$ psia.
5.13 $\dot{m} = 899.42$ kg/s, $A_2 = 0.386$ m^2.
5.14 $\dot{m} = 103$ lbm/sec, $A_* = 0.33744$ ft^2, $A_2 = 0.53665$ ft^2.
5.15 $p_2 = 63.9$ psia, $\dot{m} = 2029$ lbm/sec.

CHAPTER SIX
6.1 $p_2 = 6.465$ psia, $V_2 = 656.6$ ft/sec.
6.2 $p_2 = 29,307$ pascals, $V_2 = 176$ m/s.

6.3 $R_1 = 0.96856$.
6.4 $R_1 = 0.95677$.
6.5 $\mathbf{M}_2 = 1.873$, $\dot{m} = 1.582$ 1bm/sec.
6.6 $\mathbf{M}_2 = 1.873$, $\dot{m} = 15.54$ kg/s.
6.7 $K_{1,2} = 13.464$.
6.8 $\mathbf{M}_2 = 0.768$, TPR $= 1.15995$.
6.9 $L = 208.9$ ft.
6.10 $L = 6.315$ m.
6.11 $p_{t1} = 19.61$ psia, $p_1 = 17.65$ psia.
6.12 $p_2 = 182{,}891$ pascals, $\mathbf{M}_2 = 0.4263$, $V_2 = 190.6$ m/s.
6.13 $(K_{1,3})_3 = 1.72$, TPR$_{1,3} = 1.28953$.

CHAPTER SEVEN
7.1 $\mathbf{M}_1 = 0.176$, $\mathbf{M}_2 = 0.411$, $p_2 = 8.44$ psia.
7.2 $\mathbf{M}_1 = 0.184$, $\mathbf{M}_2 = 0.273$, $p_2 = 66{,}383$ pascals.
7.3 $T_{t2} = 920°$R, $\mathbf{M}_2 = 0.260$.
7.4 $T_{t2} = 550.6$ K, $\mathbf{M}_2 = 0.242$.
7.5 $\mathbf{M}_2 = 0.3$.
7.6 $q_{\text{Rejected}} = 59.795$ Btu/lbm.
7.7 $q_{\text{Rejected}} = 180{,}707$ J/kg.
7.8 $\mathbf{M}_2 = 0.9$, TTR $= 0.3498$.
7.9 $\mathbf{M}_2 = 0.313$, TTR $= 0.4683$.
7.10 $s_2 - s_1 = -0.101$ Btu/lbm-°R.
7.11 $s_2 - s_1 = -719.6$ J/kg$-$K.
7.12 $T_{t1} = 558.2°$R, $T_{t2} = 934.3°$R, $p_{t2} = 10.025$ psia.
7.13 TTR $= 0.77975$, TPR $= 1.01515$.
7.14 TPR $= 0.96820$, $\mathbf{M}_2 = 0.41380$, $p_2 = 16.334$ psia, $p_{t2} = 18.377$ psia.
7.15 TTR $= 0.52336$.

CHAPTER 8
8.1 $q_{\text{ADD}} = 12.986$ Btu/lbm.
8.2 $p_2 = 4.196$ psia.
8.3 $s_2 - s_1 = 0.13488$ Btu/lbm-°R.
8.4 $q_{\text{add}} = 32{,}751$ J/kg.
8.5 $p_2 = 54{,}233$ pascals.
8.6 $s_2 - s_1 = 374.673$ J/kg-K.
8.7 $\mathbf{M}_2 = 0.825$, TPR $= 1.474$.
8.8 $\mathbf{M}_2 = 0.480$, TPR $= 1.589$.
8.9 $\Delta p = 7.26$ psi.
8.10 $q_{\text{add}} = 0.0326$ Btu/lbm.
8.11 $\Delta p = 93{,}933$ pascals.
8.12 $q_{\text{add}} = 419$ J/kg.
8.13 $K_{\text{iso}} - K_{\text{adi}} = (-)\,0.063$.

CHAPTER 9

9.1 $T_2 = 843.75°R$, $T_{t2} = 899.99°R$, $p_2 = 45$ psia, $p_{t2} = 56.41$ psia.

9.2 $\Delta s = 0.02244$ Btu/lbm-°R.

9.3 $T_2 = 1068.8$ K, $T_{t2} = 1125$ K, $p_2 = 712{,}500$ pascals, $p_{t2} = 852{,}571$ pascals.

9.4 $\Delta s = 199.57$ J/kg-K.

9.5 $p_{*1} = 45.438$ psia, $p_{*2} = 28.755$ psia, $p_{*3} = 6.39$ psia, $D_{exit} = 12.99$ in.

9.6 $X = 0.367$ L (where X and L are measured from the throat).

9.7 $p_{*1} = 328{,}125$ pascals, $p_{*2} = 179{,}371$ pascals, $p_{*3} = 32{,}732$ pascals, $D_{exit} = 1.416$ m.

9.8 $X = 0.5656$ L (where X and L are measured from the throat).

9.9 $M_1 = 1.648$.

CHAPTER 10

10.1 $M_2 = 0.672$.

10.2 $R_2 = 0.7077$.

10.3 $M_2 = 0.4342$.

10.4 $R_2 = 0.7103$.

10.5 $M_2 = 0.47519$.

CHAPTER 11

11.1 $p_2 = 23.22$ psia, $p_{t2} = 25.74$ psia.

11.2 $T_{t2}/T_{t1} = 1.23618$.

11.3 TPR $= 1.37136$, TTR $= 0.99365$.

11.4 $p_2 = 19.31$ psia, $p_{t2} = 19.58$ psia, $T_2 = 619.86°R$, $T_{t2} = 622.27°R$, $M_2 = 0.140$.

11.5 $p_2 = 45.36$ psia, $p_{t2} = 47.06$ psia, $T_2 = 730.98°R$, $T_{t2} = 738.68°R$, $M_2 = 0.229$.

INDEX

Absolute pressure, 6, 16
Absolute temperature, 6, 16, 17, 21
Acoustic velocity, 60, 62, 171
Adiabatic critical state, 100
Adiabatic flow, 98–102
Adiabatic loss coefficient, 107–111
Adiabatic process, 21, 27, 28, 73
Adiabatic system, 5, 8, 18
Air, properties of, 25

Basic identity, 19, 99
Bernoulli, D., 1, 30
Blasius, P. R. H., 36
Boltzmann, L., 1
Boyle, R., 19, 21
Boundary layer, 30

Caratheodory, C., 8, 16
Carnot, S., 1, 16, 21
Charles, J. A. C., 19, 20
Choking flow, 91, 107, 117, 181–183
Clapeyron, E., 20
Clausius, R. J. E., 1, 17
Colebrook, C. F., 36
Conservation, 2, 46
    energy, 2, 53–56, 223, 224
    mass, 2, 47–49, 60, 61, 223
    momentum, 2, 49–53, 60, 61, 223
Continuity, 47–49, 60, 63, 174, 223
Control volume, 46, 47
Convective heat transfer coefficient, 135–137, 226
Converging-diverging nozzle, 90, 91, 106, 181
Conversion constants, 3
Critical pressure:
    first, 181, 183
    second, 181, 182, 184
    third, 181–183

Critical pressure ratio, 76, 85, 100, 131, 153
Critical state, 114, 152

Darcy-Weisbach equation, 107, 152, 157, 224
DeLaval nozzle, 90, 91, 106, 181
Density, 6
Diabatic flow, 129
Diffuser, 85
Dynamic viscosity, 7, 30–33

Effective roughness, 37
Energy, 224
    conservation, 2, 53–56, 223, 224
    internal, 6, 9, 10, 16, 54
    kinetic, 14, 54
    potential, 14, 54
Enthalpy, 6
Entropy, 6, 16–19, 99, 130, 151, 172, 180
Equation of state:
    Clapeyron, 20
    Kelvin, 21
    perfect gas, 23
    Regnault, 20
Euler, L., 1, 30
Euler equation, 51

Fanno approximation, 232
Fanno flow, 101, 219, 228
Fanno tables, 121–124
First law, 8–13, 19
Flow:
    number, 77, 92, 159, 191
    work, 14
Fluid properties, air, 25
Fortran, 227
Friction, 1, 11–13, 15, 34
    factor, 34–41, 98
    tables, 40, 41

Gas:
   ideal, 21
   perfect, 23
Gas constant, specific, 23, 25
Gas properties, 5–7
   air, 25
Gas tables:
   Fanno, 121–124
   generalized, 193–219
   isentropic, 87
   isothermal, 166
   normal shock, 177, 178
   Rayleigh, 143
Gay-Lussac, J. L., 19–21
General energy, 14, 15, 55, 56
Generalized flow function, 107, 108
Generalized loss coefficient, 73–78
Generalized map: 79
   Fanno, 119
   isothermal, 163–165
   Rayleigh, 139

Heat, 9, 10
   transfer, 1
   transfer coefficient, 135–139, 226
Hybrid pressure ratio, 109

Ideal gas, 21
Impulse function, 133
Internal energy, 6, 8, 9, 16, 54
Isentropic critical pressure ratio, 76, 85
Isentropic critical state, 85, 191
Isentropic exponent, 23
Isentropic flow equation, 84
Isentropic process, 27–29, 60, 74, 84, 219
Isobaric process, 26
Isochoric process, 26
Isotherm, 8, 19, 21, 27, 150, 230, 231
Isothermal loss coefficient, 158–161
Isothermal process, 150, 220
Isothermal tables, 166

Joule, J. P., 1, 13, 23

Kelvin, 1, 9, 21
Kinematic viscosity, 7, 30
Kinetic energy, 14, 54

Laminar flow, 34
Laplace, P. S., 62
Laws:
   Boyle, Mariotte, 19
   Charles—Gay-Lussac, 19
   ideal gas, 21
   perfect gas, 23, 24

Loss coefficient, 98, 107–119, 224
   overall, 116

Mach, E., 63
Mach angle, 64, 65
Mach cone, 65
Mach equation, 65–69
Mach number, 64
Macroscopic, 6
Mass:
   conservation, 47–49, 60, 223
   flow rate, 69
Mariotte, E., 19, 20
Momentum, 61, 223
   conservation, 49–53, 61, 223
Moody plot, 36–39

Navier, L. M. H., 30
Newton, I., 2, 62, 135
Newton-Raphson method, 113, 163, 185, 228
Nikuradse, J., 34–37
Normalized gas dynamics function, 75–78, 86, 191
Normal shock:
   process, 171, 220
   tables, 177, 178
Nozzle, 85, 90, 106, 181
Nusselt, W., 135

One-dimensional flow, 1, 49, 52, 56, 73
Overall loss coefficient, 116–119
Overexpanded nozzle, 182

Path function, 6, 8, 10, 13
Perfect gas, 1, 19, 23, 61, 99
Pitot tube, 93, 186, 187
Plenum, 22, 91
Polytropic process, 25, 26
Potential energy, 14, 54
Prandtl, L., 1, 30, 34, 137
Pressure:
   absolute, 6, 16
   critical, 85, 100, 131, 153, 181
   empirical, 6
   static, 68, 76, 80, 88, 93, 107, 175, 178, 186, 187
   total, 29, 68, 76, 84, 93, 107, 108, 117, 133, 175, 178, 182, 186, 187, 226
Process, 10, 25–27
Properties of air, 25

Ratio, critical pressure, 76, 85, 100, 114, 131, 153
Rayleigh approximation, 234
Rayleigh Pitot tube relation, 186, 187